ACID RAIN INFORMATION BOOK

ACID RAIN
INFORMATION BOOK

Second Edition

1984

Edited by

David V. Bubenick

GCA/Technology Division
Bedford, Massachusetts

70939

np | NOYES PUBLICATIONS
Park Ridge, New Jersey, USA

Copyright © 1984 Noyes Publications
Library of Congress Catalog Card Number: 83-21986
ISBN: 0-8155-0967-7
Printed in the United States

Published in the United States of America by
Noyes Publications
Mill Road, Park Ridge, New Jersey 07656

10 9 8 7 6 5 4 3 2 1

Library of Congress Cataloging in Publication Data

Main entry under title:

Acid rain information book.

   Rev. ed. of: Acid rain information book /
Frank A. Record. 1982.
   Bibliography: p.
   Includes index.
   1. Acid rain. II. Bubenick, David V. II. Record,
Frank. Acid rain information book.
TD196.A25A29 1984   363.7'394   83-21986
ISBN 0-8155-0967-7

Foreword

This book discusses the major aspects of the acid rain problem which exists today; it points out the areas of uncertainty and summarizes current and projected research by various government agencies and other concerned organizations. This edition is a revised and greatly enlarged version of the original *Acid Rain Information Book* published in 1982. The wealth of information published in the two years since the first edition was completed made this revision both necessary and desirable—in order to provide a more complete picture of the acid rain situation.

Several recently released studies place the responsibility, or blame, for acid rain on one industrial source or another. This book does not intend to point a finger; rather it attempts to present, simply, acid rain information.

Acid rain, caused by the emission of sulfur and nitrogen oxides to the atmosphere and their subsequent transformation to sulfates and nitrates, is one of the most widely publicized and emotional environmental issues of the day. The potential consequences of increasingly widespread acid rain demand that this not altogether surprising phenomenon be carefully evaluated. This review of the literature reveals a rapidly growing body of knowledge, but also indicates major gaps in understanding which need to be narrowed, and unanswered questions which should be resolved.

The book is organized in a logical progression from sources of pollutants affecting acid rain formation to the atmospheric transport and transformation of those pollutants and finally to the deposition of acid rain, the effects of that deposition, monitoring and modeling procedures, and possible mitigative measures and regulatory options. This information is followed by a discussion of uncertainties in the understanding of the acid rain phenomenon and a description of current and proposed research by responsible government agencies and other concerned organizations.

The information in the book is from *Acid Rain Information Book—Final Report, Second Edition,* edited by David V. Bubenick of GCA/Technology Division, prepared for the U.S. Department of Energy, May 1983.

The table of contents is organized in such a way as to serve as a subject index and provides easy access to the information contained in the book.

Advanced composition and production methods developed by Noyes Data are employed to bring this durably bound book to you in a minimum of time. In order to keep the price of this book to a reasonable level, it has been partially reproduced by photo-offset directly from the original report and the cost savings passed on to the reader. Due to this method of publishing, certain portions of a few of the figures may be less legible than desired.

Acknowledgements

This document, as well as its predecessor, is the result of the combined efforts of many staff members of GCA/Technology Division. Responsibility for this report was divided as follows: Section 2—Sources Affecting Acid Rain Formation—was prepared by David V. Bubenick, assisted by John A. Dirgo and Douglas R. Roeck; Section 3—Atmospheric Transport, Transformations, and Deposition Processes—by Frank A. Record; Section 4—Monitoring Programs and Results—by Frederick M. Sellars and Douglas R. Roeck; Section 5—Regional Transport and Deposition Modeling—by Alan D. Goldman; Section 6—Adverse and Beneficial Effects of Acid Precipitation—by Arlene W. Levin and Robert J. Kindya; Section 7—Regulatory Alternatives and Mitigative Strategies—by Lisa A. Baci, Arlene W. Levin, and David V. Bubenick; Section 8—Summary of Issues, Uncertainties, and Further Research Needs—contributed to by several project team members and organized by David V. Bubenick; and Section 9—Current and Proposed Research on Acid Precipitation—by Lisa A. Baci. As Project Manager, Mr. Bubenick selected the project staff, monitored project execution, and reviewed all draft, draft final, and final manuscripts.

The GCA Project Manager wishes to thank Robert Kane, DOE Project Officer, for his assistance in assembling selected material for review and for his continuing guidance throughout the project. The careful review of the draft and revised draft copies of this document provided by DOE staff and selected members of the Acid Deposition Assessment Staff and Interagency Task Group I is also appreciated.

The collection of reference material was greatly expedited by GCA's librarian, Josephine Silvestro. Project reference materials were coordinated by Evelyn Limberakis. The Project Manager wishes to express his appreciation to GCA's Technical Publications staff for their expert preparation of this manuscript.

The single most important source of information for this project was GCA's original Acid Rain Information Book. That report, which is a compendium of acid rain information through 1980, was updated and revised in light of the wealth of information published in the past 2 years, resulting in the present document.

NOTICE

Contents and Subject Index

Executive Summary

INTRODUCTION

Acid rain is one of the most widely publicized environmental issues of
the day. It has been known for many years that the chemical content of
precipitation can vary as a result of the scavenging of atmospheric gases and
particles. It was not until the 1950's, however, that organized monitoring
programs in northern and western Europe identified the magnitude and
widespread nature of the acid rain phenomenon. The probability that a
regional acid rain problem also exists in the northeastern United States and
adjacent parts of Canada was not widely recognized until the early 1970's.

The potential consequences of widespread acid precipitation demand that
this phenomenon be carefully evaluated. Review of the literature shows a
rapidly growing body of knowledge, but also reveals major gaps in
understanding that need to be narrowed. This document discusses major aspects
of the acid rain phenomenon, points out areas of uncertainty, and summarizes
current and projected research by responsible government agencies and other
concerned organizations.

Acid Precipitation and Its Measurement

The free acidity of a solution such as rain is determined by the
concentration of hydrogen ions present. It is commonly expressed in terms of
a pH scale where pH is defined as the negative logarithm of the hydrogen ion
concentration. The pH scale extends from 0 to 14, with a value of 7
representing a neutral solution. Values less than 7 indicate acidic
solutions; values greater than 7 indicate basic solutions. Because the scale
is logarithmic, each whole number increment represents a tenfold change in
acidity. For example, as the pH of a solution decreases from 6 to 4, its
acidity is increased by a factor of 100.

Precipitation includes all forms of water that condense from the
atmosphere and fall to the ground. Unpolluted precipitation is frequently
assumed to have a pH of 5.65, the same value as distilled water in equilibrium
with atmospheric carbon dioxide under laboratory conditions. Hence, the term
acid rain has come to mean rainfall with a pH of less than 5.65, although
background levels below this value have been recorded for unpolluted
precipitation in some remote locations.

Precipitation removes gases and particles from the atmosphere by two
processes: (1) rainout, which is the incorporation of material into cloud
drops that grow in size sufficiently to fall to the ground, and (2) washout,

1

which occurs when material below the cloud is swept out by rain or snow as it falls. Together, these two processes account for wet deposition of acidic material on the earth's surface. Pollutants are also removed from the atmosphere in the absence of precipitation by direct contact with the ground and vegetation and by gravitational settling. This process is called dry deposition. Effects of the two types of deposition on the environment are not readily distinguishable. Both types are usually implicitly included under the popular term acid rain.

Contaminants in the atmosphere can shift the pH of precipitation either way. For example, soil particles of the West and Midwest tend to be basic and can increase the pH. In contrast, soil particles from the eastern United States are frequently acidic. The presence of such acid particles, or sulfuric or nitric acid aerosols, could lower the pH.

Role of Atmospheric and Terrestrial Systems

Figure 1 depicts the role of atmospheric and terrestrial systems in transforming and transporting acid precipitation precursor pollutants from natural and manmade sources to a variety of receptors. The introduction of contaminants into the atmosphere is followed by transport, dispersion, transformation, and deposition on the earth's surface. Here, acidic substances may have either adverse or beneficial effects on vegetation, and may accelerate the erosion of stone or the corrosion of metals. After deposition, acidic products may be buffered by alkaline soils or carried by seepage and runoff into lakes, thus, potentially lowering the pH of the water and affecting the aquatic ecosystem.

Report Organization

The remainder of this summary and the subsequent report follows the logical progression from sources of pollutants affecting acid rain formation to the atmospheric transport and transformation of those pollutants and finally to the deposition of acid rain, the effects of that deposition, and possible mitigative measures. This information is followed by a discussion of uncertainties in the understanding of the acid rain phenomenon and a description of current and proposed research.

SOURCES AFFECTING ACID RAIN FORMATION

Although manmade emissions of sulfur and nitrogen air pollutants are considered to be a major source of acid rain precursors, no quantitative cause-effect relationship between pollutant emissions from individual and regional sources or source categories and the measured acidity of precipitation at receptor areas situated some distance downwind has yet been determined. This situation results from the very complex nature of many chemical and physical processes that are involved in the transformation, transport, and deposition of the complex mixture of substances comprising acidic precipitation. Contributions of possible acid rain precursors and inhibitors from natural sources are also important. It is apparent that more

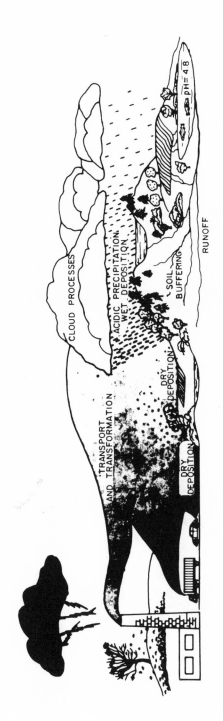

Figure 1. Schematic representation of the role of atmospheric and terrestrial systems in the acid rain phenomenon.

work must be done on tracing the release of pollutants, determining their conversion and transport rates, and measuring their deposition rates in order to evaluate the effects of modification of the various source contributions on the acid precipitation in receptor areas.

Natural Sources of SO_x and NO_x

To assess the magnitude and distribution of anthropogenic contributions of SO_x and NO_x from individual sources or from source areas, a knowledge of background levels is necessary. A common approach consists of performing a mass balance of the pollutants in a known air volume using approximations of the emission, atmospheric transformation and transport, scavenging, and removal of the pollutant. Budgets of this type have been useful in estimating the magnitudes of natural emission processes in sulfur and nitrogen compound systems. Although natural sources of SO_x and NO_x may be significant, they are globally distributed, whereas manmade emissions tend to be concentrated near population centers.

The natural sources of sulfur compounds are generally defined to include seaspray containing sulfates, hydrogen sulfide from volcanic eruptions, and biogenic sulfur compounds originating from the bacterial decomposition of organic matter. Of these major source categories, biogenic sulfur compounds are believed to be the most significant natural source. Estimation of emissions of sulfur from natural processes is tenuous at best, however, and even the direct measurements that have been made can vary widely.

Recent estimates of natural sulfur emissions have been revised downward from earlier figures. The latest available estimate of 147×10^6 metric tons of sulfur per year represents approximately 60 percent of the total global sulfur burden. Globally, man's activities account for 40 percent of all sulfur emissions. In eastern North America, the anthropogenic contribution is probably much higher. One recent study indicated that maximum potential biogenic emissions were in approximately the same range as manmade emissions but that estimates of the actual natural component were much lower. Thus, in eastern North America, anthropogenic sources may account for as much as 90 percent of total sulfur emissions. Other studies have indicated similar levels for large areas of Europe.

Relative to global and regional SO_x emission estimates, the inventories for NO_x and related nitrogen compounds are much less certain, particularly for the fraction produced by natural sources. Global fluxes of nitrogen compounds are based largely on extrapolation of experimentally-determined, small-scale emission factors or use of mass balances to obtain crude estimates for unknown sources. Estimated ratios of natural emissions of NO_x from terrestrial and aquatic sources to those from anthropogenic sources have ranged from 15:1 to 1:1 because of the variability in the natural source component estimate. Global estimates of natural NO_x emissions suggest that natural terrestrial sources of NO and NO_2 and tropospheric production of NO_x-N by lightning can be significant contributors to the total NO_x background. The principal source of gaseous NO_x in terrestrial systems appears to be chemical decomposition of nitrates.

Anthropogenic Sources of SO_x and NO_x Emissions

Based on information available from the National Emissions Data System (NEDS) files as of 1982, total annual emissions for SO_x and NO_x in the United States are 29.1 and 24.0×10^6 tons, respectively. Major source categories contributing to these two pollutants and their percentage of national emissions are given in Table 1. It can be seen that fossil fuel combustion (coal and oil) and industrial processes (principally primary metal production) are the largest contributing sources of SO_x emissions. In addition to fossil fuel (including coal, oil, and natural gas) combustion, transportation also contributes a significant portion of total U.S. NO_x emissions.

TABLE 1.   CATEGORICAL DISTRIBUTION OF MANMADE U.S. SO_x AND NO_x
EMISSIONS FOR 1982, IN MILLIONS OF TONS

Major source category	SO_x emissions (percent of U.S.)	NO_x emissions (percent of U.S.)
Stationary fuel combustion	22.8 (78.5)	13.5 (56.1)
Coal	18.2 (62.5)	7.0 (29.1)
Oil	4.3 (14.8)	1.5 (6.2)
Gas	0.2 (0.7)	4.8 (20.0)
Industrial processes	5.3 (18.2)	0.82 (3.4)
Primary metals	2.5 (8.8)	0.06 (0.3)
Chemical manufacturing	0.97 (3.3)	0.14 (0.6)
Petroleum	0.88 (3.0)	0.29 (1.2)
Mineral products	0.52 (1.8)	0.23 (1.0)
Transportation	0.91 (3.1)	9.4 (38.9)
Gasoline	0.23 (0.8)	5.2 (21.7)
Diesel fuel	0.43 (1.5)	3.9 (16.1)
Total U.S.	29.1	24.0

The NEDS emission inventory is maintained by EPA's Office of Air Quality Planning and Standards (OAQPS). Although other inventories are available for estimating SO_x and NO_x emissions, most of these use the NEDS data base as a starting point. Because it is geographically inclusive of the major source categories for criteria pollutants and because it has a structured updating system, the NEDS inventory is one of the most comprehensive emission data bases for describing the magnitude and distribution of current emissions on a national scale.

Although the magnitude of the SO_x and NO_x emission problem is important, of at least equal concern to the acid rain problem is how these emissions are distributed across the country. Emission density maps developed

from the NEDS inventory show that most of the emissions occur in the eastern
half of the country. The regional distribution of both of these pollutants is
depicted in Table 2.

TABLE 2.   REGIONAL EMISSIONS OF SO_x AND NO_x COMPARED TO POPULATIONS
(PERCENT OF U.S. TOTALS)

EPA region	States	Percent of U.S. population	Percent of U.S. SO_x total	Percent of U.S. NO_x total
I	CT, ME, MA, NH, RI, VT	5.3	2.6	2.4
II	NJ, NY, PR, VI	12.2	6.0	5.6
III	DE, DC, MD, PA, VA, WV	10.7	15.0	10.3
IV	AL, FL, GA, KY, MS, NC, SC, TN	16.8	22.2	17.4
V	IL, IN, MN, MI, OH, WI	20.4	27.5	20.0
	Eastern region subtotal	65.4	73.3	55.7
VI	AR, LA, NM, OK, TX	10.8	8.8	21.4
VII	IA, KS, MO, NE	5.1	6.5	6.7
VIII	CO, MT, ND, SD, UT, WY	3.0	3.0	4.8
IX	AZ, CA, HI, NV, GU, AS	12.2	6.7	8.3
X	AK, ID, OR, WA	3.5	1.7	3.1
	Western region subtotal	34.6	26.7	44.3
	Total	100	100	100

Historical trends indicate that emissions of both SO_x and NO_x
increased steadily from 1940 to 1970. The large growth in electric utility
SO_x emissions was only partially offset by the reduction in industrial and
residential/commercial emissions, produced by switches from coal to oil and
gas in the 1940s and 1950s. Transportation, industrial, and utility sources
have contributed most to increased NO_x emissions from 1940 to the present.
Sulfur dioxide emissions reached a peak of 32.1 million tons in 1970 while
maximum NO_x emissions of 25.1 million tons were recorded in 1973. Over the
most recent 5-year period from 1977 to 1982, SO_x emissions decreased by
7.6 percent and NO_x emissions increased by 10.6 percent. Current
projections estimate emission levels of approximately 27 to 33 million tons
for SO_x and 19 to 25 million tons for NO_x by the year 2000.

Based on future energy scenarios defined in the National Energy Policy Plan (NEPP, also known as the Third National Energy Plan--NEP III), it appears that utility and industrial combustion and transportation will continue to be the major sources of SO_x and NO_x. Significant reductions are projected for both utility combustion and transportation because of stringent emission standards now being applied to new plants and vehicles. Future changes in emission standards, pollution control technology, and fuel mix will, of course, affect the projected emissions of SO_x and NO_x. Sizable increases (greater than 25 percent) in electric generating capacity are planned by 1989 for all but the three northeastern EPA Federal Regions (Regions I, II, and III). Historically, the Northeast's contribution to total U.S. SO_x and NO_x has been decreasing, and it appears that the extent of interregional transfer of airborne sulfur and nitrogen oxides produced by coal burning in regions lying to the west may be an important environmental issue for the Northeast.

Factors Affecting SO_x and NO_x Emissions

Because coal-fired boilers are major contributors of SO_x emissions, the sulfur content of this fuel is an important factor. Nearly all of the available sulfur is discharged in the form of SO_2 and SO_3^- because of complete conversion and low sulfur retention in the coal ash. Recent experiments have shown that under conditions of high excess oxygen, coal-fired boilers may also emit small quantities of primary sulfates. Oil-fired boilers emit higher levels of SO_3^- and primary sulfates, for a given amount of fuel sulfur, than coal-fired boilers. Possible explanations for this observation are the higher flame temperatures in oil-fired boilers and the catalytic oxidation of sulfur by trace metals found in fuel oils.

Emissions of NO_x from fuel combustion depend on the type of boiler and the manner in which it is operated. One of the most important variables is excess air and how it relates to temperature. At a given furnace temperature the quantity of NO_x formed decreases as excess air decreases, due to the reduced oxygen concentration in the flame zone. For coal-fired boilers, emissions of NO_x are highest for cyclone boilers and much lower for either pulverized coal or stoker-fired boilers. With oil firing, tangentially-fired boilers have lower average NO_x emission levels than other firing methods.

Both SO_x and NO_x emissions vary seasonally. SO_x emissions from fuel combustion are highest in the winter while, on a nationwide basis, NO_x emissions are highest in the summer. These seasonal patterns are different for different areas of the country. NO_x emissions from transportation sources depend on both the amount of travel (highest in the summer) and the emissions per vehicle mile (which decrease as temperature increases).

The type and degree of application of SO_x and NO_x control technologies play an important role in pollutant reduction. Since approximately 80 percent of SO_x emissions result from fuel combustion (shown in Table 1), control strategies focus on this source category. The use of low sulfur coal, although the geographic availability of this fuel is limited, or the physical cleaning of higher sulfur coal allow some installations to meet emission limitations without resorting to flue gas desulfurization (FGD) systems. Most of the wet FGD systems now operating are applied to eastern high sulfur coal with efficiencies of up to 90 percent. Dry sorbent FGD and fluidized-bed combustion (FBC) technologies are also receiving considerable attention for reducing SO_x and, in the case of FBC, also NO_x emissions. Limestone injection multistaged burners, although not commercially available, may prove suitable for simultaneous SO_x and NO_x reductions. A variety of regenerable processes that produce a sulfur-based by-product are being developed for both coal and oil combustion. For oil-fired boilers, fuel additives containing magnesium have been used effectively to reduce primary sulfate emissions.

Nitrogen oxide emissions are presently controlled primarily through combustion modifications rather than the application of hardware. These methods include: low excess air firing, use of overfire air or staged combustion, low NO_x burners, reduced combustion intensity and peak furnace temperatures, and ammonia injection. These combustion modifications are the most cost-effective options currently available for achieving low levels (~5 to 60 percent) of NO_x control. Flue gas treatment systems, such as selective catalytic reduction, are capable of higher control efficiencies but are not widely available at this time.

Other Sources

In addition to the principal sources, "secondary" contributors or inhibitors are important in the formation of acid rain. Ammonia is generally found as an alkaline vapor able to neutralize either sulfuric or nitric acid in the atmosphere and may increase the pH of rain and snow. Recent studies of the chemical composition of precipitation have shown high correlations between ammonium and sulfate and/or nitrate ions. The consistency of these correlations supports the role of ammonia in the neutralization of acid precipitation. Most ammonia emissions are released into the atmosphere by natural and biological processes, such as the decay and decomposition of organic matter, forest fires, and volatilization from land and ocean masses. Anthropogenic sources account for a small percentage of the total ammonia emissions. Atmospheric ammonia concentrations vary geographically over the continental United States, suggesting considerable regional differences in acid precipitation neutralization by ammonia. Lowest levels have been reported in the Northeast.

Average rainwater acidity in the northeastern United States has been calculated from representative samples to be 62 percent sulfuric acid, 32 percent nitric acid, and 6 percent hydrochloric acid (HCl). Despite its low but significant percentage in precipitation, HCl is a strong acid whose sources and mechanisms of formation have not been completely identified. The natural sources of chloride include salt spray from the oceans, volcanic gases, and upper atmospheric reactions. Anthropogenically-produced chlorine and chlorides are emitted in various manufacturing and process operations; primarily in the manufacturing, handling, and liquefaction of chlorine gas and HCl. The combustion of coal by power generating facilities also releases chlorides into the atmosphere because midwestern United States and Appalachian coals contain 0.01 to 0.5 percent chlorine by weight.

Ozone and other photochemical oxidants may play a role in the conversion of SO_x and NO_x to sulfates and nitrates. Under conditions conducive to the formation of photochemical smog, airborne acid sulfate levels have been found to closely parallel the usual diurnal variations in ozone. Photo-oxidation of SO_2 in the gas phase by strong oxidizing radicals and direct oxidation of SO_2 by ozone in the liquid phase are both plausible mechanisms of sulfate formation. The scavenging of ozone by NO_x in the plumes from fuel burning installations may increase nitric acid production.

Atmospheric CO_2, along with other gases and soluble particles, determines the background pH of precipitation. The extent to which SO_x, NO_x, ammonia, and chlorides contribute to rain water acidification depends on background pH. Although the potential synergistic reactions of these substances are largely a matter of speculation and hypothesis at this time, further research can be expected to reveal the extent of their contributions to acid rain.

Another factor in the formation or neutralization of acid precipitation is the presence of natural and manmade dusts. Natural dusts from the central and midwestern United States are alkaline and may react with and neutralize strong acids in the atmosphere. In the eastern United States, however, natural dusts are slightly acidic. A similar role has been postulated for coal-fired fly ash emissions, which are often alkaline. Some investigators have even suggested that fly ash removal by particulate control devices may have indirectly contributed to acid rain formation. Fly ash and other carbon soot particles may play a more direct role in acid rain formation by catalytic oxidation of SO_2 by metallic constituents, such as vanadium pentoxide, or by absorption-oxidation in the presence of large amounts of water. Vanadium pentoxide is also formed in the combustion of residual oil and, therefore, may influence the fate of SO_2 from oil-fired power plants. The catalytic oxidation of SO_2 needs greater study, as it may be an important route in the transformation of SO_2 to sulfate particles. The conversion of SO_x and NO_x to their more stable particulate sulfate and nitrate forms increases their atmospheric lifetime, facilitates transport, and may contribute to the regional nature of the acid rain phenomenon.

ATMOSPHERIC TRANSPORT, TRANSFORMATION, AND DEPOSITION PROCESSES

Manmade pollutants are injected into the atmosphere at heights ranging from a few feet, as is the case with auto exhaust, to more than 1000 feet in the case of tall stacks. Significant quantities of many of these same substances are also emitted over a wide range of heights from natural sources, for example, decaying vegetation and volcanoes. Once introduced into the atmosphere, the fate of all such substances depends on the physical processes of dispersion, transport, and deposition, and on complex chemical transformations that take place between the point of emission and the time of delivery to ground-level receptors. The residence time within the atmosphere of these emitted substances may be brief or may extend over several days, weeks, or even years, depending upon such properties as their reactivity and solubility in water and, in the case of particles, their physical size. Related determining factors include the height of release, amount of solar radiation, presence of precipitation, and the nature of the underlying earth's surface.

Transport and Diffusion

Once substances are in the atmosphere, they are subject to natural processes of dilution and bulk or advective transport. Dilution is accomplished by random fluctuations in the wind, by wind shear, and by convection. Advection is the bulk transport of material by the mean wind. Transport distances (source to receptor) relevant to the acid deposition phenomenon can be estimated by the combined residence times of acid rain precursors and their acidic end products--a period believed to average 3 to 5 days, but one that is highly dependent upon the amount of precipitation experienced en route.

The spatial and temporal distributions of acid precipitation in North America are strongly influenced by large-scale climatological features. Of particular importance are the prevailing wind patterns that transport pollutants from major industrial areas, and the location of frequent storm tracks. In combination, these two features make the acid rain phenomenon of special concern to the northeastern United States and the neighboring parts of Canada. In addition, precipitation is enhanced when moisture-laden air is forced to ascend topographic barriers, such as the Adirondack mountains.

Chemical Transformations During Transport

Investigators agree that the phenomenon of acid precipitation (wet deposition) is caused by the presence of the three strong acids: H_2SO_4 (sulfuric acid), HNO_3 (nitric acid), and HCl (hydrochloric acid). Of these, H_2SO_4 and HNO_3 are by far the most important, but their relative contribution varies with geographical area and with season. It is also agreed that the two principal anthropogenic sources of atmospheric acidity are emissions of sulfur oxides and nitrogen oxides.

Conversion of sulfur dioxide to sulfuric acid in the atmosphere may occur as a result of two types of reactions. In polluted atmospheres, homogeneous oxidation of sulfur dioxide proceeds after gas-phase collision with strong oxidizing radicals such as $HO\cdot$, $HO_2\cdot$, and $CH_3O_2\cdot$. The source of these radicals is hydrocarbon-NO_x emissions, which through daytime photo-oxidation produce oxidizing radicals as intermediate products. The rate of oxidation is believed to depend on the initial ratio of hydrocarbons to NO_x, temperature, dewpoint, solar radiation, and the absolute concentrations of the reactive pollutants. Typical estimated conversion rates range from 0.1 to 10 percent per hour.

The second type of reaction involves both gaseous and liquid or solid phases. Three heterogeneous mechanisms believed to be important in the atmospheric conversion of sulfur dioxide are: (1) catalytic oxidation in water droplets by transition metals, (2) oxidation in the liquid phase by ozone or hydrogen peroxide, and (3) surface-catalyzed oxidation of sulfur dioxide on collision with solid particles, particularly elemental carbon (soot). Oxidation rates for these heterogeneous reactions in the atmosphere are not known.

The conversion of NO_x to nitric acid takes place through a series of complicated reactions during which nitrogen oxides switch back and forth between various stages of oxidation and eventually end up as nitrates. Because of the complexity of the chemical processes involved in the production of acidic products from nitrogen oxides in the atmosphere and the spatial and temporal variations of key parameters controlling these processes, rates of conversion of nitrogen oxides to nitrates can be expected to vary greatly.

Thus the chemical and physical processes acting during transport and deposition are exceedingly complex, involving both gas-phase, homogeneous reactions, and heterogeneous reactions between gas molecules and liquid or solid aerosols. The chemical pathways followed and the rates of transformation appear to be highly dependent upon the composition of the polluted air and the presence of solar radiation. At the present time, only a relatively few of the many possible complex interactions among pollutants are considered when modeling chemical transformations within the atmosphere. More complete knowledge of the physical and chemical processes involved during transport and deposition is needed for the realistic evaluation of alternative control strategies.

There is general agreement that a reduction in SO_2 emissions would probably bring about a reduction in the production of sulfate aerosol and, to a lesser extent, the acidity of precipitation. However, recent studies have led some investigators to conclude that the reduction in the sulfuric component of acid rain would be smaller than that indicated by a one-to-one relationship. On the other hand, it is thought that the reduction in the dry deposition of sulfur components would approximate reductions made in SO_2 emissions. The supporting theoretical argument is that oxidizing agents are a limiting factor in the formation of acids. In addition, some reactions are slowed as pH drops. Confirmation of this hypothesis could lead to a control strategy based on concurrent changes in reactive hydrocarbon and nitrogen oxide emissions as well as a reduction in SO_2 emissions.

Neutralization of Acidity

The acidity (pH) of precipitation is determined by the chemical nature and relative proportion of acids and bases in solution. Major cations and anions present typically include hydrogen (H^+), ammonium (NH_4^+), potassium (K^+), sodium (Na^+), calcium (Ca^{++}), magnesium (Mg^{++}), nitrate (NO_3^-), sulfate ($SO_4^=$), chloride (Cl^-), and phosphate ($PO_4^\equiv$); but the concentrations of the individual ions that determine the ionic balance and resultant acidity sometimes vary greatly from one geographic area to another, and from season to season. Thus, sulfate and nitrate are not quantitative indicators of acid deposition unless the relative alkali deposition is negligible or corrected for neutralization. In principle, changes in pH can be brought about as well by changes in the concentrations of neutralizing substances as by changes in the concentrations of the strong acids. Substances recognized for their ability to neutralize the atmosphere's acidic load include wind-blown soil particles and ammonia.

Evidence of the neutralizing effect of airborne soil particles was found in a study of the impact of land use on the chemical composition of precipitation in the north central United States. Event precipitation and snow core samples were taken along a transect extending from southeastern North Dakota to northeastern Minnesota for a period of approximately 1 year. Land use along the transect varied from prairie-agricultural in the west to forested in the east. The study indicated that soil and anthropogenic sources each contributed importantly to the composition of both rain and snow, with soils being more important in the west and anthropogenic sources in the east. After studying elemental and component ratios, the investigators concluded that sulfate and nitrate at the western sites appeared to be primarily soil-derived, whereas this was not the case at the eastern forested sites. They also concluded that the major influence of wind-blown soil on precipitation chemistry disappeared only a short distance east of the priarie-forest transition, being associated chiefly with particles of short atmospheric residence times.

As further evidence of the neutralizing effect of soil particles in the Midwest, an analysis of precipitation data collected by the Illinois State Water Survey showed that the drop in pH from 5.6 to 4.7 that occurred between 1954 data and 1960 data was associated with a decrease in the concentration of calcium and magnesium and not with an increase in sulfates or nitrates. Furthermore, 1954 was a year of severe drought in both the northeastern and midwestern states and dust storms were a common occurrence in those years. It was also pointed out by the investigator that current levels of alkaline dust in United States precipitation are considerably lower than those observed during the 1955 to 1956 or 1959 to 1963 periods and that this change may be a cause of the observed lower pH values.

Ammonia is produced from a variety of natural and anthropogenic sources, and is able to neutralize both sulfuric and nitric acids. In urban atmospheres, the sulfate anion is usually present as neutral ammonium sulfate or partially neutralized ammonium bisulfate. The effect of ammonia in precipitation may be complicated by its dissolving to form the ammonium ion NH_4^+, the presence of which may increase the conversion rate of SO_2 to sulfurous and then to sulfuric acid.

Deposition Processes

The processes by which pollutants are transferred from the atmosphere to the earth's surface are conveniently divided into two categories called wet and dry deposition. Wet deposition encompasses those processes that remove gases, liquids, or solids by precipitation. Dry deposition includes those processes that do not involve precipitation, namely: (1) the absorption or adsorption of gases by exposed surfaces such as vegetation, soil, water, and manmade structures; (2) gravitational settling of relatively coarse particles; and (3) impaction of fine particles on vegetation and other surfaces. The effectiveness of the various deposition processes is a function of the physical and chemical characteristics of the particular substance, the nature of the receiving surface, and meteorological factors.

The relative importance of wet and dry deposition of acidic products and precursor gases is dependent upon the characteristics of receptor surfaces and the frequency, rate, total amount, and form of precipitation. Over western Europe and much of North America, wet and dry deposition are believed to be about equal in removing SO_2 and its oxidized end products from the atmosphere. However, the relative importance of these processes in producing acidity in watersheds is not yet fully understood.

MONITORING PROGRAMS AND RESULTS

Although it is unquestionable that acid rain is falling, conflicting conclusions have been drawn as to whether or not there is a trend toward increasing acidity. While some researchers strongly believe that the phenomenon is worsening, others insist the data are inconclusive. The major reason for the disagreement among investigators is the lack of consistently measured long-term monitoring data at those locations where acid rain is presently occurring.

Past and Present Monitoring Activities

The first reported 20th century acid rain monitoring network was set up in Sweden in the mid-1940's. This network gradually expanded into the rest of Scandinavia and finally throughout all of Western Europe where it became known as the European Air Chemistry Network.

Concern over acidic precipitation spread to the United States in the early to mid-1970's when high acidity levels were noted in the Hubbard Brook watershed of New Hampshire. Since that time, acidic precipitation has also been documented throughout the northeastern United States, in northern Minnesota, near the Continental Divide in Colorado, in California, Hawaii, Florida, and in areas of the Northwest and Canada.

Current Monitoring Programs

Recent concern over the possible adverse effects of acid precipitation has resulted in a resurgence of interest in precipitation monitoring. The types of sampling systems currently used include: bulk collection (wet and dry deposition collected together), wet samplers, and wet/dry collectors (wet and dry samples collected separately). Of these, wet deposition monitoring results are believed to be most reliable.

In North America there are now over 70 monitoring networks; major ones being the National Atmospheric Deposition Program (including 97 sampling locations in the continental United States, Alaska, Hawaii, and American Samoa); the NOAA/WMO Precipitation Chemistry Network (including 130 sites worldwide, 10 of which are located in the continental United States); the MAP3S/RAINE network (which includes 9 sites in the northeastern United States); and the Canadian Network for Sampling Precipitation (which includes 56 stations across Canada). Although there are some limitations with respect to the current acid rain monitoring data base (differences--in some cases--

between networks arising with respect to monitoring techniques, quality
assurance, analytical procedures, dry deposition sampling methods, and the
need for additional sampling locations in the western United States), it has
been shown that good agreement can be obtained when data from many networks
are compared. Given the number of sites now in place or soon to be
operational, improvements being made in equipment, and the greater consistency
of quality assurance techniques for sampling and analysis, the future
availability of high-quality wet deposition data looks promising. However,
the potential of existing instrumentation and equipment for monitoring and
analyzing dry deposition exhibits much less promise. Sampling and analysis
techniques for other meteorological phenomena such as dew, frost, and fog must
be developed or greatly improved since pH tends to be depressed for low volume
forms of precipitation.

Geographic Distribution of Acid Deposition

The occurrence of acid rain is extensive enough so as to be referred to
as a worldwide phenomenon. Virtually all industrialized areas of the world
are affected, with Scandinavia, the northeastern United States, and southern
Canada receiving the most highly acidic rain according to past and current
monitoring data. Figure 2 depicts mean pH values across North America as
measured at WMO stations for the 1974-1975 period. The acid rain phenomenon
in the northeastern United States is a subject of great controversy as related
to its origin. The dominant theory suggests that pollutants transported from
the Midwest are primarily responsible, while other theories assert that local
sources are largely to blame. Undoubtedly, both local and distant sources of
SO_x and NO_x contribute to acid rain deposition in the Northeast. The
Electric Power Research Institute (EPRI) concluded from results of its Sulfate
Regional Experiment that major SO_x sources in the Ohio River Valley could
result in sulfate episodes as far away as 300 miles downwind. Whereas acid
rain in the Northeast has a higher ratio of sulfate to nitrate ions, acid rain
in California is predominantly composed of nitrate ions and is believed to be
primarily locally generated. In addition to acid rain, acid fog having a
measured pH of as low as 1.7 has been observed in California, also having a
high nitrate component.

Regardless of where they are measured, detailed observations of
precipitation pH show that there are frequently very large variations in
acidity not only from storm to storm at individual sites but also spatially
and temporally within the same precipitation event. Due to the complexity of
the mechanisms involved, it appears that precipitation acidity varies with
type of storm, precipitation rate, spatial and temporal differences in cloud
structure, and the time during the storm when measurements are taken.

Long-Term Trends

Because of the lack of long-term monitoring data, acidity trends in the
United States have necessarily been based on comparisons of recent monitoring
data with calculated pH values for the 1950-1960 time period. These
comparisons indicate an apparent increase in acidic precipitation in the
Northeast and in Florida (as shown in Figure 3) and California. Although
arguments have been presented that challenge the validity of calculated pH

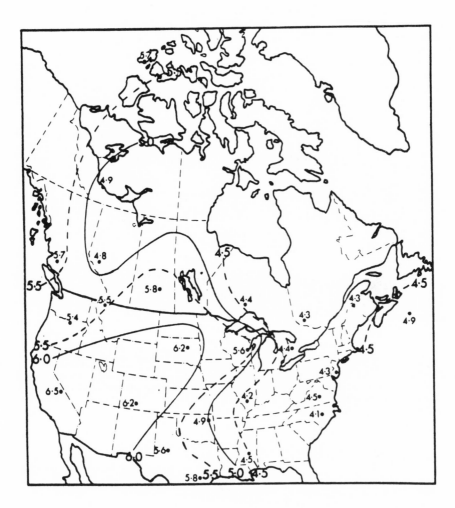

Figure 2.   Precipitation amount weighted mean pH at North American
WMO stations for 1974–1975.

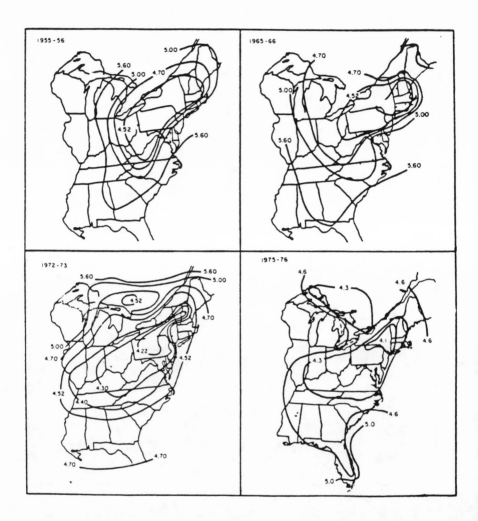

Figure 3.   Isopleths of the weighted annual average pH of precipitation
in the eastern United States in 1955-1956, 1965-1966,
1972-1973, and 1975-1976.

data, the original investigators (after reevaluation of the data) still
believe there is a trend toward more acidic precipitation. The accumulation
of data from existing monitoring networks around the country will hopefully
resolve any questions regarding long-term trends.

Short-Term Trends

Short-term or seasonal trends in acid precipitation are more readily
apparent than long-term trends and indicate that, in general, summer rains are
more acidic than winter precipitation. This has been found to be true both in
the Northeast and in Florida and is attributed to both higher summer
temperatures (which result in higher reaction rates for atmospheric
pollutants) and the fact that convective showers in the summer are more
efficient in scavenging sulfates and nitrates from the atmosphere than are
winter frontal storms.

REGIONAL TRANSPORT AND DEPOSITION MODELING

Due to widespread concern regarding the causes and effects of acid
precipitation, long-range (regional) atmospheric transport and deposition
models are being applied to investigate source/receptor relationships.
Although modeling is the accepted technique for predicting short-range
concentrations of regulated pollutants, the development and validation of
long-range transport models to describe acid deposition are in their early
stages. Therefore, no long-range models have received official approval for
regulatory applications. However, the use of long-range transport models is
generally considered to be the best currently available methodology for
investigating the transport, transformation, and deposition of atmospheric
pollutants on a regional scale.

Only a few results from long-range acid deposition modeling studies have
appeared in the general literature to date. A summary of the results from six
of these studies, believed to represent the state of the art, is presented in
this report, along with a brief description of each model. For convenience,
the discussion has been separated into two parts. The first three models,
here designated as event simulation models, use hourly meteorological data and
perform the basic transport, diffusion, transformation, and removal
calculations once per hour. The results are particularly well suited to the
calculation of short-term (episode) averages, although in principle the time
period can be extended to 1 year or longer. The second three models,
designated as statistical models, use long-term averages of meteorological
data to describe mean plume position and spread, and transformation and
deposition rates, and are therefore more efficient for long simulation periods.

Event Simulation Models

The initial testing of long-range transport models has been carried out principally by predicting concentrations of SO_2 and aerosol sulfate over regional-scale distances and comparing model results with ambient concentrations of the two pollutants. These pollutants were selected in part because of the ready availability of SO_2 emission data and ambient measurements of both SO_2 and sulfate, and in part because of their recognized role in the acid deposition problem.

Battelle, Pacific Northwest Laboratories (PNL), has developed a regional transport model for sulfur oxides that determines monthly and annual concentrations of SO_2 and $SO_4^=$, and the total monthly and annual wet deposition of sulfur. The PNL model, still in a testing and developmental stage, was only moderately successful in simulating ambient measurements. Although no conclusions can be reached from the preliminary results, the model is promising and may serve as a useful tool to judge the impacts of proposed industrial development scenarios. SRI International developed a trajectory-type regional air pollution model, EURMAP-1, that calculates long-term average concentrations, and dry and wet deposition of SO_2 and $SO_4^=$. This model was adapted for the region of eastern North America and renamed ENAMAP-1 (Eastern North America Model Air Pollution). Current predictions using ENAMAP-1 are not as close to observed values as the PNL model results. The Atmospheric Environment Service (AES) of Canada has developed an event simulation model for ambient concentrations and deposition patterns of sulfur over eastern North America. Analysis of model predictions indicates some overprediction of monthly sulfur dioxide concentrations and some underprediction of wet deposition, but generally the overall concentration patterns and episode occurrences agree quite well with measurements.

Statistical Models

Statistical models use long-term averages of meteorological data to describe mean plume position and spread, and transformation and deposition rates, and are therefore used more efficiently for simulations of long time periods. The results of three statistical simulation models prepared for eastern Canada and the northeastern United States are presented.

Argonne National Laboratory has developed the Advanced Statistical Trajectory Regional Air Pollution (ASTRAP) model for sulfur under the MAP3S program initiated by the U.S. Department of Energy. As its name suggests, this model takes a statistical approach to long-term regional modeling rather than the event simulation technique discussed earlier. Preliminary model runs have been made in the eastern United States and Canada, and the model results were then compared with measurements from the SURE data network. Major deviations between model predictions and measured data are most notable in the western portion of the modeling region, but also occur generally. The data also show a more complex distribution of sulfur deposition than that indicated by the ASTRAP model results. The Ontario Ministry of the Environment (OME) has developed a statistical model to simulate long-term ambient concentration and wet deposition patterns on a regional basis over eastern North America. The model estimates compare quite well with measurements of annual wet deposition taken from Canadian and United States networks for 1977. The Regional Climatological Dispersion Model (RCDM) simulates both sulfur dioxide and sulfate concentrations. RCDM annual predictions are in generally good agreement with regional SO_2 and $SO_4^=$ concentrations. In the areas of highest SO_2 emissions, the predicted wet sulfur deposition values are in agreement with those computed from the MAP3S and EPRI precipitation chemistry networks.

State of the Art of Regional Modeling

As indicated above, the accuracy of acid rain modeling results varies greatly with each modeling approach and is limited by a lack of detailed understanding of the complex processes controlling the transport, diffusion, chemical transformation, and deposition of pollutants; by the spatial and temporal variations of these processes; and by the inadequacy of the input data bases.

Most existing models only treat sulfur chemistry while ignoring nitrogen and other compounds; however, the acidity of precipitation is governed by a delicate balance of many ions in solution. It is generally assumed that variations in precipitation pH may be due to changes in sulfate and nitrate concentrations, to which anthropogenic sources contribute greatly in industrialized regions. It is therefore important to note that most current models do not treat total acid formation (including nitrate contributions) or acid neutralization processes. In addition, most models commonly treat sulfur chemistry in an unsophisticated, linearly parameterized manner. This limits the ability of the models to accurately predict the changes in atmospheric acid formation and deposition caused by variations in the magnitude of the emission of acidifying compounds and their precursors.

While computational and monetary restraints require that the transport and diffusion models be simple, it is necessary that the most important processes be taken into account before the models can be expected to provide a realistic evaluation of possible control strategies. It has been estimated that current models may provide only order-of-magnitude results, even for time-averaged values. The atmosphere is a very complex system, and further evaluations may well show that more sophisticated models are required to obtain useful results.

International Research

During the last several years significant efforts have been made in developing mathematical models which are capable of estimating long-range transport of acid rain precursors. In the United States over 15 different organizations have developed models; while at least three in Canada, one in Mexico, and several others in Europe are also working on model development projects. The models are continually being refined to improve their treatment of the transport, transformation, and removal processes.

In conjunction with modeling studies, acid precipitation monitoring programs have been established in many countries. In the United States there are 50 different measurement and analysis programs currently underway or recently completed, while there are 20 programs in progress in Canada, and one in Mexico.

The pollutant flux across the United States-Canadian border has been estimated by either correlating available air quality and meteorological data or using transport and deposition models. Some initial work has been done with air quality data. For example, one study used the Ontario Hydro network to show that high background SO_2 in Ontario, observed primarily in the winter, coincided with winds favoring transport from the United States. At this time, however, the primary source of transboundary flux estimates has been from models. Preliminary estimates of the transboundary flux by the ASTRAP model, described earlier, indicate that the United States contributes 4 to 5 times as much sulfur to Canada as it receives. As would be expected from the seasonal wind patterns, the summer flux is greater than the winter flux.

ADVERSE AND BENEFICIAL EFFECTS OF ACID PRECIPITATION

This section discusses the potential impacts of acidification on the environment. Most of the data available on impacts of acidic precipitation are derived from studies of the effects of increased acidity on aquatic organisms. The effects of lowering pH on fish, plant species, and other members of fresh water ecosystems are relatively well documented; therefore, the manner and severity of disruption of the affected ecosystems produced by acidification may be postulated with some confidence.

Discussion of potential impacts of acidic precipitation on terrestrial ecology rests on more tenuous evidence. The terrestrial ecosystem is a complicated biological system, and deposition of acidic precipitation exerts a complex influence on the functioning of that ecosystem. The evaluation of potential impacts is complicated by the apparent trade-offs between benefits from nutrient enhancement and the possibility of inhibition of plant growth or other detrimental effects. Most of the effects data have been generated under laboratory or greenhouse conditions using simulations of exposure of terrestrial species to acidic precipitation.

In general, there has been no clear quantification of the magnitude of the potential adverse or beneficial impacts of acidic precipitation. Whether the observed adverse effects are a local or regional phenomenon caused by poor buffering capacity of the affected lakes or soils or whether the effects are more widespread is still unresolved. Past research has centered on those areas where effects, especially aquatic effects, have been observed. Such research has therefore involved the most acid-sensitive regions, systems, and organisms. Implied impacts of acid precipitation on more highly buffered areas whose acid resistance is higher are speculative at this point. It is possible that acidic precipitation is producing or will produce responses within the ecosystem even though it is not possible at the present time to observe, record, or evaluate them. Determining what these changes are, quantifying the changes, and determining whether the changes are harmful or beneficial can only be accomplished through systematic scientific investigation over a long period of time.

Effect of Acidic Precipitation on Aquatic Ecosystems

Acidification of Lakes--

The acidity of freshwater lakes and streams appears to be stressing aquatic ecosystems in Europe and North America. The chemical composition of lakes is largely determined by the composition of influents from precipitation and watershed drainage. Softwater lakes are usually produced by drainage over acidic igneous rocks, whereas hard waters contain large concentrations of alkaline earths derived from drainage of calcareous deposits. Hardness of water is associated with alkalinity and, therefore, with the increased capacity of the water to neutralize or buffer the acidity entering a lake. Chemical weathering and ion exchange are two mechanisms in watersheds that act to neutralize incoming acidity.

Depending on various factors, lakes and watersheds exhibit a range of sensitivity to acidification. Included among these factors are the acidity of both wet and dry atmospheric deposition, the hydrology of the lake, the soil system, and the resultant chemistry of the surface water. The most important of these factors appears to be the soil system and associated canopy effects relative to the lake in question. Studies indicate that the capability of a lake and its drainage basin to neutralize the acidic inputs of precipitation is largely predicated on the composition of the bedrock of the watershed.

Although the mechanisms of acidic input into freshwater lakes and streams have been recognized, the magnitude of the contribution of acidic precipitation to lake acidification is far from resolved. Many studies have emphasized the complex nature of the interactions between precipitation and resultant water quality. A study recently completed by the U.S. Geological Survey in New York found the evidence linking precipitation acidity and stream water quality in nine water basins to be inconclusive using data compiled from 1965. Some authors caution that water quality effects usually attributed directly to the input of acidic precipitation could possibly be the result of lithospheric or ecosystem changes not caused by acid deposition. Some European investigators assign a secondary role to acidic precipitation in water quality changes. Others maintain that acidic precipitation is the causative factor.

Effects on Fish--

The death of fish in acidified freshwater lakes and streams has been more thoroughly studied, both in the laboratory and in the field, than any other aspect of lake and stream acidification. Various factors that affect the tolerance of fish to acidic waters have been identified, among which are species, strain, age, and size of the fish and physical factors including temperature, season, and hydrology. Generally, among the salmonids, rainbow trout are the most sensitive, salmon are next, and brown and brook trout are

least sensitive. These data are based on experiments conducted with fish
maintained at constant pH. Data are not available of species' response to
transient pH changes, such as spring snow melt surges.

The decline of fish populations in acidified lakes and streams has been
reported in Scandinavia, Canada, and more recently in the United States.
Although the disappearance of fish populations in Scandinavia was initially
reported as long as 50 years ago, the rate of such disappearances has sharply
increased during the past 15 years. In addition, investigators have
documented the acidification of lakes and the loss of fish in Sudbury,
Ontario, and surveys conducted in New York State's Adirondack Mountains and in
Pennsylvania have indicated an increase in the number of lakes and streams
with acid pH (<5) over time with reduced fish populations.

Disappearance of fish from affected bodies of water is usually associated
with one of two patterns. A sudden, short-term shift in pH resulting in acid
shock may cause fish mortality. Sudden drops in pH could cause fish kills at
pH levels above those normally toxic to fish. Such pH shocks often occur in
early spring when snow melt releases acidic constituents accumulated during
the winter. A gradual decrease in pH with time is a second mechanism whereby
acidification could result in elimination of fish populations. Field
observations and laboratory experiments have shown that prolonged acidity
interferes with fish reproduction and spawning so that, over time, there is a
decrease in fish population density and a shift in the size and age of the
population to older and larger fish. This pattern has been observed in some
lakes in Norway, Sweden, Canada, and the United States. However, the trend
toward increased acidity of lakes has not been determined in controlled
studies.

Studies in the Adirondacks have indicated that mobilization of toxic
metals, especially aluminum, is an additional factor that may contribute to
mortality of fish at low pH levels. Soil leaching and mineral weathering by
acidic precipitation may result in high concentrations of aluminum in surface
and ground waters. Several studies in Sweden, Canada, and the United States
have revealed high mercury concentrations in fish from acidified regions.
Elevated mercury levels in fish or freshwater lakes could have a potential
detrimental impact on both aquatic species and human health. However, studies
performed to date are far from comprehensive, and reports of results are still
controversial.

Effects on Plant Life and the Food Chain--
Elimination or reduction of a fish population is the most obvious
biological impact associated with acidification of freshwater lakes and
streams. Less obvious, but of great importance, however, are the effects of
acidification on other aquatic organisms. Organisms at all trophic levels
within the food chain may be affected. Species can be reduced in number and
variety, and primary production and decomposition may be impaired with a
resultant disruption of the entire ecosystem.

Changes in pH have caused alterations in the composition and structure of the aquatic plant communities involved in primary production. Experimental lowering of pH of lakes studied in Ontario resulted in changes in species' composition and in the standing crop and production of the phytoplankton community. The relative abundances of the algal flora also changed. In the lakes under study, differences in nutrient levels (phosphorus and nitrogen) were not responsible for these changes in primary productivity; acidity appeared to be the limiting factor.

Little quantitative information exists regarding the impacts of acidification on primary production and biomass in aquatic ecosystems. Most data are collected from experiments conducted in laboratories where artificial acidification occurred abruptly versus a quasi-steady state condition found in the environment. Generally, reductions in the diversity of the plant communities in lakes and streams and subsequent disruption in primary production reduce the supply of food and, therefore, the energy flow within the affected ecosystem. Changes in these communities also reduce the supply of nutrients. These factors limit the number of organisms that can exist within the ecosystem.

Effects on Microorganisms and Decomposition--
Acidification of lakes reduces microbiological activity and, therefore, affects the rates of decomposition and the accumulation of organic matter in aquatic ecosystems. Organic matter plays a central role in the energetics of lake ecosystems. The biochemical transformations of detrital organic matter by microbial metabolism are fundamental to nutrient cycling and energy flux within the system, and the trophic relationships within lake ecosystems are almost entirely dependent on detrital structure.

Effects on Other Aquatic Organisms--
Invertebrate communities are also affected by acidification of freshwater lakes and streams. Surveys conducted at sites in Scandinavia and North America have shown that acidified lakes and streams have fewer species of bottom-dwelling invertebrates than do waters with higher pH. Amphibians appear to be affected by acid stress in the same way as fish.

Effect of Acidic Precipitation on Terrestrial Ecosystems

Assessing the impacts of acid precipitation on terrestrial ecosystems is extremely difficult. In fact, at present, it has not been possible to observe or measure changes in natural terrestrial ecosystems that could be unequivocally attributed to acidic precipitation; however, such changes have been observed under controlled laboratory and field conditions. Therefore, it may be postulated that such effects could occur.

Effects on Vegetation--
Chemical species in the atmosphere reach plant surfaces through wet and dry deposition. Although sulfates, nitrates, and other water-soluble species may be assimilated through plant leaves, it has generally been assumed that the free hydrogen ion concentration in acidic precipitation is the component most likely to cause direct, harmful effects on vegetation. Experimental

studies have supported this assumption, but there have been no reports of foliar symptoms on field-grown vegetation in the continental United States that could be attributed to exposure to ambient acidic precipitation.

A recent study measured the effects of acid precipitation on 28 major crops that represent a total annual income in the United States of $50 billion. Crops were grown under controlled environmental conditions and exposure to simulated (sulfuric) acid rain of pH 3.0, 3.5, and 4.0, in addition to a control rain of pH 5.6. Injury to foliage and roots and effects on yield of edible portions were then determined. The results indicated that some crops were adversely affected, others benefited, some were ambiguously affected, and no effects were observed for other crops. Foliar injury and observed inhibited root growth were not necessarily associated with decreased marketable yields. The results imply that an optimum rain pH or sulfate concentration may exist for maximum productivity.

Acidic precipitation can also cause indirect effects on plants and vegetation, some of them beneficial. Some studies have shown an increase in needle length and the weight of seedlings of Eastern white pine with increasing acidity of simulated precipitation. Investigators at the Argonne National Laboratory have reported no harmful effects on soybean productivity following exposure to simulated acidic rain. In fact, they observed a positive effect on productivity as reflected by seed growth.

Research to date on the effects of acidic precipitation on the leaching of chemical constituents from vegetation has resulted in equivocal and often contradictory results. It has been demonstrated that acidic precipitation can increase the leaching of various cations and organic carbon from the tree canopy. Foliar losses of nutrient cations from bean plants and maple seedlings were found to increase as acidity of the artificial mist to which they were exposed increased. However, in experiments using Norway spruce, researchers found no evidence of change in the foliar cation content although increased leaching was observed. It has been stated that increased leaching of nutrients from foliage can actually accelerate their uptake by plants. The impacts of the increased leaching of chemical substances from vegetation by acidic precipitation is still unresolved.

Many researchers have concluded that acid rain affects vegetation by altering the nutrient conditions of the ecosystem. Forest productivity can be increased, decreased, or remain the same depending on the site, nutrient status, and the duration and rate of inputs. Short-term accumulation of sulfur and nitrogen has been observed to have beneficial effects on vegetation, whereas the long-term effects of accumulation and cycling of these nutrients is less understood. A critical level must exist between nutrient sufficiency and toxicity, where heavy metals accumulate, cation depletion occurs, and hydrogen ion concentrations increase.

Effects on Soil--
     Another area that suffers from limited investigation and inconclusive
results is the effects or consequences of increased acidity on soil and the
subterranean ecosystem. Effects have been postulated, but the picture is far
from clear. It is especially difficult to factor out the potential impacts of
acid precipitation on soil as compared to natural or anthropogenic mechanisms
resulting in soil acidification, such as agricultural fertilization. Some
authors contend that acid precipitation inputs are low compared to the
possible influences of agricultural fertilization or liming practices.

     All soils are not equally susceptible to acidification. The buffering
capacity of soil depends on mineral content, texture, structure, pH, base
saturation, salt content, and soil permeability. Studies indicate that
increases in acidification of precipitation lead to loss of cation exchange
capacity and increased rates of mineral loss (especially Ca^{++}). Although
the potential effects of acidic precipitation on soil could be long lasting,
researchers note that many counteracting forces could mitigate the overall
final effects, including the release of new cations to exchange sites by
weathering or through nutrient recycling by vegetation.

Effects of Acidic Precipitation on Human Health

     As previously observed, mobility of metallic compounds in soil is
increased at low pH levels. Given this fact, there exists a potential
indirect impact on human health through contamination of edible fish and
drinking water supplies by these metallic species. However, comprehensive
study and analysis of toxic metals in commercial or recreational fish catches
have yet to be conducted. Also, reported concentration levels of these
metallic species in analyzed waters have been well below public health
drinking water standards.

Effects of Acidic Precipitation on Materials

     Acidic precipitation can damage materials, structures, and manmade
artifacts. It has the potential to accelerate corrosion of metals and erosion
of stone. However, because a dominant factor in the formation of acidic
precipitation can be sulfur compounds, it is difficult to distinguish effects
of acidic precipitation from damage induced by sulfur pollution in general.

     Acidic precipitation can have a varying influence on corrosion of
metals. Rain may accelerate corrosion by forming a layer of moisture on the
metallic surface and by adding hydrogen and sulfate ions. However, rain may
also wash away sulfates accumulated during dry deposition and can, therefore,
retard corrosion. This problem has been investigated, and results indicate
that the mode of deposition complicates analysis of the impact of acid
precipitation.

     Just as acidic water leaches ions from soils and bedrock, acidic
precipitation may leach chemical constituents from stonework. However, at the
present time, it is not possible to attribute observed effects of atmospheric

sulfur compounds in general, or acidic precipitation in particular, to
specific chemical compounds. The precise chemical mechanisms involved in such
deteriorations are, likewise, unresolved. However, the effects are evident on
buildings, monuments, and statuary.

Models to Determine Acceptable Loadings of Acidic Materials to the Ecosystem

Developing acidic tolerance models for lakes, crops, or materials is very
difficult due to interference from other pollutants or due to direct
introduction of chemicals by man, such as fertilizer application. However,
models for relating deposition of sulfur compounds to adverse aquatic effects
have been described in the literature. All of the models are based on
empirical reports and attempt to relate sulfate deposition to critical changes
in lake pH. No similar relationships for nitrogen compound deposition were
available in the literature. To date, there have been no scientifically
accepted models to project future trends in lake acidification or recovery.

REGULATORY ALTERNATIVES AND MITIGATIVE STRATEGIES

As the debate over the cause and effect relationships of acid
precipitation has intensified, the need for understanding the regulatory
alternatives and strategies for controlling anthropogenic emissions of acid
rain precursors and mitigating the effects of acid deposition has grown.
A number of the regulatory options suggested have been refined into specific
legislative proposals and are currently being considered by Congress as part
of the debate over the Clean Air Act Reauthorization. Bills currently being
reviewed focus on SO_2 reductions in the 31 states east of, or bordering on,
the Mississippi River; most allow NO_x reductions to be traded for SO_2
reductions on a two-for-one basis. While the Senate bill provides states with
an initial opportunity to allocate required emission reductions among
themselves, all of the bills contain a formula to allocate required emission
reductions to each state based on current SO_2 emissions from electric
utilities.

Several analyses have been conducted to gauge the impacts of acid rain
control measures on industry, consumers, and the high-sulfur coal market. The
Acid Rain Mitigation Study, cofunded by DOE and EPA, is designed to examine
the impacts of a wide range of alternative regulatory options on SO_2
reduction and control costs for the electric utility industry, as well as coal
demand. Another study, which is being conducted by the Office of Technology
Assessment (OTA), is designed to provide information on a variety of issues
relating to the Long Range Transport of Air Pollutants (LRTAP) for use in the
Clean Air Act Reauthorization debate. OTA's analysis focuses on the costs to
electric utilities of achieving a series of maximum emission limits (termed
"caps") ranging from 1.0 to 4.0 pounds SO_2 per million Btu input. SO_2
emission reductions as a result of these "caps" range from 2.2 to 10.3 million
tons per year. These emission reductions include 1.5 million tons of
reductions required under current State Implementation Plans (SIPs); however,
the costs presented in the OTA report only consider those reductions that
would be required beyond SIP compliance. The OTA report also summarized the
results of several recent acid rain control cost studies. For an 8-million
ton per year reduction, which is the level specified in the bill reported out

of the Senate Committee on Environmental and Public Works, these cost estimates range from slightly under $2 billion per year to over $4 billion per year. The costs and distributional consequences of a number of approaches to allocating an 8-million ton reduction in SO_2 emissions to states have also been analyzed. In most cases, the cost estimates prepared by OTA are higher than the ones presented in other studies. The most recent study of acid rain control costs, funded by EPA, estimates that by 1995 it will cost the utility and industrial sectors between $3.3 and $4.5 billion per year to comply with the provisions of the Senate bill (S. 3041).

One of the possible options for use in a program for the management of acid deposition may be to mitigate its harmful effects in susceptible areas. Methods suggested have included increasing the pH of affected lakes, soils, forests, etc.; the development of protective coatings for exposed structures and materials; and the development of acid-resistant species of crops, trees, and fish. Only the first approach, which involves liming of lakes and/or streams, has received extensive investigation thus far.

Liming has been attempted largely in Scandinavia and on a limited scale elsewhere. Although to date no observations of long-term detrimental effects of liming have been observed, the true ecological consequences are unknown. Invariably, alkalinity and pH will increase as long as treatment continues. Phosphorus release from lake sediments should be observed, probably as a result of ion-exchange processes with bicarbonate generated from liming. Concentrations of zinc, manganese, and aluminum drop with elevations in pH. Among the biological changes that have been reported subsequent to liming are increased phytoplankton and zooplankton diversity. In fish populations whose age distribution was skewed toward older groups as a result of acidification, liming resulted in restoration of younger age groups.

Treatment of affected waters by large-scale liming programs represents major undertakings that could be logistically difficult. The economic realities involved in such programs in which the financial cost of the liming treatment is carefully balanced against the loss incurred if the treatment were not given must be evaluated in detail. This balance would be a major consideration in remote or generally inaccessible areas.

SUMMARY OF ISSUES, CONCERNS, AND FURTHER RESEARCH NEEDS

Section 8 of this report summarizes the key issues, concerns, and further research needs relating to what is known of and speculated about acid rain. Table 3 is a condensed summary of the principal areas of uncertainty associated with the acid rain phenomenon. Table 8-1, at the end of Section 8, is a rather detailed summary of the individual issues that have surfaced from a comprehensive review of the literature. These issues, which are discussed in detail throughout the report, are organized according to major subject areas: sources affecting acid rain formation; atmospheric transport, transformations, and deposition processes; monitoring programs and results; regional transport and deposition modeling; adverse and beneficial effects; and mitigative strategies. Corresponding to each issue is an indication of the level of concern as suggested in or directly inferred from the literature as a result of a lack of consensus among the experts. Examination of the

TABLE 3. PRINCIPAL AREAS OF UNCERTAINTY ASSOCIATED
WITH THE ACID RAIN PHENOMENON

Category	Extent of information gap	Will research help?	How long will research take?
Emissions			
Manmade			
• Global	Major	Yes	Years
• National	Moderate	Yes	Months-Years
• Regional	Moderate	Yes	Months-Years
• Local	Moderate	Yes	Months-Years
Natural	Major	Yes	Years
Transport, Transformation, and Deposition			
• Source to receptor transport	Major	Yes	Years
• Chemical transformations	Major	Yes	Years
• Deposition rates	Moderate	Yes	Years
Monitoring and Measurement			
• Evidence of increased acidity over increasing area	Major	Yes	Years
• Changes in lake, soil, vegetation acidity	Major	Yes	Years
• Susceptibility to change	Major	Yes	Months-Years
Regional Modeling			
• Neglect of NO_x transformations	Major	Yes	Years
• Wet vs. dry deposition	Moderate	Yes	Years
Effects			
• Fish destruction	Minor	Yes	Months
• Lake ecology	Major	Yes	Years
• Forest productivity	Major	Yes	Years
• Human health	Unknown	Yes	Years
Regulatory Alternatives and Mitigative Strategies			
• Development of control technology for precursor pollutants	Moderate	Yes	Months-Years
• Relationship between emission reductions and reduced acid deposition	Major	Yes	Years
• Feasibility of liming as a mitigation strategy	Moderate	Yes	Months-Years

issues has often led to identification of specific research needs and level of intensity that may be required to alleviate the underlying concern or uncertainty. The total resources required for these efforts are difficult to estimate because of the complexity and multidisciplinary talents needed to comprehensively address each issue. One of the most important of these factors is that the character of anthropogenic emissions will be constantly changing as future energy scenarios, pollution abatement procedures, mandated control requirements, and industrial processes are implemented.

CURRENT AND PROPOSED RESEARCH ON ACID PRECIPITATION

Many organizations in the United States sponsor research on acid rain. The Federal Government, for example, proposes to fund more than $20 million in acid rain research during FY 1983. Several states and a wide range of private organizations also conduct sizable acid rain research programs. Chapter 9 of this report provides an overview of the organizations involved in acid rain research and the types of projects that they sponsor. In addition, two programs are discussed that are designed to provide more comprehensive inventories of federal, state, and private sector research on acid rain.

Federal research on acid precipitation is being coordinated by the Interagency Task Force on Acid Precipitation (ITFAP). This Task Force, which was created by the Acid Precipitation Act of 1980, is jointly chaired by the Department of Agriculture (DOA), the Environmental Protection Agency (EPA), and the National Oceanic and Atmospheric Administration (NOAA). The other participating federal organizations are: the Departments of the Interior (DOI), Health and Human Services (HHS), Commerce (DOC), Energy (DOE), and State (DOS); the National Aeronautics and Space Administration (NASA); the Council on Environmental Quality (CEQ); the National Science Foundation (NSF); and the Tennessee Valley Authority (TVA). The Task Force also includes four Presidential appointees and the Directors of the Argonne National Laboratory, Brookhaven National Laboratory, Oak Ridge National Laboratory, and the Pacific Northwest National Laboratory.

The Task Force's primary responsibility is to develop and implement a comprehensive, 10-year National Acid Precipitation Assessment Program (NAPAP). In June 1982, the Task Force published the National Acid Precipitation Assessment Plan, which outlines the scope and proposed organization of this 10-year federal research effort. This plan divides research needs into nine basic categories: (a) natural sources; (b) manmade sources; (c) atmospheric processes; (d) deposition monitoring; (e) aquatic impacts; (f) terrestrial impacts; (g) effects on materials and cultural resources; (h) control technologies; and (i) assessment and policy analysis.

Of the approximately $18.2 million spent by the ITFAP in FY 1982, EPA was funded at $9.1 million or 50 percent, followed by DOE at 14 percent, DOI with 12 percent, DOA with 11.5 percent, NOAA at 10.4 percent, and TVA funded at about 2 percent. On the basis of research category, these funds were allocated as follows: atmospheric processes (26.5 percent), terrestrial impacts (19.9 percent), deposition monitoring (16.9 percent), aquatic impacts (16.9 percent), assessment (7.5 percent), manmade sources (6.4 percent), natural sources (3.3 percent), and effects on materials (2.7 percent).

Each of the task groups within ITFAP is currently drafting a detailed operating plan for 1983 and beyond. These plans identify current and proposed research projects, sponsored by the six agencies mentioned above, that are designed to address the research tasks outlined in the National Plan. The Interagency Task Force has also contracted with the Oak Ridge National Laboratory to develop an inventory of all federal- and state-sponsored acid precipitation research. This inventory will contain a description of all research projects funded under the NAPAP.

Although the Federal Government conducts the largest acid precipitation research program in the country, state governments, industry, trade and research organizations, and environmental interest groups also sponsor several million dollars of acid rain research each year. Over the last 3 years, the Electric Power Research Institute (EPRI) has spent over $12 million on acid rain research and anticipates spending over $6 million per year for each of the next 5 years. Several of EPRI's research projects have attracted considerable attention, particularly its Integrated Lake-Watershed Acidification Study. One of the major goals of this multimillion dollar multidisciplinary project is to produce a model that predicts how acid rain interacts with elements of the environment to affect lake acidity.

In a recent survey of research projects related to acid rain sponsored by the private sector, a total of 124 research projects were identified and described. Total private sector funding for these projects was approximately $3.1, $7.1, and $8.5 million in 1980, 1981, and 1982, respectively. The electric utility industry provided approximately 80 percent of these funds. The motor vehicles industry, coal industry, and the petroleum industry supplied 8, 6, and 4 percent of these research funds, respectively. Approximately 43 percent of the funding was devoted to research on the environmental effects of acid deposition; research on atmospheric processes and emissions/monitoring each received approximately 22 and 23 percent of the total funds expended, respectively.

1

Introduction

Acid rain is one of the most widely publicized environmental issues of the day. The potential consequences of widespread acid rain demand that the phenomenon be carefully evaluated. Review of the literature shows a rapidly growing body of knowledge, but also reveals major gaps in understanding that need to be narrowed. This document discusses major aspects of the acid rain phenomenon, points out areas of uncertainty, and summarizes current and projected research by responsible government agencies and other concerned organizations.

ACID PRECIPITATION AND ITS MEASUREMENT

The free acidity of a solution such as rain is determined by the concentration of hydrogen ions (H^+) present. It is commonly expressed in terms of a pH scale where pH is defined as the negative logarithm of the hydrogen ion concentration. The pH scale extends from 0 to 14, with a value of 7 representing a neutral solution. Values less than 7 indicate acid solutions; values greater than 7 indicate basic solutions. Because the scale is logarithmic, each whole number increment represents a tenfold change in acidity; thus, a solution with pH 4 is 10 times as acidic as one with pH 5 and 100 times as acidic as one with pH 6.

Natural precipitation includes all forms of water that condense from the atmosphere and fall to the ground. Natural, unpolluted precipitation is frequently assumed to be slightly acidic with a pH of 5.65. This is the pH of distilled water in equilibrium with atmospheric carbon dioxide, as determined under laboratory conditions. Whether 5.65 is the pH of unpolluted precipitation in nature has never been established. Nevertheless, many researchers today have accepted this assumption and refer to precipitation having a pH of less than 5.65 as acidic. Hence, the term acid rain has come to mean rainfall with a pH of less than 5.65.

Contaminants in the atmosphere can shift the pH of precipitation either way. Soil particles in the West and Midwest frequently contain carbonates, tend to be basic, and can increase the pH. In contrast, soil particles from the eastern United States are usually acidic. The presence of such acid particles, or sulfuric or nitric acid aerosols, would lower the pH. The processes affecting the acidity of precipitation are very numerous, and very complex. They include gas-to-particle transformations, photochemistry and catalytic chemistry, aqueous chemistry within cloud drops and precipitation, and regional and global atmospheric transport. The pH of precipitation is an integrated measure of the relative contributions of all of these complicated processes.

Precipitation removes gases and particles from the atmosphere by two processes: (1) rainout, which is the incorporation of material into cloud drops that grow in size sufficiently to fall to the ground, and (2) washout, which occurs when material below the cloud is swept out by rain (or snow) as it falls. Together, these two processes account for wet deposition of material on the earth's surface. Pollutants may also be removed from the atmosphere in the absence of precipitation by direct contact with the ground and vegetation and by gravitational settling. This process is called dry deposition. Effects of the two types of deposition on the environment are indistinguishable. It should be pointed out that, with the exception of a few surfaces, even the measurement of dry deposition is very difficult.

DISCOVERY OF THE PHENOMENON

It has been known for many years that the chemical content of precipitation can vary as a result of the scavenging of atmospheric gases and aerosols. In the 1850's, researchers in England described the presence of both nitric and sulfuric acid in air.[1,2] The term "acid rain" was used as early as 1872 in a book titled "Air and Rain: The Beginnings of a Chemical Climatology" published by R. A. Smith in England.[2] Modern awareness of the acid rain phenomenon and an understanding of its widespread nature, however, awaited the establishment of an organized monitoring program in northern and western Europe during the 1950's.

An analysis of data collected by the European Air Chemistry Network that was carried out in 1966 showed an area of precipitation with values below pH 4.0 centered on the Low Countries. It also showed that the area of acid precipitation had expanded during the data collection period.[3] An overview of the changing chemistry of precipitation and surface waters in Europe during this period has been presented by Oden.[4]

The probability that a regional acid rain problem similar to that found in Europe also exists in the northeastern United States and adjacent parts of Canada was brought to the attention of the scientific community by Likens and Bormann in 1974.[5] Their conclusions were based primarily on 11-year records of precipitation chemistry in north-central New Hampshire (Hubbard Brook Ecosystem Study), 1970-1971 data at several New York sites, and scattered observations elsewhere. A 1979 article by Likens et al.[6] includes isopleths that show a spread of acid rain in eastern North America between 1955-1956 and 1975-1976. Subsequent verification of these trends has been recently presented by Likens and Butler.[7] Although the observations made in the United States clearly show that acid rain is falling, the frequently reported trend toward increasing acidity is largely inferred from composite data bases acquired by different sampling networks operated over different time periods and sometimes with different sampling methods. Some investigators who have analyzed these data have concluded that they are therefore inadequate to define trends in acidity during this period. For example, in testimony presented before the Senate Committee on Environment and Public Works, R. M. Perhac stated that "...if data only from common stations are used, the reported trends fail to materialize."[8] Resolution of the issue will require long-term operation of a high-density monitoring network and the use of uniform sampling and analytical procedures.

In addition to the observations that have been made in the eastern United States, more limited observations have been made in other parts of the United States and Canada. These data have confirmed the widespread occurrence of acid precipitation in both countries. Recently, measurements made in areas far from manmade sources of precursor pollutants (e.g., the windward side of the island of Hawaii) have shown high levels of acidity.[9] These results suggest the existence of a worldwide background level of acidity considerably greater than hitherto suspected.

POSSIBLE EFFECTS

When acid precipitation has been deposited on the ground, it may alter the composition of the soils and surface waters and exert either a beneficial or a detrimental effect on indigenous plants and animals within the ecosystem. In addition, the deterioration of buildings and other corrosion effects could be accelerated. Understanding of the changes brought about by acid deposition is far from complete, but as increasing amounts of data are evaluated, there is general agreement that the effects are, on balance, detrimental to the environment. A commonly cited illustration of a change associated with the acidification of fresh waters is the decline and disappearance of fish populations (Wright et al.).[10] More subtle suspected effects include damage to other components of aquatic ecosystems, acidification and demineralization of soils, and reductions in crop and forest productivity. These effects can be cumulative or can result from peak acidity episodes (Glass et al.).[11] The extent of environmental damage is strongly dependent on the natural buffering capacity of the local soil. With regard to materials damage, it should be recognized that these effects are also produced by other chemical compounds and meteorological processes, as well as acid deposition.

FEDERAL AGENCY INTEREST AND INVOLVEMENT

Over the past several years, the Federal government has become increasingly aware of the suspected long-term impacts on human health and the environment represented by acidic precipitation. Acid rain was described by the U.S. Department of Health, Education, and Welfare as one of the most serious global environmental problems associated with fossil-fuel combustion, the other being the accumulation of carbon dioxide in the atmosphere.[12] As part of the National Energy Plan (NEP) in 1977, the President commissioned a study on potential environmental impacts of increased coal use. That report, known as the Rall Report,[13] identified acid rain in the United States as one of the six environmental problems requiring closer scrutiny. At present, however, insufficient knowledge exists with regard to the precise cause and effect relationships involved in the acid rain phenomenon, a fact that has hampered the identification and development of appropriate control and mitigation measures.

As a result of President Carter's August 2, 1979 Environmental Message directing a concerted national effort to understand the causes, magnitude, and impacts of acid rain and to identify measures that can mitigate acid rain impacts, a new initiative was proposed. The initiative called for the creation of an Acid Rain Coordination Committee whose primary responsibility was to draft a Federal Acid Rain Assessment Plan.[14] The Plan, which was developed and revised in 1980, served as the starting point for increased Federal agency involvement in various aspects of the acid rain phenomenon.

With the passage of the Acid Precipitation Act of 1980, a formal Interagency Task Force was established to coordinate all Federal research on acid precipitation and develop and implement a comprehensive, 10-year, $50-million National Acid Precipitation Assessment Program (NAPAP). This Task Force is jointly chaired by the Department of Agriculture (DOA), the Environmental Protection Agency (EPA), and the National Oceanic and Atmospheric Administration (NOAA). The other participating Federal organizations are: the Departments of the Interior (DOI), Health and Human Services (HHS), Commerce (DOC), Energy (DOE), and State (DOS); the National Aeronautics and Space Administration (NASA); the Council on Environmental Quality (CEQ); the National Science Foundation (NSF); and the Tennessee Valley Authority (TVA). The Task Force also includes four Presidential appointees and the Directors of the Argonne National Laboratory, Brookhaven National Laboratory, Oak Ridge National Laboratory, and the Pacific Northwest National Laboratory.

In June 1982, the Task Force published the National Acid Precipitation Assessment Plan,[15] which outlines the scope and proposed organization of this 10-year Federal research effort. The Plan divides research needs into nine basic areas: natural sources, manmade sources, atmospheric processes, deposition monitoring, aquatic impacts, terrestrial impacts, effects on materials and cultural resources, control technologies, and assessment and policy analysis. DOE is responsible for coordinating the research of the manmade sources task group.

During the past year, several bills containing regulatory proposals to control the manmade precursor emissions of acid rain have been introduced in Congress. They are presently being reviewed by the Senate Environment and Public Works Committee and the House of Representatives' Energy and Commerce Committee. Important features of these bills are presented in Section 7.

REPORT ORGANIZATION

The remainder of this report follows the logical progression from sources of pollutants affecting acid rain formation (Section 2) to the atmospheric transport and transformation of those pollutants (Sections 3 and 5), and finally to the deposition of acid rain (Sections 4 and 5), the effects of that deposition (Section 6), and possible regulatory strategies or mitigative measures (Section 7). This information is followed by a discussion of uncertainties in the understanding of the acid rain phenomenon (Section 8) and a description of current and proposed Federal, state, and private sector research (Section 9).

213
315

REFERENCES

1. Chamberlain, J., H. Foley, D. Hammer, G. MacDonald, O. Rothaus, and
   M. Ruderman. The Physics and Chemistry of Acid Precipitation. Jason/SRI
   International, Technical Report JSR-81-25, November 1981.

2. Cowling, E. B. Acid Precipitation in Historical Perspective. Env. Sci.
   and Tech., 16(2)110A-123A, 1982.

3. Barnes, R. A. The Long Range Transport of Air Pollution - A Review of
   European Experience. J. Air Pollution Control Assoc., 29(12):1219-1235,
   1979.

4. Oden, S. The Acidity Problem - An Outline of Concepts. In: Proceedings
   of the First International Symposium on Acid Precipitation and the Forest
   Ecosystem. USDA Forest Service and Ohio State University, Columbus,
   Ohio, 1975.

5. Likens, G. E. and F. H. Bormann. Acid Rain: A Serious Regional
   Environmental Problem. Science, 184:1176-1179, 1974.

6. Likens, G. E., R. F. Wright, J. N. Galloway, and T. J. Butler. Acid
   Rain. Sci. Am., 241(4):43-51, 1979.

7. Likens, G. E. and T. J. Butler. Recent Acidification of Precipitation in
   North America. Atmos. Environ., 15(7):1103-1109, 1981.

8. Perhac, R. M. Testimony for the Electric Power Research Institute Before
   the Subcommittee on Environmental Pollution of the Senate Committee on
   Environment and Public Works, 1980.

9. Mondaca, B. G., ed. Geophysical Monitoring for Climatic Change, Summary
   Report 1978. U.S. Department of Commerce, NOAA, Env. Res. Lab., Report
   No. 7, Boulder, Colorado, 1979.

10. Wright, R. F., T. Dale, E. T. Gjessing, G. R. Hendrey, A. Henriksen, M.
    Johannessen, and I. P. Muniz. Impact of Acid Precipitation on Freshwater
    Ecosystems in Norway. In: Proceedings of the First International
    Symposium on Acid Precipitation and the Forest Ecosystem. USDA Forest
    Service and Ohio State University, Columbus, Ohio, 1975.

11. Glass, N. R., G. E. Glass, and P. J. Rennie. Effects of Acid
    Precipitation. Env. Sci. and Tech., 13:1350-1355, 1979.

12. U.S. Department of Health, Education, and Welfare. Report of the
    Committee on Health and Environmental Effects of Increased Coal
    Utilization. Washington, D.C., 1978.

13. U.S. Department of Health, Education, and Welfare. Report of the
    Committee on Health and Environmental Effects of Increased Coal
    Utilization. Washington, D.C., 1977.

14. Acid Rain Coordination Committee.   The Federal Acid Rain Assessment
     Plan.   Executive Office of the President, Council on Environmental
     Quality, Draft Report, August 1980.

15. Interagency Task Force on Acid Precipitation.   National Acid
     Precipitation Assessment Plan.   Washington, D.C., June 1982.

2

Sources Affecting Acid Rain Formation

INTRODUCTION

   Although manmade emissions of sulfur and nitrogen air pollutants are
considered to be major sources of acid rain precursors, no quantitative
cause-effect relationship between pollutant emissions and the measured acidity
of precipitation has been determined. Also, no direct cause-effect
relationships have yet been determined between individual and regional sources
or source categories and receptor areas situated some distance downwind from
these sources. This situation results from the very complex nature of the
many chemical and physical processes that are involved in the transformation,
transport, and deposition of the complex mixture of substances comprising
acidic precipitation. Contributions of possible acid rain precursors from
natural sources are also important. It is apparent that much work should be
done on tracing the release of pollutants, determining their conversion and
transport rates, and measuring their deposition rates in order to evaluate the
effects of modification of the various source contributions on acidic
precipitation in receptor areas.

   In view of these uncertainties, this section of the report focuses on
assessing the magnitude and distribution of the precursors of acid rain from
anthropogenic and natural sources. A list of acidic or potentially acidifying
substances involved in acid rain formation includes:

   •   sulfur compounds and radicals: sulfur dioxide (SO_2), sulfur
       trioxide (SO_3^-), hydrogen sulfide (H_2S), dimethyl sulfide
       (($CH_3)_2S$ or DMS), dimethyl disulfide (($CH_3)_2S_2$ or DMDS),
       carbonyl sulfide (COS), carbon disulfide (CS_2), sulfate (SO_4^-),
       sulfuric acid (H_2SO_4), methyl mercaptan (CH_3SH or MeSH);

   •   nitrogen compounds and radicals: nitric oxide (NO), nitrous
       oxide (N_2O), nitrogen dioxide (NO_2), nitrite (NO_2^-), nitrate
       (NO_3^-), nitric acid (HNO_3), ammonium (NH_4^+), ammonia (NH_3);
       and

   •   chlorine compounds and radicals: chlorine (Cl^-), hydrochloric
       acid (HCl).

Precipitation acidity is primarily attributed to the strong mineral acids
H_2SO_4 and HNO_3. The immediate precursors of these acids are the manmade
and naturally-produced gases SO_x (SO_2 and SO_3^-) and NO_x (NO and
NO_2). Natural sources of SO_x and NO_x are generally distributed

globally, while anthropogenic emissions tend to be concentrated regionally near population centers.

In addition to the principal sources, other pollutants that are involved in the formation (e.g., chlorides) or neutralization (e.g., ammonia) of acid rain have been identified. The role of metal catalysts such as vanadium, manganese, and iron, and the potential synergistic reactions of ozone, carbon dioxide, volatile organic compounds, and particulates with the principal causative agents of acid rain need to be analyzed. Many of these pollutants are produced by both stationary and mobile sources. Their roles in smog formation, in the contribution to background acidity in rain, and as sources or sinks of acidic components and precursors of precipitation need further investigation.

The basic source assessment methodology used to map the quantities of the principal sources of acid precipitation is the emission inventory. The most recently available data from the National Emissions Data System (NEDS) have been used in this report as a basis for describing the current trends in the magnitude and distribution of SO_x and NO_x. Although the reliability of the NEDS inventory has been questioned and a number of other inventories are available, the use of NEDS is practical for the following reasons: it has been in operation for several years; it serves as the basis or beginning point for several other inventories; it has a structured updating system; and it is geographically inclusive of the major point and area sources of SO_x and NO_x in the United States. It appears that on a large regional or national scale, the NEDS data base is in general agreement with other inventories.

NATURAL SOURCES

To assess the magnitude and distribution of manmade (anthropogenic) contributions of SO_x and NO_x from individual sources or from source areas, a knowledge of background levels is necessary. A common approach consists of performing a mass balance of the pollutants in a known air volume using approximations of the emission, atmospheric transformation and transport, scavenging, and removal of the pollutant. Budgets, as they are often referred to, have been especially useful in sulfur and nitrogen compound systems by allowing an estimate to be made of natural emission processes, on which few, if any, applicable field data are available. Although the magnitude of some natural sources of SO_x and NO_x may be significant, they are globally distributed, whereas manmade emissions tend to be much more concentrated. In polluted urban airsheds, it appears that anthropogenic sources of these pollutants dominate.

Sulfur Oxides

Naturally-produced sulfur compounds are generally believed to constitute a significant fraction of the atmospheric sulfur burden.[1-13] Non-biogenic sources include geothermal emissions of SO_2 and H_2S deriving mainly from volcanoes, and sea spray, containing sulfates, formed above the oceans. Biogenic sulfur compounds, such as H_2S, DMS, CS_2, and COS, originate from the decay of animal and plant tissue, marine algae, anaerobic microbiological activity, and other in-situ inland soil processes.[14] Figure 2-1 shows the

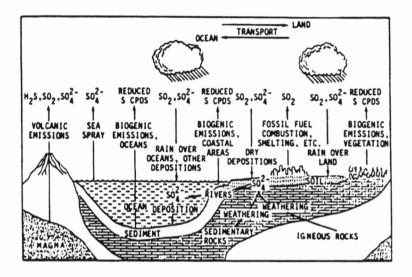

Figure 2-1. The atmospheric sulfur cycle.[13]

principal processes by which sulfur compounds are emitted into and removed from the atmosphere.[13] Whereas the quantity of atmospheric sulfur contributed annually from anthropogenic sources, volcanoes, and sea spray can be determined with a reasonable degree of accuracy, biogenic emissions are not yet amenable to direct measurement or calculation, and as such the emission rate is usually set equal to the source deficit that results from global sulfur budgets.

The predominant sulfur compound emitted from volcanic activity is generally SO_2[15] with possibly significant amounts of H_2S under relatively low temperatures and reducing conditions.[16,17] Estimates of volcanic emissions, based on the premise that the gases emitted contain a constant known proportion of sulfur and that their weight is related to the lava flow measured, range from as low as 0.75 to 3.9 Tg* S per year,[6,18] depending on the fixed ratio assumed. Recently, the use of remote-sensing correlation spectrometry has revealed greater emissions, as high as 10 Tg S per year.[12] Excluding large eruptions, an average global value is generally taken to be 5 Tg S per year.[13,19] Whereas volcanism has been found to significantly affect the sulfate concentration in polar ice,[20,21] its contribution in most industrialized areas appears to be small in comparison to other natural sulfur emitters.

The amount of sulfur emitted into the atmosphere in the form of sea spray, which evaporates to leave solid particles of $NaCl$ and Na_2SO_4, depends on the sulfate content of seawater (generally agreed to be 0.27 percent) and the extent to which sulfate ions are enriched relative to sodium and chloride ions during spray formation.[13,22] Although the major portion of sea salt aerosols are short-lived due to their relatively large size, Eriksson[1,23] estimated that approximately 10 percent is carried over and deposited on land surfaces. His estimate of 44 Tg S per year is generally accepted for the total emission of sulfur from sea spray. Based on Eriksson's estimate, Galloway and Whelpdale[24] obtained a flux estimate of 0.06 Tg S per year for sea spray corresponding to internal ocean waters within eastern Canada, and concluded that its contribution for eastern North America was very small compared to anthropogenic sources.

By far the most significant natural sources of atmospheric sulfur are biogenic in origin. Biogenic sulfur compounds originate from nonspecific bacterial reduction (anaerobic and aerobic) of organic sulfur; i.e., plant decomposition, marine algae, and soils,[25,26] and from specific sulfate-reducing (anaerobic) bacteria, generally present in fine-grained muds.[26,27] The biogenically-produced fraction is difficult to characterize either qualitatively or quantitatively. This is due to the irregularity of the source strength over the globe and to difficulties in measuring source strength. In addition, there is a lack of knowledge concerning how environmental factors (such as temperature or soil type) affect the emission of biogenic sulfur compounds and the reactions of these compounds in the atmosphere.

---

*One teragram (Tg) = 10^{12} grams (g) = 10^9 kilograms (kg) = 10^6 metric tons (tonnes, t) = 1.1 x 10^6 short tons.

Table 2-1 is a summary of the available literature values for natural biogenic sulfur emissions from salt and fresh water marshes (open ocean estimates are provided for comparison), from various inland soils and vegetative cover, and from the decomposition of organic matter.[24]   Apart from the variations from site to site that may be due to the different sampling and analytical methods used by these investigators, other factors such as the temperature at the time of sampling and the types of soils measured may be significant. Based on measurements of biogenic sulfur gas flux at 21 sites, representing nine major soil orders within the SURE (Sulfate Regional Experiment) study area, Adams et al.[33,36] found that inland soils contribute significantly to the total biogenic sulfur flux in this area. Emissions from this source, representing less than 1 percent of the manmade emissions in the study area, were a strong function of soil order (i.e., coastal saline marshes, poorly drained inland organic soils, and dry mineral soils). Flux measurements taken by Aneja et al.[14,34] on North Carolina coastal salt marshes varied greatly as a function of soil type and moisture content. Both investigators reported that higher sulfur emission rates were strongly correlated with higher temperatures.

Other factors may also be important in assessing the amount of sulfur released as gases by biological activity. Rice, Nochumson, and Hidy[37] compared estimates of sulfur from biogenic origins with anthropogenic emissions of sulfur from sulfur dioxide in seven geographical sectors in the United States. The total biogenic contribution was defined to include mobilization of sulfur in the biosphere, combined with the "quasi-natural" sources of animal husbandry, fertilizer, crop losses, and acid mine drainage. The total upper bound emission estimates, corresponding to 100 percent sulfur mobilization, were found to be in approximately the same range as the estimated anthropogenic emissions in all but one region. In Ohio, Florida, Wisconsin, and Virginia, the highest estimate exceeded anthropogenic emissions. Mine drainage also represented a large fraction of the exchangeable sulfur in all regions. However, under the assumption that only 10 percent (perhaps more realistic) of the available biogenic sulfur pool is released to the atmosphere, the contribution from natural sulfur gases in the eastern United States, where high levels of sulfate are observed, is minor.[37] These results highlight the fact that the estimation of emissions of sulfur gases from biogenic and natural processes is tenuous at best without direct measurements which, as shown in Table 2-1, can also vary widely. Clearly, additional measurements are needed if biogenic fluxes are to be adequately parameterized with respect to such important factors as meteorology and source type.

Although global and regional suflur budgets have been estimated, few reliable measurements exist. The numbers for natural emissions have been lowered considerably from some of the early estimates shown in Table 2-2 to 147×10^6 metric tons sulfur per year, which is approximately 59 percent of the total global sulfur burden. Of this percentage, biogenic emissions typically make up nearly two-thirds, sea spray constitutes slightly less than one-third, and the remainder is attributed to volcanic activity. Conversely, the fraction produced by manmade contributions has been constantly revised with, in general, an increasing anthropogenic estimated input. Cullis and Hirschler[13] have observed that between 1956 and 1976 man's contribution has been increasing at an average rate of 2.2 percent per year.

TABLE 2-1. LITERATURE VALUES OF NATURAL EMISSIONS OF SULFUR COMPOUNDS[a]

Reference	Source	Compound	Emission rate ($mg\ S\ m^{-2}y^{-1}$)	Remarks
Friend, 1973[7]	Land Ocean	H_2S Sulfide	387 133	Estimated to balance global budget
Liss and Slater, 1974[28]	Ocean	DMS	10	Calculated value
Hitchcock, 1975[29]	Marine algae Vegetation Soils	DMS	0.14 3.6 10-33	From anaerobic decay of organic matter; value of 10 is preferred
Granat, 1976[10]	Anaerobic bacterial reduction of SO_4	H_2S, DMS, others	53	Required to balance budget
Maroulis and Bandy, 1977[30]	Ocean	DMS	6	Conclusion: marshes, shallow bays, land were not much stronger sources than open ocean
Jaeschke and Haunold, 1977[31]	Swamps, tidal flats, anaerobic soils	H_2S	26	
Hansen et al., 1978[32]	Sediment of shallow coastal area	H_2S	$1.8\text{-}44 \times 10^4$	Probably anaerobic bacterial reduction of SO_4; mainly at night, 2 cm H_2O, high temperature, limited extent

(continued)

TABLE 2-1 (continued)

Reference	Source	Compound	Emission rate ($mg\ S\ m^{-2}y^{-1}$)	Remarks
Adams et al., 1978[33]	Soils	H_2S, COS, DMS, MeSH, CS_2, DMDS	1.3–7.5	H_2S dominant; daily averages; wet soils; flux proportional to temperature
	One soil	H_2S, COS, MeSH	7.24×10^4	Tidal area; isolated case
	Grass (inland)	COS, DMS, CS_2	0.4–4.2	
	Marsh grass	H_2S, COS, CS_2, DMS, DMDS	$< 8 \times 10^2$	
	Sea water	COS, DMS, CS_2	4–22	
Aneja et al., 1978[34]	Salt-marsh grass	DMS, H_2S	660	Average values; emission rates increase with increasing temperature
	Mud flats	H_2S, DMS	220	
Delmas et al., 1979[35]	Soils (humid forest)	H_2S	70	Average value (near a salt marsh)
	Soils (temperate regions)	H_2S	44	Average value (France)

aModified from Galloway and Whelpdale.[24]

TABLE 2-2. ESTIMATES OF GLOBAL ATMOSPHERIC SULFUR EMISSIONS FROM NATURAL AND MANMADE SOURCES, 10[6] METRIC TONS SULFUR PER YEAR[a]

| Natural | | | | Manmade | Total manmade plus natural | Relative manmade contribution | | Reference |
| Biogenic | | Sea spray | Volcanoes | | | % of total | % of natural | |
Land	Sea		Total[b]					
110	170	44	–	324	40[c]	364	11	12	Eriksson (1960)[1]
70	160	45	–	275	40[c]	315	13	15	Junge (1963)[2]
110	170	45	–	325	40[c]	365	11	12	Eriksson (1963)[3]
70	30	44[d]	–	144	70[e]	214	33	49	Robinson and Robbins (1968)[4]
68	30	44[d]	–	142	70[e]	212	33	49	Robinson and Robbins (1972)[5]
71	18	44[d]	1	134	50[e]	184	27	37	Kellogg et al. (1972)[6]
58	48	44[d]	2	152	65[e]	217	30	43	Friend (1973)[7]
3	28	44[d]	3	178	65[e]	143	45	37	Bolin and Charlson (1976)[8]
3	34	44[d]	3	84	65[e]	149	44	77	Hallberg (1976)[9]
5	27	44[d]	3	79	65[e]	144	45	82	Granat (1976)[10]

(continued)

TABLE 2-2 (continued)

| Natural | | | | Manmade | Total manmade plus natural | Relative manmade contribution | | Reference |
| Biogenic | | Sea spray | Volcanoes | Total[b] | | | % of total | % of natural | |
Land	Sea								
106	46	44[d]	–	196	70[e]	266	26	36	Garland (1977)[11]
60	26	44[d]	10	140	60[e]	200	30	43	Davey (1978)[12]
48	50	44[d]	5	147	86[f]	233	37	59	Cullis and Hirschler (1980)[13]
48	50	44[d]	5	147	93[g]	240	39	63	Cullis and Hirschler (1980)[13]
48	50	44[d]	5	147	104[h]	251	41	71	Cullis and Hirschler (1980)[13]

[a] Modified from Cullis and Hirschler (1980)[13] and Szabo, Esposito, and Spaite (1982).[38]

[b] Total does not include estimates of sulfate emissions due to fertilizer application to soil or rock weathering.

[c] Based on 1956 emission data.

[d] Other investigators have used Eriksson's 1960 estimate for the contribution of sea spray.

[e] Based on emission data from the mid-1960's.

[f] Based on 1970 emission data.

[g] Based on 1974 emission data.

[h] Based on 1976 emission data.

These estimates of natural SO_x emissions indicate that, although it can be highly variable, the natural-emission component of the sulfur cycle is sizable relative to anthropogenic emissions on a global basis. This is not the case, however, in eastern North America. Galloway and Whelpdale[24] have prepared detailed sulfur budgets for eastern North America (see Table 2-3) showing that manmade emissions account for over 90 percent of the total emissions in the region. Natural emissions account for approximately 4 percent of the total, with inflow from outside the region contributing the remainder. On the basis of other research conducted in the United States and Europe,[39] natural processes (emissions from terrestrial activities, marine processes in coastal zones, and sea-salt advection) were found to contribute about 10 percent to the total SO_x emitted in the eastern United States, which is well below the global estimate of approximately 60 percent (Table 2-2). Similar conclusions were also reached for industrialized areas of Europe.[39]

Nitrogen Oxides

Relative to global and regional SO_x emission estimates, the inventories for NO_x and related nitrogen compounds are much less certain, particularly for the fraction produced by natural sources. Global fluxes of nitrogen compounds are based largely on extrapolation of experimentally-determined, small-scale emission factors, or use of mass balances to obtain crude estimates for unknown sources. Robinson and Robbins[40] estimated the ratio of natural emissions of NO_x from terrestrial and aquatic sources to those from anthropogenic sources to be approximately 7:1. An earlier estimate[5] indicated a higher ratio of 15:1. The downward revision was based on a 55 percent lower estimate of the amount of NO_x contributed by natural sources. By way of comparison, Söderlund and Svensson[41] concluded that the ratio of NO_x emissions from natural versus manmade sources could range from approximately 1:1 to 5:1. The uncertainties associated with global estimates of natural NO_x emissions along with their contributing sources are highlighted in Table 2-4 (depicting NO_x and related compounds) and Table 2-5 (depicting NO and NO_2).

The data presented suggest that natural terrestrial sources of NO and NO_2 and tropospheric production of NO_x-N by lightning can be significant contributors to the total NO_x background. Although 40 to 108 Tg NO_x-N per year have been estimated to be released from terrestrial sources, most of it is reabsorbed with only 8 to 25 Tg NO_x-N escaping to the troposphere.[41] Söderlund and Svensson also suggest that the principal source of gaseous NO_x in terrestrial systems is chemical decomposition of nitrates.

During lightning discharges, tropospheric production of NO_x has been estimated to account for 8 to 40 Tg NO_x-N per year.[45,47,48] If these higher estimates are correct, lightning could account for as much as 50 percent of the total atmospheric production of NO_x on a global basis.[45] This level is comparable to other estimates of global manmade NO_x emissions.[49,50]

TABLE 2-3.   ATMOSPHERIC SULFUR INPUTS FOR EASTERN NORTH AMERICA[a,24]

Term	Magnitude ($Tg\ S\ yr^{-1}$) for Eastern:					
	Canada		U.S.A.		North America	
Manmade emissions	2.1	(47)[b]	14	(91)	16	(93)
Natural emissions						
Sea spray, internal	0.06	(1)			0.06	(-)[c]
Terrestrial biogenic	0.06	(1)	0.04	(-)	0.1	(1)
Marine biogenic	0.2	(4)	0.4	(2)	0.6	(3)
Inflow from oceans	0.04	(1)	0.02	(-)	0.06	(-)
Inflow from west	0.1	(2)	0.4	(2)	0.5	(3)
Inflow to U.S. from Canada			0.7	(5)		
Inflow to Canada from U.S.	2.0	(44)				
Total	4.6	(100)	15.6	(100)	17.4	(100)

[a]Area includes Ontario, Quebec, the Atlantic Provinces, the Gulf of St. Lawrence, approximately one-half of the Hudson Bay, and in the United States, all area east of 92°W (approximately east of the Mississippi River).

[b]Numbers in parentheses indicate percent of total emissions (natural and manmade).

[c]Dashes indicate negligible contribution.

TABLE 2-4. ESTIMATES OF GLOBAL EMISSIONS OF OXIDES OF NITROGEN AND RELATED COMPOUNDS (Tg N/yr)

	Delwiche, 1970[42]	Burns and Hardy, 1975[43]	Söderlund and Svensson, 1976[41]	Robinson and Robbins, 1975[40]	Liu et al., 1977[44]	Chameides et al., 1977[45]
NO_x emissions from land to atmosphere	NA	NA	40-108	NA	NA	NA
NO_x emissions from land and sea	NA	NA	NA	210 (NO)	NA	NA
NO_x formed by combustion	NA	15	19	15	NA	NA
NO_x formed by industrial processes	30	30	36	NA	40	NA
Atmospheric NH_3 transformation to NO_x	NA	30	3-8	NA	NA	NA
NH_3 emissions to atmosphere	NA	165 (land and sea)	113-244 (land)	870 (land and sea)	NA	NA
Atmospheric production of NO_x by lightning	NA	10	NA	NA	NA	30-40

NA = Not available.

TABLE 2-5. ESTIMATES OF THE GLOBAL EMISSIONS OF NO_x (NO AND NO_2) (Tg N/yr)

	Burns and Hardy, 1975[43]	Söderlund and Svensson, 1976[41]	Robinson and Robbins, 1975[40]	Crutzen and Ehhalt, 1977[46]	Chameides et al., 1977[45]
Natural emissions from land to atmosphere	NA	21-89	NA	NA	NA
Natural emissions from land and sea to atmosphere	NA	NA	210	NA	NA
Tropospheric production by lightning	10	NA	NA	8-40	30-40
Stratospheric production from N_2O	5	0.3	2	NA	NA
Atmospheric production from NH_3	NA	3-8	NA	NA	NA
Production during combustion	15	19	15	NA	NA
Other industrial production	30	36	NA	NA	NA

NA = Not available.

ANTHROPOGENIC SOURCES OF SO_x AND NO_x EMISSIONS

Magnitude and Distribution

Nationwide emissions of sulfur oxides (SO_x) and nitrogen oxides (NO_x) are summarized in this section. These two pollutants, which are the primary precursors in acid rain formation, rank third and fifth, respectively, when compared to national discharges of the other three criteria pollutants (viz., particulates, hydrocarbons, and carbon monoxide). For purposes of assessing the magnitude and distribution of SO_x and NO_x emissions, data from the 1977 National Emissions Data System (NEDS)[51] were originally reviewed and then updated with point and area source data contained in the NEDS computer files as of July 1982. The base year (date-of-record year) in both cases above may be misleading. For example, it has been observed that early 1982 NEDS files generally represented a 1978/1979 data base, with some data being as old as 1975.[52] However, in view of frequent updating, especially of power plant emissions, the representative average base year for these emissions has been taken to be 1980. Similarly, for the published 1977 NEDS figures, the representative base year may be taken as 1975. It is worthwhile to point out that the comparison of date-of-record emissions for 1977 and 1982 did not reveal any major shifts in the percent contribution from various source types. However, total SO_x decreased by approximately 7.6 percent, NO_x increased by nearly 10.6 percent, and some state totals of these emissions shifted over this 5-year period.

Total emissions of SO_x and NO_x for 1982 (date-of-record) are shown to be 29.1 and 24.0×10^6 tons, respectively. Stationary fuel combustion is a major contributor of both pollutants as shown in Figures 2-2 and 2-3. In the case of SO_x, fuel combustion accounts for 78 percent of the total, whereas for NO_x, its contribution is 56 percent. The second most important source of SO_x emissions is industrial processes, which account for about 18 percent of the total. Industries pertaining to primary metals (8.8 percent), petroleum (3.0 percent), chemical manufacturing (3.3 percent), and mineral products (1.8 percent) are the major sources. A further breakdown of these industrial process SO_x emissions is possible: copper smelters account for 75 percent of primary metal emissions; process heaters and catalytic cracking operations account for about 60 percent of petroleum industry emissions; sulfuric acid and elemental sulfur production make up 67 percent of the chemical manufacturing category; and cement manufacturing contributes about 90 percent of SO_x emissions in the mineral products industry.

Figure 2-3 indicates that the transportation category is second in importance to fuel combustion, accounting for 40 percent of total NO_x emissions. About 56 percent of the transportation contribution is produced by gasoline combustion, and 41 percent is produced by diesel fuel combustion.

Although the magnitude of the SO_x and NO_x emission problem is important, of at least equal concern is how these emissions are distributed across the country. Figures 2-4 and 2-5 represent 1982 emission density maps for SO_x and NO_x, respectively, wherein emissions per square mile are indicated by progressively darker areas. It is readily apparent that most of the SO_x emissions occur in the eastern half of the country. In fact, the

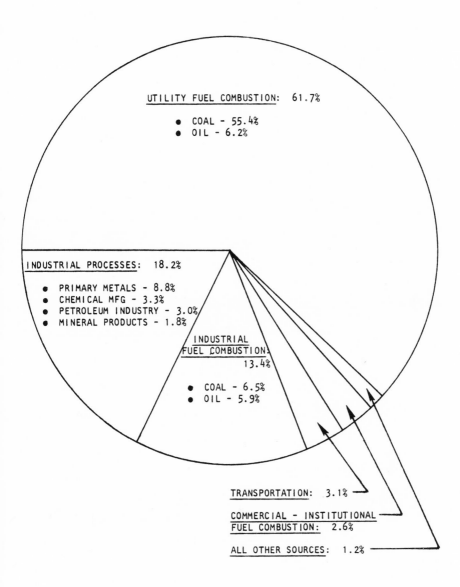

UTILITY FUEL COMBUSTION: 61.7%

- COAL - 55.4%
- OIL - 6.2%

INDUSTRIAL PROCESSES: 18.2%

- PRIMARY METALS - 8.8%
- CHEMICAL MFG - 3.3%
- PETROLEUM INDUSTRY - 3.0%
- MINERAL PRODUCTS - 1.8%

INDUSTRIAL
FUEL COMBUSTION:
13.4%

- COAL - 6.5%
- OIL - 5.9%

TRANSPORTATION: 3.1%

COMMERCIAL - INSTITUTIONAL
FUEL COMBUSTION: 2.6%

ALL OTHER SOURCES: 1.2%

Figure 2-2.   Percentage of 1982 national SO$_x$ emissions
by source category.

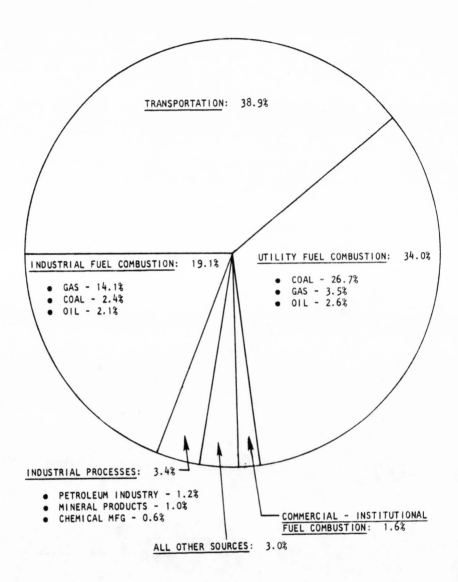

Figure 2-3. Percentage of 1982 national NO_x emissions
by source category.

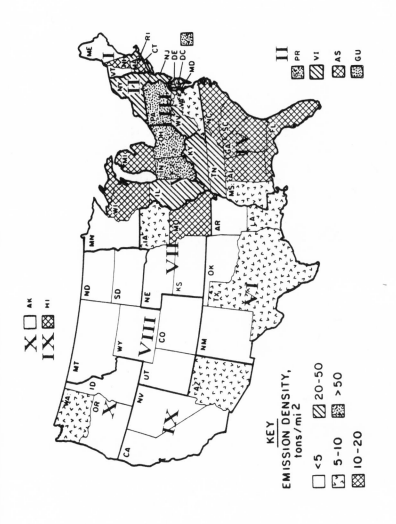

Figure 2-4. Characterization of U.S. SO$_x$ emission density by state (1982).

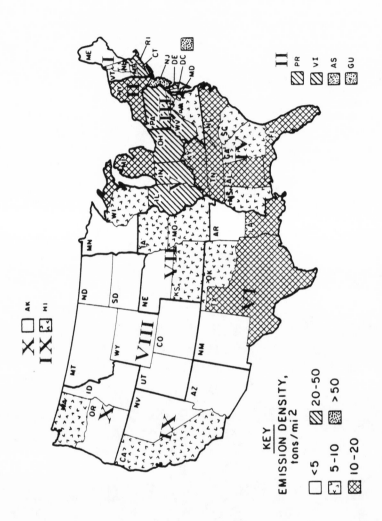

Figure 2-5. Characterization of U.S. NO$_x$ emission density by state (1982).

26 states east of the Mississippi River account for 20.6×10^6 tons or
71 percent of the total SO_x emissions in the country. Although emission
estimates on a state-by-state basis are more accurate than those made using
smaller subdivisions [i.e., counties or Air Quality Control Regions (AQCRs)],
emission density maps for SO_x and NO_x (Figures 2-6 and 2-7, respectively)[53]
by county are provided to indicate the "hot spots" within each state. It
should be noted that the date-of-record year for Figures 2-6 and 2-7 is 1977,
and the average representative year may be earlier.

To provide additional insight into the major contributing states and the
important source categories in each state, two tables have been prepared.
Table 2-6 provides a list of 20 states that together constitute at least
80 percent of total U.S. SO_x emissions. Total state emissions, percent of
U.S. total, and the major source categories comprising at least 80 percent of
the states' emissions are indicated. Electric generation by bituminous coal
(abbreviated in the table as EG/BC) is seen to be a major factor in most of
these high-ranked states. Table 2-7 shows 25 states that contribute (in the
aggregate) at least 80 percent of total national NO_x emissions. A breakdown
for each state is given only between total fuel combustion and transportation
because NO_x emissions are fairly evenly split among the numerous fuel
combustion subcategories. The fuel combustion and transportation categories
together comprise 90 percent or more of the total NO_x emissions in each of
the states listed in Table 2-7. Also, the fuel combustion category accounts
for the majority of the NO_x emissions in all of these 25 states except for
California, Florida, New Jersey, Virginia, and Washington.

Regional Summaries--
     Besides looking at emissions on a state basis, it is also of interest to
determine which sections or regions of the country are important in terms of
magnitude and source distribution. The following discussion summarizes
emissions by EPA region. (These regions are highlighted on the statewide
emission density maps, Figures 2-4 and 2-5.) Because stationary fuel
combustion and transportation are dominant categories in most states, other
source categories are mentioned only if they are significant. Population
statistics cited in these regional summaries represent 1980 data.[54]

*   Region I--(Connecticut, Maine, Massachusetts, New Hampshire, Rhode
     Island, Vermont). The New England area is not especially noted for
     heavy industry, nor are there many coal-burning utility or
     industrial facilities. The region contains 5.3 percent of the U.S.
     population but contributes only 2.6 percent of total NO_x and 2.4
     percent of total SO_x.

*   Region II--(New Jersey, New York, Puerto Rico, Virgin Islands).
     This region makes up about 12.2 percent of the U.S. population. The
     region contributes only 6 percent and 5.6 percent of U.S. SO_x and
     NO_x emissions, respectively.

*   Region III--(Delaware, District of Columbia, Maryland, Pennsylvania,
     Virginia, West Virginia). This region, consisting of the five
     mid-Atlantic states and the District of Columbia, accounts for
     10.7 percent of the population. Total SO_x is 4.3×10^6 tons

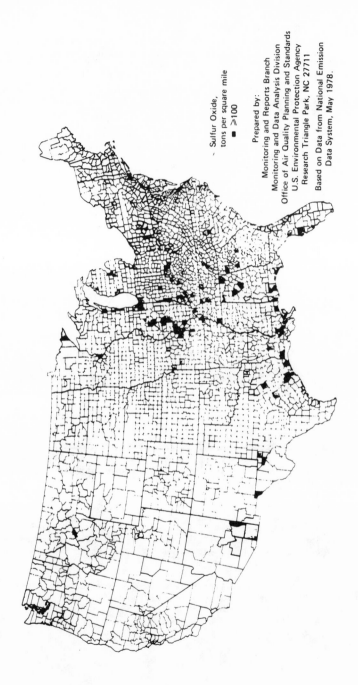

Sulfur Oxide,
tons per square mile
■ ≥100

Prepared by:
Monitoring and Reports Branch
Monitoring and Data Analysis Division
Office of Air Quality Planning and Standards
U.S. Environmental Protection Agency
Research Triangle Park, NC 27711
Based on Data from National Emission
Data System, May 1978.

Figure 2-6.   SO$_x$ emission density by county.[53]

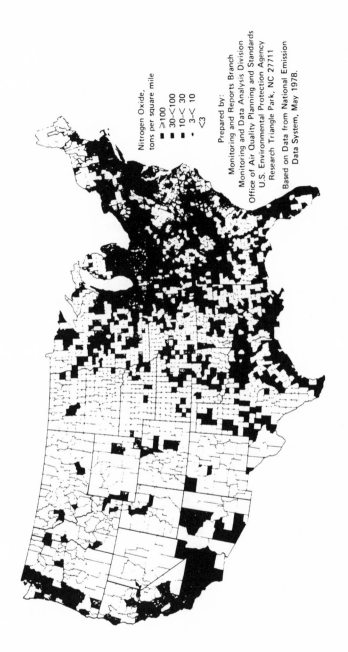

Nitrogen Oxide,
tons per square mile

≥100
30–<100
10–< 30
3–< 10
<3

Prepared by:
Monitoring and Reports Branch
Monitoring and Data Analysis Division
Office of Air Quality Planning and Standards
U.S. Environmental Protection Agency
Research Triangle Park, NC 27711

Based on Data from National Emission
Data System, May 1978.

Figure 2-7. NO_x emission density by county.[53]

TABLE 2-6.   NATIONAL DISTRIBUTION OF 1982 SO_x EMISSIONS

State (by rank)	SO_x emissions (10^6 tons)	% of U.S. SO_x total	Major source(s)--% of state
1. Ohio	2.78	9.6	EG/BC--79.9; IF/BC--11.7
2. Pennsylvania	2.32	8.0	EG/BC--61.5; PM--14.1; IF/BC--7.5
3. Indiana	1.90	6.5	EG/BC--82.5
4. Texas	1.60	5.5	CM--24.6; IF--16.0; PM--13.6; EG/L--11.6; PI--11.1; T--5.9
	Subtotal	29.6	
5. Illinois	1.50	5.1	EG/BC--74.4; IF/BC--7.5
6. Missouri	1.31	4.5	EG/BC--87.4
7. Kentucky	1.20	4.1	EG/BC--87.5
8. West Virginia	1.15	3.9	EG/BC--84.9
9. Florida	1.13	3.9	EG/RO--32.8; EG/BC--31.1; CM--9.5; IF/RO--7.3
	Subtotal	51.1	
10. Tennessee	1.12	3.8	EG/BC--84.6
11. New York	1.07	3.7	IF/RO--24.8; EG/RO--22.3; EG/BC--21.7; CIF/RO--8.2; IF/BC--7.3
12. Arizona	0.93	3.2	PM--82.8
13. Georgia	0.895	3.1	EG/BC--84.0
14. Michigan	0.875	3.0	EG/BC--63.0; IF/BC--11.7; PM--9.2

(continued)

TABLE 2-6 (continued)

	State (by rank)	SO_x emissions (10^6 tons)	% of U.S. SO_x total	Major source(s)--% of state
15.	Alabama	0.84	2.9	EG/BC--66.7; IF/BC--10.7; CM--4.0
16.	Wisconsin	0.71	2.4	EG/BC--69.9; IF/BC--14.6
17.	North Carolina	0.64	2.2	EG/BC--68.6; IF/RO--16.0
18.	California	0.565	1.9	PI--22.0; T--20.8; IF/RO--19.5; EG/RO--9.2; CM--7.6; PM--4.0
19.	New Mexico	0.475	1.6	PM--51.9; EG/BC--16.5; PI--14.4
20.	Louisiana	0.41	1.4	CIF/RO--29.9; PI--18.7; IF/DO--9.6; T--8.8; CM--7.0; EG/RO--6.6
		Total	80.3	

KEY:
- EG = Electric generation (external combustion only)
- IF = Industrial fuel use
- CIF = Commercial/institutional fuel use
- BC = Bituminous coal
- RO = Residual oil
- DO = Distillate oil
- L = Lignite
- PI = Petroleum industry
- PM = Primary metals
- CM = Chemical manufacturing
- T = Transportation

TABLE 2-7.   NATIONAL DISTRIBUTION OF 1982 NO$_x$ EMISSIONS

State (by rank)	NO$_x$ emissions (10^6 tons)	% of U.S. NO$_x$ total	Percentage of state emissions attributable to:	
			Fuel combustion	Transportation
1. Texas	3.41	14.2	73.5	22.3
2. California	1.44	6.0	32.1	57.9
3. Ohio	1.20	5.0	59.2	38.1
	Subtotal	25.2	60.8	33.9
4. Illinois	1.16	4.8	59.8	36.3
5. Pennsylvania	1.13	4.7	58.8	37.1
6. Indiana	0.85	3.5	63.2	32.6
7. New York	0.76	3.2	49.3	48.6
8. Louisiana	0.75	3.1	62.0	25.8
9. Florida	0.73	3.0	45.6	48.6
10. Michigan	0.73	3.0	54.6	41.3
	Subtotal	50.5	58.8	36.1
11. Missouri	0.61	2.5	56.1	37.8
12. North Carolina	0.58	2.4	55.2	42.4
13. Kentucky	0.58	2.4	61.1	34.6
14. Alabama	0.57	2.4	62.7	32.6
15. Georgia	0.56	2.3	50.9	44.8
16. Tennessee	0.56	2.3	56.2	39.0
17. West Virginia	0.56	2.3	80.9	15.1
18. Kansas	0.50	2.1	66.2	31.8
19. Oklahoma	0.44	1.8	58.1	36.8
20. New Jersey	0.43	1.8	41.6	54.3
21. Wisconsin	0.42	1.8	51.4	45.5
22. Minnesota	0.41	1.7	50.0	47.6
23. Virginia	0.40	1.7	39.3	54.1
24. Washington	0.35	1.4	34.9	55.4
25. New Mexico	0.34	1.4	73.3	23.9
	Total	80.8	58.0	37.2

(15 percent of the U.S. total) and total NO_x is 2.4×10^6 tons or 10.3 percent of total U.S. emissions. Aside from fuel combustion and transportation, primary metals (two zinc smelting complexes) contribute 14 percent of Pennsylvania's SO_x emissions.[55]

- Region IV--(Alabama, Florida, Georgia, Kentucky, Mississippi, North Carolina, South Carolina, Tennessee). This region in the southeastern United States, made up of eight states, represents 16.8 percent of the U.S. population. Sulfur oxide emissions are 6.5×10^6 tons (22.2 percent of the U.S. total), whereas NO_x emissions are 4.2×10^6 tons (17.4 percent of U.S. emissions). The only significant industry besides fuel combustion and transportation contributing to emissions is chemical manufacturing, which accounts for about 9.5 percent of Florida's SO_x total, probably attributable to 14 sulfuric acid plants located in the state.

- Region V--(Illinois, Indiana, Michigan, Minnesota, Ohio, Wisconsin). Region V has higher emissions of both SO_x and NO_x than any other region. It contains more people than any other region (approximately 20 percent of the U.S. population), but accounts for 27.5 percent of total SO_x and 20 percent of total NO_x emissions. Stationary fuel combustion is by far the most important source of SO_x emissions in the region with the following percent contribution from each state in the region (followed, in parentheses, by percent contributions from electric generation by bituminous coal):

  - Indiana   - 95 (83)

  - Ohio   - 95 (80)

  - Wisconsin - 93 (70)

  - Illinois   - 89 (74)

  - Minnesota - 88 (54)

  - Michigan   - 81 (63)

- Region VI--(Arkansas, Louisiana, New Mexico, Oklahoma, Texas). The five south-central states in this region represent about 10.8 percent of the U.S. population and account for about 9 percent of total SO_x and 21.4 percent of total NO_x. The high NO_x contribution is primarily from Texas, which leads the country in this category, contributing 14.2 percent of the U.S. total. Sulfur oxide emission sources other than fuel combustion that are important in this region are: Texas--57 petroleum refineries, 14 sulfuric acid plants, 1 copper smelter and 4 zinc smelters; New Mexico--8 petroleum refineries and 1 copper smelter; and Louisiana--32 petroleum refineries.

- Region VII--(Iowa, Kansas, Missouri, Nebraska). These four states in the central United States account for 5.1 percent of the population, 6.5 percent of SO_x emissions, and 6.7 percent of NO_x emissions.

- Region VIII--(Colorado, Montana, North Dakota, South Dakota, Utah, Wyoming). The six mountain states in the north-central United States account for only 3.0 percent of the population, 3.0 percent of SO_x emissions, and 4.8 percent of NO_x emissions.

- Region IX--(Arizona, California, Hawaii, Nevada, Guam, American Samoa). Four states and the territories of Guam and American Samoa make up this region, which represents about 12.2 percent of the U.S. population. This region contributes 6.7 percent of total SO_x emissions and 8.3 percent of total NO_x emissions. Other than fuel combustion, large emissions of SO_x are produced by 7 copper smelters in Arizona and 42 petroleum refineries in California. Also, 58 percent of NO_x emissions in California are produced by transportation.

- Region X--(Alaska, Idaho, Oregon, Washington). The three northwestern states of Idaho, Oregon, and Washington and the state of Alaska constitute Region X, which accounts for 3.5 percent of the population, but only 1.7 percent of SO_x emissions and 3.1 percent of national NO_x emissions.

To determine the extent of any correlation between SO_x and NO_x emissions and population, linear regression analyses were performed on both a state and regional basis using the 1982 (date-of-record year) NEDS data. Correlation coefficients, denoted by r (with ± 1 being a perfect linear correlation), obtained were as follows:

- SO_x, regional, r = + 0.884;

- NO_x, regional, r = + 0.766;

- SO_x, state,   r = + 0.604; and

- NO_x, state,   r = + 0.749.

As indicated, the correlation coefficients are stronger on a regional basis than on a state basis for both pollutants, but none (except for the SO_x regional coefficient) appears to be statistically significant. The higher coefficient for regional SO_x compared to state SO_x may be attributed to the fact that utilities in one state often supply electricity to neighboring states and thus the emissions are not directly a function of the supplying state's population. The similarity between the state and regional coefficients for NO_x is probably due to the fact that NO_x emissions are more equally spread among all types of fuel combustion sources as well as the transportation sector. However, an explanation of the fact that the NO_x regional coefficient is so much lower than the SO_x regional coefficient is not readily apparent.

Historical Data--
    Nationwide estimates of SO_x and NO_x are available from the EPA emission estimates[53,56] for 1940 through 1982. These data are shown graphically in Figures 2-8 and 2-9 for SO_x and NO_x, respectively. Between 1940 and 1960, the estimated total U.S. emissions of SO_x to the atmosphere increased very little, from 21.9 x 10^6 tons/yr to 24.1 x 10^6 tons/yr, whereas NO_x increased from 6.7 x 10^6 tons/yr to 11.5 x 10^6 tons/yr. Although the data from 1970 to 1982 are more reliable than those for the years 1940, 1950, and 1960, both pollutants show a significant increase from 1960 to 1970. In the period from 1960 to 1976, SO_x reached its peak in 1970 with 32.1 x 10^6 tons/yr, viz., a 46 percent increase from 1940; whereas NO_x rose to 25.1 x 10^6 tons/yr in 1973, representing a 273 percent increase from 1940 and a 117 percent increase from 1960.[56]

    The large growth in utility SO_x emissions was compensated in part by reduction in industrial and residential/commercial emissions, produced by switches from coal to oil and gas in the 1940's and 1950's. Most utility emissions are from coal, reflecting the impact of new sources equipped with flue gas desulfurization (FGD) systems[57] in the 1970's, and the impact of mandated fuel switching (resulting from the Energy Supply and Environmental Control Act--ESECA and the Power Plant Industrial Fuel Use Act--PIFUA). Transportation, industrial, and utility sources contributed most to increased NO_x emissions.

    Based on the NEDS date-of-record years of 1977 and 1982, SO_x emissions decreased by 2.4 x 10^6 tons or 7.6 percent, while NO_x emissions increased by 2.3 x 10^6 tons or 10.6 percent over this 5-year period. With respect to SO_x, states (from Table 2-6) that experienced significant declines (with percent decrease in parentheses) were: Ohio (-14.7), Kentucky (-26.4), Arizona (-25), Michigan (-28.3), and Alabama (-19.2). Increases in SO_x emissions were recorded in Texas (+3.9), Florida (+14.3), and Georgia (+27.9). With two exceptions, all of these changes were due to electric generation by bituminous coal; Arizona's decrease was due to a reduction in the primary metal (copper smelter) sector while Florida's increased emissions were due to the chemical manufacturing (sulfuric acid) industry. With respect to NO_x, the most significant increase occurred in Texas where emissions rose 60 percent above 1977 levels, while California NO_x emissions increased by 12.5 percent. These two states were ranked first and second in 1977 and remain in that order at the present time. Other significant percentage increases occurred in Kansas (+43 percent), Georgia (+16 percent), and West Virginia (+16 percent), although the magnitude of NO_x emissions in these states is much less than either Texas or California. For these five states, NO_x emission increases were due to fuel combustion sources.

Projections--
    Figures 2-10 and 2-11 present the national trends discussed above for SO_x and NO_x, respectively, along with projections to the year 2000.[57] These emission estimates are based on several future energy scenarios that have been studied at Brookhaven National Laboratory under the sponsorship of DOE's Office of Environmental Assessments.[57] These scenarios are defined in

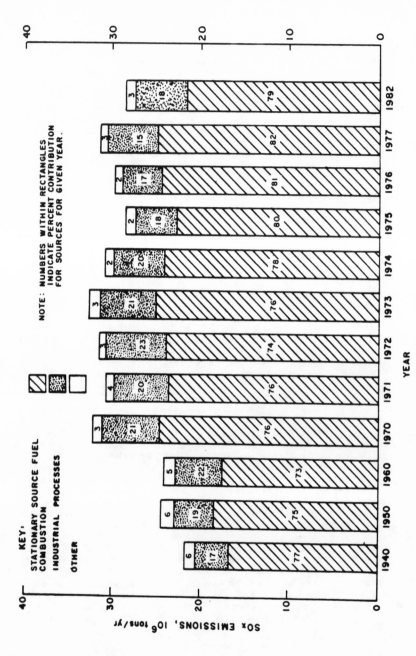

Figure 2-8. Trends in national SO$_x$ emissions since 1940.[53,56]

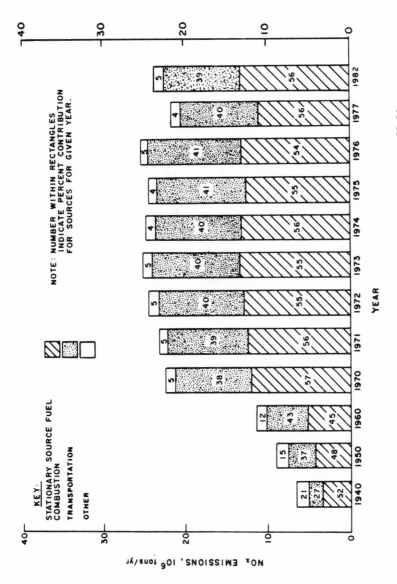

Figure 2-9.   Trends in national NO_x emissions since 1940.53,56

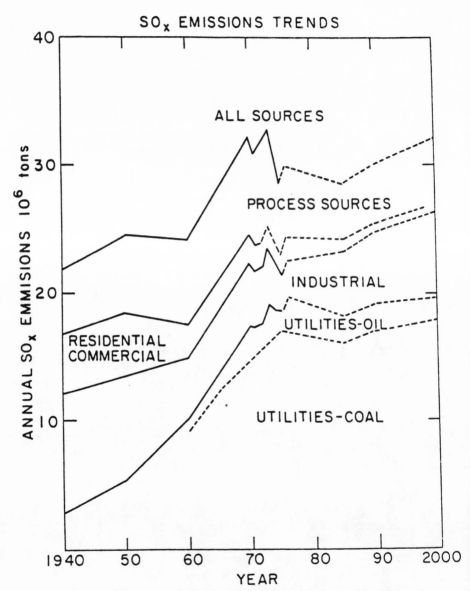

Figure 2-10. SO_x emissions trends for the U.S., 1940-2000
(projections based on NEP II).[57]

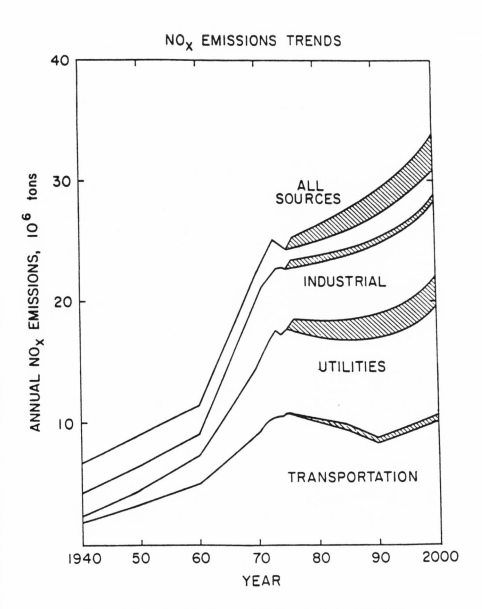

Figure 2-11.   NO$_x$ emissions trends for the U.S., 1940-2000
(projections based on NEP II).[57]

the Second National Energy Plan (NEP II), with future-year data adjusted to correspond to the 1975 EPA data to present continuous trends. The shaded areas on Figure 2-11 represent the range of scenarios defined in NEP II for NO_x. Transportation will continue to be a major source of NO_x, although the dip noted in Figure 2-11 between 1975 and 1990, corresponding to the imposition of emission controls, may not be realized due to waivers being given to automobile manufacturers. More recent projections, based on the National Energy Policy Plan[58] (also known as NEP III), show somewhat different trends for SO_x and NO_x emissions. In the year 2000, SO_x emissions are projected to be between 26.8 and 32.9 million tons; the range for NO_x emissions is 19.2 to 24.7 million tons.

Although these figures give a complete picture of national trends, a regional-scale analysis emphasizing planned coal-fired electric generating capacity (an important contributor to SO_x and NO_x emissions) will aid in assessing environmental impacts. Table 2-8 shows current and planned increases in electric generating capacity by EPA region for coal and oil over the period 1979 through 1989 based on the results of a survey conducted by the National Coal Association.[59] It is important to note that sizable increases (greater than 25 percent) in coal burning occur in all but three northeastern regions (Regions I, II, and III). Historically, the Northeast's contribution to total U.S. SO_x and NO_x has been decreasing (based on the NEP II and NEP III scenarios mentioned above); viz., 30 percent of the SO_x in 1970, 25 percent in 1975, and 18 percent projected in the year 2000; and 20 percent for NO_x in 1970, 17 percent in 1975, and 14 percent in the year 2000.[57] In view of these facts, it appears that the extent of interregional transfer of airborne sulfur and nitrogen oxides produced by coal burning in regions lying to the west may be an important environmental issue for the Northeast.

Local Sources--
    Although long-range transport of SO_x and NO_x from coal-fired power plants appears to be a significant factor for the Northeast, local sources of SO_x and NO_x may also contribute to the acid rain phenomenon in this region as well as in other parts of the country. It has been suggested (as will be discussed in more detail under Factors Affecting Source Emissions--Combustion Variables) that local oil-fired sources are especially suspect for two reasons:[60]

1. Burning of both distillate and residual oil produces large quantities of primary sulfates, which are formed in the furnace and need not undergo chemical reaction to participate in the formation of acid rain. Small residential and commercial boilers emit a much higher percentage of primary sulfates than do utility oil-fired boilers.[61]

2. Burning of residual oil releases large quantities of finely divided catalytic materials, such as vanadium and carbon, which can catalyze the transformation of sulfur dioxide to sulfate as these substances remain suspended in the atmosphere.[62]

TABLE 2-8.   CURRENT AND PLANNED INCREASES IN U.S. ELECTRIC GENERATING
CAPACITY BY EPA REGION, 1979-1989[59]

EPA region	Current (1978) capacity (MW)	Planned increase (MW)			Percent increase		
		Coal	Oil	Total	Coal	Oil	Total
I	11,984	600	–	600	5	–	5
II	23,580	1,550	850	2,400	6	3.5	10
III	49,948	9,547	1,820	11,367	19.1	3.7	22.8
IV	83,545	31,522	2,222	33,744	37.7	2.7	40.4
V	84,875	21,730	1,350	23,080	25.6	1.6	27.2
VI	73,771	37,886	480	38,366	51.4	0.6	52
VII	22,725	11,870	–	11,870	52.2	–	52.2
VIII	12,274	15,770	–	15,770	128	–	128
IX	29,386	7,896	–	7,896	26.9	–	26.9
X	1,329	530	–	530	40	–	40
Totals	393,417	138,901	6,722	145,623	35.3	1.7	37

In addition to the Northeast, acidification of lakes in Florida and California may be partially attributable to local source contributions.[38] In California, for example, there are a significant number of petroleum refineries and nearly all stationary combustion facilities burn oil or natural gas. In Florida, the majority of the fuel burning facilities use residual oil and there is probably an important contribution from the state's sulfuric acid and phosphate mining industries. On the other hand, researchers in Florida have noted that the more acidic rain is associated with air masses from the north.[63] Both of Florida's northern bordering states are large coal-burning states; 92 percent of Georgia's electric generation is by coal and 76 percent of the state's SO_x emissions are due to coal burning. In Alabama, the figures are 98 and 80 percent, respectively. These data may suggest that long-range transport is a factor in Florida's acid rain problem. In both Florida and California, it should be noted that emissions of NO_x are significant--especially from mobile transportation sources--and may also contribute to local rain acidification. These issues are discussed in detail in Section 4.

Canadian Emission Inventory--

The data cited in this section for SO_x and NO_x emissions in Canada are primarily from the work of Voldner, Shah, and Whelpdale.[64] This inventory has been developed by the Canadian Department of the Environment as part of its Long-Range Transport of Air Pollutants (LRTAP) Program. The inventory consists of point and area sources mainly for 1974,[65] but in some cases updated to 1976 and 1977.

Total annual emissions are given as 6.5×10^6 short tons for SO_2 and 2.2×10^6 short tons for NO_2. (These values are 21 and 10 percent, respectively, of SO_x and NO_x emissions in the United States for the same period.) Emission density maps for each of these pollutants are shown in Figures 2-12 and 2-13, where the numbers cited represent ktonnes/yr.[64] Point sources contribute 80 percent of the total SO_2 emissions, and area sources such as transportation and residential fuel combustion account for 85 percent of total NO_2 emissions. Ontario, where 90 percent of the sources are classified as point sources, contributes 40 percent of all SO_2 emissions. These sources are concentrated in several areas. For example, the Sudbury smelting complex in Ontario combined with the utility sector account for 80 percent of the point source emissions, and in Alberta, the Oil Sands development and natural gas fields account for 90 percent of point source emissions. Quebec, where 71 percent of the sources are classified as point sources, accounts for 23 percent of total SO_2 emissions.

Although data are currently unavailable for long-term projections of Canadian sulfur emissions, they should be similar to trends in the United States.[66] Canadian smelter emissions are expected by the end of the century to produce SO_2 emissions ranging from current levels to 60 percent of these levels as older plants are phased out and replaced by newer and better-controlled facilities. As with SO_2 emissions, NO_2 projections are expected to follow U.S. trends with increases primarily in the utility sector.[66]

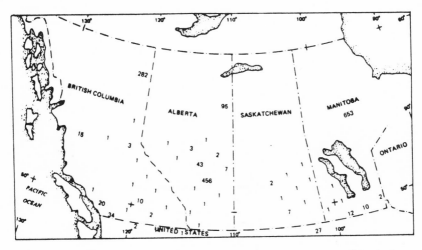

a.   SO₂ emissions in western Canada from all sources (10³ MT/yr).

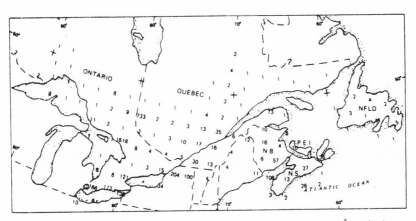

b.   SO₂ emissions in eastern Canada from all sources (10³ MT/yr).

Figure 2-12.   Total SO$_2$ emissions in Canada.[64]

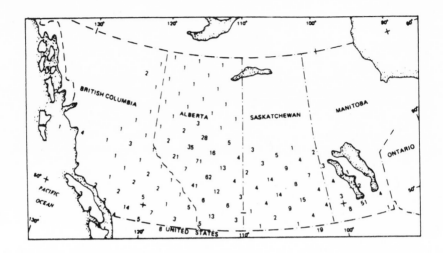

a.   NO$_2$ emissions in western Canada from all sources (10^3 MT/yr).

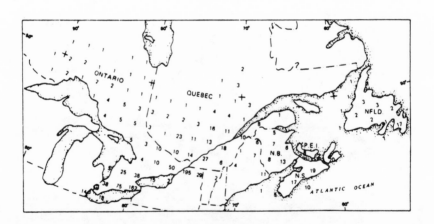

b.   NO$_2$ emissions in eastern Canada from all sources (10^3 MT/yr).

Figure 2-13.   Total NO$_2$ emissions in Canada.[64]

Factors Affecting Source Emissions

Uncontrolled Emissions From Combustion Sources--
The amount of uncontrolled SO_x emissions from a utility or industrial boiler depends on the amount and sulfur content of the fuel burned, the type and operating characteristics of the boiler, and other chemical and physical properties of the fuel. In the combustion of bituminous and anthracite coals, approximately 95 percent of the coal sulfur is emitted as gaseous SO_2 and SO_3^-; conversion of sulfur compounds in these fuels to SO_2 is 90 to 100 percent complete.[67,68] The remaining coal sulfur may be emitted as particulate sulfates or may combine with the slag or ash in the furnace and be disposed of as solid waste. The degree of SO_3^- formation, usually 1 to 2 percent of total SO_x, depends on combustion conditions, with, in general, a leaner fuel mixture forming more SO_3^-.[69] Other factors that will affect SO_3^- formation are boiler age, boiler design, and method of firing.

Sulfur retention in anthracite and bituminous coal ash is generally low, ranging from less than 1 percent at high ashing temperatures (1200°C) to 15 percent at low ashing temperatures (750°C).[70] There is some experimental evidence that sulfur in coal of high alkaline ash content tends to concentrate in the ash during combustion. A high-sodium lignite may retain over 60 percent of the available sulfur in the boiler,[71,72] whereas a low-sodium lignite may contain less than 10 percent of the available sulfur in the boiler ash.[73,74]

Experiments recently carried out by EPA to determine the percentage of fuel sulfur that is emitted as sulfate, have shown that in the case of coal combustion, approximately 1 to 3 percent of the sulfur is emitted as primary sulfate.[75] Several investigators have shown that excess boiler oxygen enhances the emission of primary sulfates from both oil-fired and coal-fired boilers.[75,76] In the presence of excess oxygen, SO_2 is oxidized to SO_3^- which then hydrolyzes to H_2SO_4. Sulfuric acid has been identified as the major constituent of the total water-soluble sulfate emissions from both oil and coal firing.[77] In general, industrial oil-fired boilers operate at higher excess oxygen levels and are found to emit a larger proportion of primary sulfates compared to utility boilers burning oil of the same sulfur content. This observation is also generally true of coal-fired boilers.

Homolya and Cheney[75] have also shown that for the same sulfur content in the fuel, primary sulfate emissions from oil combustion are from 5 to 10 times higher than those from coal. One explanation may be the higher flame temperature in oil-fired boilers which would exacerbate the formation of H_2SO_4, SO_3^-, and particulate sulfates by combination of SO_2 with atomic oxygen in the flame.[78] Moreover, the presence of specific metal species found in hydrodesulfurized and blended residual fuel oil, especially vanadium (~20 ppm) and nickel (~5 ppm),[79] serves to enhance the SO_2-atomic oxygen reaction by acting as catalysts thus leading to a higher rate of SO_3^- and SO_4^- formation.[80] Also, the high ash content entrained in the flue gases from a coal-fired boiler may tend to neutralize the acid that is formed, thereby accounting for the lower sulfate formation in coal-fired units. For oil-fired boilers, the percentage of primary sulfate can be calculated by knowing the vanadium concentration in the oil and the percent of excess oxygen.[79,81] However, at this time, the precise mechanism leading to sulfate formation in oil-firing is not well-defined.[80]

The extent of sulfate formation may also be influenced by specific boiler design parameters including the type and number of burners, residence time and temperature distribution in the boiler, and the size of the boiler tube surface area. It has been known for many years that an oxygen level in excess of stoichiometric for a given boiler will affect the formation of primary sulfates and H_2SO_4 by enhancing catalytic action on heat exchange surfaces.[82] Another source of primary sulfate emissions is frequent soot-blowing operations; the soot may contain sulfate produced by catalytic effects of trace fuel contaminants.

Emissions of NO_x from coal-fired power plants depend on the type of boiler and the manner in which it is operated. One of the most important variables is excess air and how it relates to temperature.[83] For a given furnace temperature distribution, the quantity of NO_x formed decreases as the excess air decreases. This is because of the reduced oxygen concentration in the high temperature flame zone in the furnace where the NO_x is formed. Reductions in the oxygen content decrease emissions of both fuel NO_x (generated by the oxidation of nitrogen in the fuel) and thermal NO_x (generated by the oxidation of nitrogen in combustion air). Reductions in temperature, however, produce significant reductions only in thermal NO_x.

The type of boiler is also important in determining expected NO_x emissions. Cyclone boilers produce greater amounts of NO_x than pulverized coal-fired boilers, and these emissions are greater than those from stoker boilers.[84] This is reflected in EPA emission factors[85] for each of the three boiler types as shown below.

Boiler type	Emission factor (lb NO_2/ton coal)
Pulverized	18
Stoker	15
Cyclone	55

These trends are consistent with the fact that cyclones have the highest heat release rates and furnace temperatures and that stokers have the lowest.

Emissions of NO_x from wet bottom boilers are higher than those from dry bottom boilers, which operate at lower temperatures. Lowest temperatures are

found in tangentially-fired units.[83] An analysis of 53 coal-fired utility
boilers showed no apparent correlation between NO_x emissions and boiler
size.[86]

With regard to oil firing, an analysis of NO_x emissions from 31
oil-fired utility boilers,[69,87] showed that for tangentially-fired units the
average NO_x emissions were 0.27 $lb/10^6$ Btu, while for all other types it
was 0.55 $lb/10^6$ Btu. Comparison of these rates with EPA emission factors
shows that the emission rates for tangentially-fired units are 20 percent
lower; whereas for other types they are 25 percent lower. A similar
comparison for 28 gas-fired boilers[69,87] shows a 7 percent difference
between average measured emission rates and EPA emission factors for
tangentially-fired units; and 19 percent for other units. In both of these
cases emission rates were lower than predicted by EPA emission factors.

Although the age of a boiler may affect the release of SO_x and NO_x
somewhat (due to decreased thermal transfer over time), the allowable
emissions for boilers predating New Source Performance Standards (NSPS) and
State Implementation Plans (SIPs) will have a greater impact on total
emissions. Older utility boilers are generally located in urban population
centers and have shorter stacks, hence the local impact may be greater than
from combustion units located in remote areas and having taller stacks.
Individual SIPs sometimes make this distinction and disallow the older plants
from emitting disproportionately higher emissions. In any event, the
retirement of these older units may be important to the acid rain issue, since
newer boilers replacing the older units over time would be required to meet
more stringent emission control levels.

Controlled Emissions From Combustion Sources--

Sulfur Oxides--Emissions of sulfur oxides can be reduced by burning lower
sulfur fuels, pretreating the fuel with reactive sorbents that retain sulfur
during combustion, and using a variety of flue gas desulfurization (FGD)
techniques. These methods can reduce SO_x emissions by as much as 90 to 95
percent and may affect primary sulfate emissions.

Over 100 billion tons of coal, representing 42 percent of all recoverable
reserves, are of sufficiently low sulfur content that they could be burned
without pretreatment or control and would not exceed an emission level of
1.2 $lb/10^6$ Btu.[88] (This is equivalent to burning 3.5 percent sulfur coal
having a heating value of 12,000 Btu/lb with an 85 percent control
efficiency.) Reserves are coals that are economically minable using currently
available technology; recoverability ranges from ~50 percent for underground
reserves to ~85 percent for surface reserves. Because the vast majority of
recoverable reserves are located in the western United States as shown in
Table 2-9,[88,89] their geographic availability is somewhat limited. A
significant portion of the eastern low-sulfur coal reserves are dedicated to
the production of metallurgical coke. Data comparing primary sulfate
emissions from low- and high-sulfur coal are inconclusive at present. Primary
sulfate emissions may be proportional to total sulfur emissions from
combustion facilities but will be affected by differences in ash composition,
specific boiler design parameters, and possibly the control technology used.

TABLE 2-9. ESTIMATES OF RECOVERABLE RESERVES OF RAW COAL CHARACTERIZED BY EMISSION RATE OF SULFUR DIOXIDE FROM UNCONTROLLED COMBUSTION[88,89]

Region	Recoverable reserve (millions of tons)	Emission rate of sulfur dioxide							
		1.2 lb $SO_2/10^6$ Btu		0.8 lb $SO_2/10^6$ Btu		0.6 lb $SO_2/10^6$ Btu		0.4 lb $SO_2/10^6$ Btu	
		% of reserve	Millions of tons	% of reserve	Millions of tons	% of reserve	Millions of tons	% of reserve	Millions of tons
Eastern	58,000	12	7,000	2	1,200	<1	0	0	0
Eastern Midwest	51,000	1	510	0	0	0	0	0	0
Western Midwest	13,000	5	650	2	260	0	0	0	0
Western	140,000	70	98,000	41	57,000	16	22,000	2	2,800
Total U.S.	262,000	42	106,160	22	58,460	8.4	22,000	1.1	2,800

Physical coal cleaning involves the separation of waste from coal by techniques based on differences in physical properties. Mineral or inorganic sulfur is often present as pyrite (FeS_2), which has a higher specific gravity than coal. Depending on the degree of size reduction and physical characteristics of the coal, approximately 35 to 70 percent of the mineral sulfur can be removed, as well as a significant amount of ash.[88] However, 30 to 70 percent of the coal sulfur can be present as organic sulfur. This sulfur was part of the plant material from which the coal was derived and cannot be removed by physical separation.[88] Thus, the overall sulfur removal effectiveness for physical cleaning can range from 10 to 50 percent, with 25 percent as a typical value. Chemical coal cleaning processes that are under development have the potential to remove nearly all of the inorganic sulfur plus some of the organic sulfur as well.[88]

Fluidized-bed combustion (FBC) is a developing technology capable of removing sulfur oxides as they are formed during the combustion process. Coal is burned in a turbulent bed of limestone which becomes calcined and subsequently reacts with SO_2 produced by the oxidation of coal sulfur. In the United States several manufacturers have built pilot-scale and industrial-sized systems and are now offering commercial-scale FBCs up to a capacity of 60,000 lb coal/hr.[90] After 4 years of testing on a 2,000 lb coal/hr unit, the Electric Power Research Institute (EPRI) concluded that 99 percent combustion efficiency, 90 percent SO_2 control at a Ca/S ratio of 2-to-1, and NO_x emissions of 0.2 $lb/10^6$ Btu can be achieved.[91] EPRI and the Tennessee Valley Authority (TVA) have built a 20 MW_e pilot plant and are planning a 200 MW_e demonstration plant scheduled to be fully operational by 1990.[91]

Flue gas can be desulfurized by both wet and dry removal processes. The dry process is a recent development that involves the injection of a lime slurry into a spray dryer countercurrently with the flue gases. The lime reacts with SO_2 to form a dry, solid product which is removed from the flue gas by a fabric filter or an electrostatic precipitator. In 1979 EPA concluded that 70 percent SO_2 removal using a lime sorbent is technically feasible and economically attractive when compared to wet scrubbing applied to coal-fired boilers burning 1.5 percent sulfur coals.[92] Full-scale systems, designed to achieve 70 percent SO_2 removal and higher, are being built.

Wet flue gas desulfurization systems have been applied to coal-fired boilers in the United States since the early 1970s. The current installed capacity on utility boilers is 34,000 MW_e and 70,000 MW_e additional capacity is planned or under construction.[93] The vast majority of current installations are limestone- or lime-based systems in which SO_x reacts with a slurry to produce a wet $CaSO_4/CaSO_3$ sludge that requires disposal. Other throwaway systems include sodium carbonate scrubbing and the double alkali process; the latter is claimed to be more reliable than limestone systems and has demonstrated SO_2 removal efficiencies in excess of 99 percent.[88,92] Federal New Source Performance Standards, based primarily on long-term demonstration experience with limestone and lime FGD systems, require most new utility boilers to achieve 85 percent SO_2 reduction.[92]

A variety of regenerable processes that produce a sulfur-based by-product are being developed as alternatives to the more commonly applied throwaway processes. The Wellman-Lord process has been applied to oil-fired boilers in Japan and on two coal-fired boilers in the United States.[94] Regenerable processes are designed to achieve the same SO_2 removal efficiencies as throwaway FGD processes.

Flue gas desulfurization systems, as shown in Table 2-10,[93] may be designed to remove SO_2, under certain conditions, with greater than 90 percent removal efficiency.[94] However, the results of an extended series of EPA tests at a conventional coal-fired boiler equipped with a wet-limestone FGD unit, showed that sulfate and SO_2 removal efficiencies can be very dissimilar.[95] Whereas SO_2 levels were reduced by 76 percent, which was within design specifications in this case, total sulfate removal was less than 30 percent. Other results in the same study showed increases in primary sulfate in the scrubber outlet stream. These increases may be produced by gaseous H_2SO_4 penetration of the scrubber demisters forming H_2SO_4 aerosol and by scrubber liquor reentrainment.

Although electrostatic precipitators, used to control particulate emissions from boilers using FGD systems, usually have little effect on overall SO_2 emissions, they may help to reduce total sulfate emissions by 50 percent or more.[75] However, conditions in hot-side electrostatic precipitators may promote sulfate formation. Arcing of corona discharges may cause localized hot spots at high temperatures as well as produce ozone, which can oxidize SO_2 to SO_3.[96] Also, because sulfate particles are generally submicron in size, they are not efficiently collected by electrostatic precipitators, thereby leading to sulfate enrichment of fine particulate matter in the outlet stream.[75,76,96]

Fuel additives usually containing magnesium have been used effectively to reduce primary sulfate emissions from oil-fired boilers.[75] These additives are selected for their ability to minimize the formation of SO_3 by reacting with or absorbing SO_3 and H_2SO_4. The reaction products are then retained in the bottom ash in the boiler or combine with fly ash which may then be collected by an electrostatic precipitator.

The above discussion serves to briefly highlight the control techniques currently available for reducing SO_2 emissions from combustion facilities, as well as the uncertainties associated with their capabilities to reduce primary sulfate and H_2SO_4 in flue gas streams. Underlying this discussion is the implicit question of whether reductions in SO_2 will lead to linear reductions in ambient sulfate levels. Although the implications of this association fall more fully in the province of Sections 3 and 4 of this report, from a control point of view it may be premature to conclude that reductions in SO_2 emissions will totally mitigate sulfate exposure. It has been suggested, for example, that since elevated sulfate levels are primarily associated with meteorological conditions and pollutants (some emanating from sources other than power plants) conducive to photochemical activity, it is conceivable that the total conversion of SO_2 to sulfates is strongly affected by the oxidant levels established through photochemical reactions, not by the total SO_2 present, which is independent of oxidant levels.[97] Further research is clearly needed to establish the effectiveness of SO_2 removal techniques as they relate to mitigation of ambient sulfate levels, as

TABLE 2-10. CONTROL TECHNOLOGIES FOR REDUCING SO_2 EMISSIONS FROM COMBUSTION SOURCES[93]

System	Effectiveness[a] ($\% SO_2$ reduction)	Applicability	Uncertainty	Waste disposal	Problems
Wet FGD Limestone Lime	75-90 (higher with additives)	All fuels	Cost is a function of size, sulfur content, location, redundancy, and equipment, and whether ash removal is included.[b]	Preferably oxidized to gypsum, otherwise settling problems in ponds and land-fill unless chemically fixed.	Waste disposal because of volume. Utilities skeptical of costs and relia-bility.[b]
Dual Alkali	90+	All fuels		As above.	As above.
Wellman Lord	90+	All fuels	Uncertain market by-products.	Potential water pollution problem.	High cost.
Dry scrubber	50-90	Low sulfur fuels	Performance data sparse.	Lime systems have minimal problems, whereas soda-based units have potential water pollution problems.	Waste disposal involves large volumes, opera-tional difficulties with variations in coal characteristics.
Low-Sulfur Fuel	—	Coal	Incremental costs, availability of supplies.		Boiler derating, effects on precipi-tator, transporta-tion, logistics.
Physical Coal Cleaning	Effective up to 25% sulfur removal.	Used for high pyritic sul-fur coals.	Coal variability and expansion of existing facilities.	Water pollution and solid waste disposal.	Energy losses, maintaining quality control.

[a]From Reference 94.

[b]This comment is equally applicable to all processes in this table.

well as the effectiveness of controls of those pollutants responsible for establishing oxidant levels.

Nitrogen oxides--Emissions of nitrogen oxides from coal- and oil-fired boilers are controlled primarily through combustion modifications, which include low excess air, overfire air, reduced combustion intensity, low NO_x burners, and NH_3 injection.[98] Flue gas treatment (FGT) systems are available and under development but have, in general, only been applied to oil-fired boilers in Japan.[98] Some FGT systems are designed to remove NO_x and SO_x simultaneously.[99]

Combustion modifications presently in use are the most cost-effective options for achieving low levels of NO_x control, viz., 5 to 60 percent, which is, at present, sufficient to meet existing NSPS levels. Each of these techniques is briefly described below.

- Low excess air consists of reducing the amount of combustion air to the minimum required to maintain acceptable furnace cleanliness, CO levels, and soot burnout.[98,100] Because less oxygen is available in the flame zone, both thermal NO_x and fuel NO_x formation are reduced. NO_x reductions of 5 to 25 percent are achievable with the effectiveness varying according to specific boiler design and age.[100,101]

- Overfire air, or staged combustion, is designed to initiate combustion in a fuel-rich zone and complete combustion in a lower temperature fuel-lean zone. Fuel NO_x is reduced because less oxygen is available during the initial combustion stage (volatilization), whereas thermal NO_x is reduced because peak temperatures are lowered.[100] Staged combustion can be achieved by removing selected burners from service or by reducing air to the burners and adding overfire air.

- The use of low NO_x burners for pulverized coal-firing is a recently-developed variation of staged combustion with achievable NO_x reduction efficiencies in the range of 45 to 60 percent. Low NO_x burners are generally designed to reduce flame turbulence, delay fuel/air mixing, and initiate combustion under fuel-rich conditions. In addition, these conditions may be suitable for controlling SO_x emissions by reacting sulfur species with calcium oxide. Limestone Injection Multistage Burners (LIMBs), although not commercially available, are the subject of major EPA research programs.

- Reduced combustion intensity lowers NO_x emissions by lowering peak temperatures. Boiler load reduction is effective in reducing combustion intensity in existing units, whereas new units can be designed with larger furnace volumes.[98]

- Ammonia injection can, under certain conditions, reduce NO_x to N_2 resulting in removal efficiencies in the range of 40 to 60 percent. The ammonia must be injected into the furnace at locations where the gas temperature is 1460 to 1860°F.

The effectiveness, operational, environmental, and cost impacts, and availability of these combustion modification NO_x control techniques for pulverized coal-fired boilers are presented in Table 2-11. The effects of combustion modifications on sulfate emission rates have not been measured. Reduced oxygen concentrations in the furnace can be expected to reduce the oxidation of SO_2 to SO_3.[98] Overfire air and low NO_x burners may also cause small reductions in SO_3 emissions, whereas ammonia injection may increase SO_3 emissions.[98]

Flue gas treatment systems may be applied to utility and industrial boilers if NO_x reductions beyond those achievable through combustion modification are required. Near-term applications will probably be limited to special cases in such NO_x-sensitive geographical areas as the California South Coast Air Basin. Many wet and dry FGT systems have been investigated in the laboratory and on pilot- and commercial-scales in Japan,[98] the vast majority of applications involving oil-fired boilers. FGT applications to coal-fired boilers have been seriously considered only within the last 3 years.

Selective catalytic reduction (SCR) is the only method that has demonstrated a 90 percent NO_x control capability and is commercially available.[103] In this method, ammonia is added to the flue gas and the mixture is passed over a catalyst bed to promote the reduction of NO_x. Although generally proprietary, such catalysts as vanadium oxide and titanium oxide have been demonstrated effective in lowering NO_x emissions. An SCR system is being installed on a commercial-scale coal-fired boiler in Japan, while in the United States SCRs are planned for a pilot-scale coal-fired unit and a commercial-scale oil-fired unit.[103]

Catalysts used in the selective catalytic reduction process may increase the oxidation of SO_2 to SO_3. The SO_3 may be emitted, collected in FGD equipment, deposited in the SCR system, or collected by particulate control equipment. Excess ammonia may react with SO_3 to produce NH_4HSO_4. It is anticipated that when particulate control equipment is used downstream of the SCR equipment, minor amounts, if any, of these sulfates will be emitted.[98]

Other Variables--
Variations in NO_x emissons can be expected because of seasonal variation in power production from fossil-fuel generating plants. On a nationwide basis, the variation is estimated at 15 percent; greatest production is in the summer and least is in the spring.[104] However, greater variation as well as different seasonal patterns have been reported for different areas of the country.[105] Factors that influence seasonal variabilities in mobile source emission of NO_x include temperature dependencies of emissions per vehicle mile traveled (viz., a 35 percent reduction as temperature increases from 20 to 90°F)[106] and changes in seasonal vehicle miles traveled (viz., nationwide, production is 18 percent higher in summer than in winter).[107] The potential impact of diurnal variations associated with motor vehicle traffic on ambient air quality are also important. Representing mobile sources by annual emissions data may underestimate their potential for producing short-term (peak) concentrations.

TABLE 2-11. COMBUSTION MODIFICATION TECHNIQUES FOR NO_x CONTROL ON PULVERIZED COAL-FIRED BOILERS[98]

Technique	Effectiveness[a] (% NO_x reduction)	Operational impact	Cost impact[b]	Environmental impact	Availability
Low excess air	5 - 25	Increased boiler efficiency.	Increased efficiency offsets capital and operating costs.	Possible increased CO and organic emissions.	Available
Overfire air	5 - 30	Possible increased slagging, corrosion. Perhaps slight decrease in boiler efficiency.	Major modification. Marginal increase in cost for new units.	Possible increased particulate and organic emissions.	Commercially offered but not demonstrated for this boiler/fuel category.
Reduced Combustion Intensity	5 - 25	None. Best implemented as increased furnace plan area in new designs.	Major modification. Marginal increase in cost for new units.	None	Technology transfer required from utility industry.
Low NO_x Burners	45 - 60	None expected.	Potentially most cost-effective.	None expected.	1981 to 1983[c]
NH_3 Injection	40 - 60	Possible implementation difficulties. Fouling problems with high sulfur fuels, load restrictions. Close operator attention required.	Several fold higher than conventional combustion modifications.	Possible emissions of NH_3 and byproducts.	Commercially offered but not demonstrated.

[a]Effectiveness based on control applied singly.

[b]Incremental cost impact noting capacity/cost of boiler to which control is applied.

[c]Reference 102.

Variations in SO_x emissions can also be expected due to seasonal
variation of major sources. Seasonal average grid SO_x emissions from the
Sulfate Regional Experiment (SURE) program (including utility, industrial,
commercial, residential, and transportation sources) show a peak in SO_2
during the winter months.[108] During the summer, high temperature and
atmospheric moisture content and the persistence of anticyclones contribute to
sulfate formation and the regional accumulation of sulfates and other air
pollutants. This phenomenon is discussed in detail in Section 3.

Of the industrial process sources discussed earlier, the primary metals
industries (principally copper, lead, and zinc) are potentially the largest
SO_x emitters. Factors affecting SO_2 emissions from smelters include the
quantity of raw ore processed, the ore sulfur content, the process
configuration, and the degree of sulfur removal and control for each process
step. The major portion of SO_2 is formed in the roasting, smelting,
sintering, and converting processes.[109]

Quality of Data Bases

The emission inventory that serves as the basis for estimates of the
magnitude and distribution of SO_x and NO_x described earlier in this
section, is NEDS,[51] which is operated through the EPA Office of Air Quality
Planning and Standards (OAQPS). This inventory contains point and area source
(including mobile) emissions data for the criteria pollutants that can be
assembled according to individual facilities, AQCRs, states, and the nation
for a variety of source categories. Although the reliability of the NEDS
inventory has been questioned and a number of other inventories are available,
the use of NEDS is practical for the following reasons: it has been in
operation for several years; it serves as the basis or beginning point for
several other inventories; it has a structured updating system; and it is
geographically inclusive of the source categories of interest in the present
study.

The NEDS inventory contains information for both point and area sources.
Point sources are defined as facilities that have a potential to emit
100 short tons/year or more of any of the criteria pollutants, although
smaller point sources sometimes reported by the states are included here. All
other sources (including mobile sources and the unreported point sources less
than 100 tons/year) are defined as area sources. Point source data were
originally obtained from state air pollution control agencies. These agencies
are required to submit revised data for certain sources on an annual basis.
Information reported for point sources includes the type of process, operating
rates and schedules, pollution control device and efficiency, stack
parameters, location data, fuel type and ash, sulfur, and heat contents, and
emission rates. Emissions data consist of stack measurements, engineering
calculations, emission factors, or, in some cases, a "guessed" estimate.

The NEDS area source file contains data on mobile sources, small
stationary sources, and miscellaneous sources such as forest fires and retail
gasoline distribution. States are not required to submit area source data.

Rather, the area source inventory is developed from data published by other Federal agencies and from validated data collected from state agencies. Area source data are updated annually by EPA's National Air Data Branch (NADB).

In concept, the NEDS data base should be a good indicator of emissions for most geographical areas. However, in reality, the data base may contain inaccuracies. Some of the factors that may contribute to the uncertainty are presented below:[51]

- unclassifiable source type, resulting in missing emissions or guessed estimates.

- mistakes and biases in the reported data,

- lack of complete and timely reporting by state agencies,

- emission factors of low reliability and/or inappropriate application,

- missing industrial process emissions from facilities that emit less than 100 tons/year, and

- inaccuracies in the procedures used to compile the NEDS area source data.

Inaccuracies introduced by the first item are considered to be minor in comparison to other sources of error.[51] Major mistakes in the data are investigated using edit programs or by reviewing NEDS output reports at NADB. However, other investigators have encountered such errors when using NEDS to develop other emission inventories.[110,111] Inaccuracies may exist in the area source data for small geographical areas,[51] presumably caused by the methods used to allocate statewide data to the county level. Although the area sources should constitute the difference between the total emissions and point source emissions, some point sources that emit less than 100 tons/year may not be included. In small geographical areas where these sources constitute a significant portion of the total emissions, the NEDS emissions inventory will be biased.[51]

Emission factors introduce uncertainty in the emission inventory, particularly as the region of interest narrows. An emission factor is simply the mass of emissions per unit of production or consumption. If a number of these are averaged for a particular type of operation (e.g., an oil-fired boiler) the result is an emission factor that is generally representative of the operation. EPA has compiled emission factors for numerous source types based on the results of measurements and engineering analyses.[85] Although these emission factors often provide fairly accurate estimates of average emissions, when applied to geographical areas where the distribution of sources is different from the national or industry average, the accuracy of the estimate decreases.

EPA has prepared nationwide emission estimates and compared them with emission totals derived from NEDS.[51] Nationwide fuel use, industrial production, and other appropriate data were used to determine activity levels for each source category. National average emission factors and pollution control device efficiencies were also used. This methodology is advantageous because all sources are taken into account. It has the disadvantages that measured emission rates from individual sources are not used and that the effect of location (important in mobile source emissions) is not taken into account. A comparison of EPA estimated emissions and NEDS emissions reveals that the totals for SO_x and NO_x agree to within approximately 5 and 15 percent, respectively, although for some source categories, the deviation exceeds 20 percent.[51]

Several emission inventories have been cited in the literature. Dykema and Kemp[111] have developed a nationwide inventory of NO_x, particulate, hydrocarbon, and CO emissions from stationary combustion-related sources. An inventory of SO_x, NO_x, particulate, and hydrocarbon emissions for the eastern United States and southeastern Canada was developed for the Sulfate Regional Experiment (SURE).[110] Brookhaven National Laboratories has developed an emission inventory for the northeast United States as part of the MAP3S program.[64] To aid long-range transport studies, Clark[112] has developed an inventory of Canadian and United States emissions east of the Rocky Mountains. Galloway and Whelpdale[24] used an inventory of sulfur emissions to develop a sulfur budget for eastern North America. The United States-Canada Research Group on the LRTAP program has cited an inventory composed of the United States portion of the SURE inventory and an updated Canadian inventory.[66] EPA is completing efforts to develop an inventory for the Northeast Corridor, which involves a careful review and update of each state's emission inventory and use of NEDS data for a few states. The NEDS and SURE data bases were used as an information source for most of these studies.

Although it does not include the total United States, the SURE emission inventory is very comprehensive (particularly from a modeling viewpoint) and possesses the following features:

- it encompasses the eastern United States, and southern Quebec and Ontario;

- the criteria pollutants are divided into component species (SO_2, sulfate, NO, NO_2, and hydrocarbons by reactivity);

- seasonal and diurnal variations in emissions are included; and

- hourly emissions of SO_x from the larger power plants are included for selected months.

The SURE inventory was partially derived from NEDS and expanded to include the features noted above. A fairly recent development, it has been adopted as the basis for many regional and individual point source inventory studies as well as long-range transport studies.

The United States portion of the SURE emissions inventory has been compared with the NEDS emission inventory for the same region.[51,110,113] This comparison shows that for total SO_x and NO_x emissions, the two inventories differ by less than 10 percent. Comparison of the SURE inventory with Galloway and Whelpdale's sulfur budget for the eastern United States[24] shows that sulfur emissions differ by less than 10 percent.[114]

Attempts have been made to evaluate the accuracy of several of the inventories mentioned above. Accuracy, as defined here, is simply an aggregate estimate of the uncertainties attached to individual reported and calculated data contained in the inventory. Klemm and Brennan[110] have reported an accuracy (uncertainty) of 17 percent for SO_2 and NO_x emissions in the SURE region. Dykema and Kemp indicate an accuracy of about 11 percent for their nationwide inventory of NO_x emissions from stationary source combustion processes.[111] Galloway and Whelpdale report an accuracy of 15 percent for the sulfur inventory they used.[24] It should be noted that these accuracy estimates relate to regional and national annual emissions; they do not describe seasonal variations or the accuracy at the state or small geographical area level.

Several other data bases exist for emission inventory analysis. Historically, most of these have been based on the NEDS data base with various degrees of modification, correction, or updating of specific source categories. Using different engineering assumptions, time frames, and emission factors, these inventories have produced slightly different results in terms of the magnitude and distribution of criteria pollutant emissions. As such, it is difficult to determine which is the best inventory, although those that are continually updated are presumably more accurate. It appears that on a large regional or national scale, the NEDS data base is in general agreement with other inventories. In examining such an emission inventory for smaller component regions, however, the emission estimates are subject to higher uncertainties. These greater uncertainties, which exist for NEDS as well as other emission inventories, arise from the manner in which the inventories are developed (e.g., use of nationwide emission factors for some sources which may not apply when examining smaller individual component regions). However, the NEDS inventory remains as one of the most comprehensive for describing the magnitude and distribution of emissions on a national scale.

Since 1975, 15 emission inventories have been developed and used by EPA and DOE personnel and contractors to some degree in various acid rain programs in the United States.[115] A tabulation of these inventories, which are updated periodically by NADB and used to better define the interrelationships between NEDS and other inventories, is presented in Table 2-12.[115] Since it is desirable that eventually one single emission inventory be accepted as the official data base for all acid rain studies, several important recommendations for improvements in future regional-scale applications should be stressed.[52]

TABLE 2-12.   EMISSION INVENTORIES FOR ACID RAIN STUDIES[115]

Name: Emissions History Information System

Compiler: OAQPS/EPA

Sponsor: OAQPS/EPA

Purpose: To provide input to the National Trends document published annually
            by OAQPS.

Extent: Pollutants: TSP, SO_x, NO_x, HC, CO
            Geography: Total national emissions by source category
            Sources: All emitting sources in the nation are included
            Time Frame: National emission levels available for 1940, 1950,
                         1960, and all years 1970-1980

Comments: In calculating national emissions, the system accesses both the
            NEDS data base and numerous national references.

Name: Northeast Corridor Regional Inventory (NECRMP)

Compiler: GCA and individual states

Sponsor: AMTB/OAQPS/EPA

Purpose: To provide input to photochemical oxidant model developed by OAQPS
            to be used by States in analyzing regional transport and strategies.

Extent: Pollutants: NO_x, VOC, CO
            Geography: 14 eastern States plus DC
            Sources: All area and point sources
            Time Frame: 1979 data gathered but will be projected to 1980 for
                         use by the model.

Comments: The NEDS data base from previous years was updated by GCA and
            individual States as part of the NECRMP program. It is expected
            that the NECRMP data base will soon be submitted to NADB for
            updating NEDS; will be allocated to hourly basis, to grids
            (approximately 20 x 20 km), and by organic compound by computerized
            allocation system using standardized algorithms.

(continued)

TABLE 2-12 (continued)

Name: OAQPS Historical Trends

Compiler: NADB and Pacific Environmental Services

Sponsor: OAQPS/EPA

Purpose: To provide a beginning data base for the U.S. Acid Rain Work
            Group 3-B.

Extent: Pollutants: SO_x, NO_x
            Geography: 33 States in the eastern U.S.
            Sources: - State-wide summaries
                         - All area and point sources included
            Time Frame: 1950-1978

Comments: Manual data base developed by NADB under a $5K contract with PES in
            early 1980. This inventory is a large set of manual tabulations
            showing state-by-state SO_x and NO_x emission trends from 1950 to
            1978. Data are based on published Bureau of Mines data, DOE
            reports, and emission factors used for National Air Pollutant
            Emissions Estimates: 1970-1978.

Name: U.S. SO_x Emission Inventory

Compiler: MITRE Corp.

Sponsor: ORD/EPA

Purpose: To prepare an emissions inventory of nonpower plant emitters for
            the U.S./Canada transboundary acid rain assessment started in 1980.

Extent: Pollutants: SO_x only
            Geography: - Eastern U.S.
                         - Only state wide totals are available except for
                           selected areas which are done by ARMS areas (jointly
                           agreed to by U.S. and Canada for the acid rain
                           project).
            Sources: Emissions agglomerated into nine emitting categories
                         excluding utilities. (Power plant emissions are being
                         compiled separately by E.H. Pechan using the AIRSHED
                         utility model.)
            Time Frame: - 1980
                         - Annual emissions

Comments: All activity and economic data in the data base are taken from the
            Strategic Environmental Assessment System (SEAS) with emission
            factors, control efficiencies, and sulfur contents generally
            obtained from NADB. Large errors in residential/commercial oil
            combustion and kraft pulp mill emissions were found but since
            contract is completed, error corrections may not soon be made.

(continued)

TABLE 2-12 (continued)

Name: U.S. SO_x/NO_x

Compiler: E.H. Pechan & Associates

Sponsor: ORD/EPA

Purpose: Emission Trends (1976-1980) of 238 largest utility emitters in U.S.

Extent: Pollutants: SO_x and NO_x
            Geography: Nationwide
            Sources: Utilities only (largest 238 emitters)
            Time Frame: - 1976 through 1980
                         - Annual emissions only

Comments: E.H. Pechan & Associates used standard DOE forms representing 1976-
            1980 as the basis for fuel consumption and fuel quality data. In
            addition, data on FGD systems are obtained from EPA Utility FGD
            Survey prepared by PEDCo for IERL. DOE data are based primarily on
            FPC Form 4 and Form 423, as opposed to AIRTEST which used FPC
            Form 67 data.

Name: AIRTEST-80

Compiler: Teknekron Research

Sponsor: EPA

Purpose: Acid rain study

Extent: Pollutants: SO_x
            Geography: Eastern U.S.
            Sources: Power plants only
            Time Frame: - Projected to 1980 based on DOE statistics on power
                             generation and fuel quality. (FPC Forms 4 and 423)
                         - Annual emissions only

Comments: AIRTEST-80 contains estimated power plant SO_2 emissions for 1980
            developed by Teknekron Research, Inc. upon initiation of U.S.-
            Canada Memo of Intent in 1980. AIRTEST-80 uses DOE plant
            generation and fuel quality data; these data are not of consistent
            years and were projected to represent 1980 as best as possible.
            1980 DOE generation and fuel quality data were not available when
            AIRTEST-80 was developed.

(continued)

TABLE 2-12 (continued)

Name: Sulfate Regional Experiment (SURE)

Compiler: GCA

Sponsor: Electric Power Research Institute

Purpose: For use by Teknekron in episode modeling, long-term transport of
          sulfate, and Utility Simulation Model

Extent: Pollutants: SO_x, NO_x, TSP, HC
          Geography: Eastern U.S.
          Sources: Power plant data received via special questionnaires;
                       all other sources represented by 1975 NEDS data.
          Time Frame: - Originally 1977-78 but updated by Teknekron to best
                         represent 1979 (SURE II inventory).
                       - Annual emissions as well as daily levels for some
                         facilities.

Comments: The inventory was developed for the Electric Power Research
          Institute by GCA. 1975 NEDS data served as the starting point and
          was updated based on data collected from individual plants by GCA.
          Teknekron used these data and made adjustments producing "SURE II."

Name: MAP3S

Compiler: Brookhaven National Laboratory

Sponsor: DOE

Purpose: To provide data input for A/Q forecasting and econometric models
          developed by Brookhaven.

Extent: Pollutant: All criteria pollutants
          Geography: Nationwide with selected Canadian emitters included in
                       data base.
          Sources: All area and point-source categories
          Time Frame: - 1978
                       - Annual

Comments: Data base started with 1976 NEDS file with data on Canadian
          emitters obtained from Environment Canada. Improvements from the
          SURE I and II data base were then added and further in-house data
          improvements were made; the final data system is called MAP3S.

(continued)

TABLE 2-12 (continued)

Name: Strategic Environmental Assessment System (SEAS)

Compiler: MITRE Corp.

Sponsor: EPA and DOE

Purpose: Data base developed for input into multimedia econometric model.
            System was developed in 1974-78 under extensive contracts with EPA.

Extent: Pollutants: Multimedia emission/effluent quantities are calculated
                        via variable emission coefficients which are based on
                        projections of economic activity.
            Geography: Nationwide but can be disaggregated to state levels.
            Sources: Plant-specific data are not available. The SEAS system
                        is based on the estimates of uncontrolled emissions and
                        must assume industry-wide existing control efficiencies
                        which leads to very large errors. University of
                        Maryland INFORUM model provides data input in the form
                        of economic interrelationships between 185 different
                        industrial categories.
            Time Frame: SEAS forecasts from any base year having "hard" data,
                        thus emissions for any year can be estimated. 1978 is
                        the baseline for "hard" data.

Comments: None

Name: Major Fuel Burning Installations (MFBI)

Compiler: DOE

Sponsor: DOE

Purpose: To monitor fuel consumption of major users in U.S.

Extent: Pollutants: The data base is a fuel-use inventory not an emissions
                        inventory.
            Geography: Nationwide
            Sources: Data for 2000 to 5000 sources collected via survey of
                        major coal, oil, and gas consumers in U.S.
            Time Frame: 1979-80 annual fuel consumption

Comments: The MFBI data base contains fuel use information inventory collected
            for large industrial fuel users by DOE. The system is not an
            emission inventory but can be used to calculate emissions by
            applying emission factors. The system was terminated in 1981.

(continued)

TABLE 2-12 (continued)

Name: Facility Energy Utilization Data System (FEUDS)

Compiler: ULTRASYSTEMS, Inc.

Sponsor: DOE

Purpose: To maintain a plant-specific data base for proprietary purposes
            (mainly DOE economic and fuel modeling studies).

Extent: Pollutants: Same as NEDS
            Geography: Nationwide
            Sources: Same as NEDS
            Time Frame: Annual - depends on NEDS input years

Comments: Entire 1978 NEDS point-source file is the FEUDS baseline with
            additional information as combustor ages and plant mailing
            addresses provided by ULTRASYSTEMS. The system is continually
            being used for a wide variety of Federal and State supported
            contracts.

Name: ICF Data Base

Compiler: ICF

Sponsor: DOE and ORD/EPA

Purpose: To project power plant emissions and their relative impact on air
            quality and to estimate the optimum costs of control.

Extent: Pollutants: SO_x, NO_x
            Geography: Nationwide
            Sources: All combustion and sources included in automated
                         data base.
            Time Frame: - Annual and seasonal emissions
                         - 1978-79 represented

Comments: Data base was developed for input to ICF forecasting model of least
            cost fuel switching strategies. This basically estimates future
            electrical demand and costs of plants to obtain adequate oil/coal
            supplies. 1978-79 coal- and oil-fired power plant data obtained
            from FPC Forms 67 and 423; industrial boiler data taken from NEDS
            and MFBI files and emission limits from SIPS.

(continued)

TABLE 2-12 (continued)

Name: Energy Data System (EDS)

Compiler: SASD/OAQPS/EPA

Sponsor: SASD/OAQPS/EPA

Purpose: To provide a rapid means of reporting fuel use and related data on
           major power plants in the U.S.

Extent: Pollutants: SO_x, NO_x, TSP
           Geography: Nationwide
           Sources: Approximately 1000 power plants are represented in EDS
           Time Frame: 1969 through 1979

Comments: Data from FPC Forms 1, 12, 67, 383, and 423 are stored in the data
           files generally from 1969 through 1979. SASD withdrew all
           resources for this system in 1979.

Name: Regional Air Pollution Study (RAPS)

Compiler: SAI and various EPA contractors

Sponsor: OAQPS/ORD/EPA

Purpose: To provide a very detailed and comprehensive inventory for ORD to
           validate dispersion and diffusion models.

Extent: Pollutants: TSP, SO_x, HC, CO, NO_x, trace materials
           Geography: St. Louis AQCR
           Sources: All area and point sources in St. Louis were
                        extensively studied and assigned to one of 2000 grids
                        in the study area.
           Time Frame: - 1975 through 1977
                        - hourly emissions either measured or estimated for all
                          emitters

Comments: The RAPS program was initiated in 1973 as a 5-year cooperative
           effort between the U.S. and U.S.S.R. St. Louis was selected as the
           U.S. city to be studied in great detail. ORD collected the ambient
           air quality data while OAQPS was assigned the development of
           inventory techniques and the collection of emissions data.

(continued)

TABLE 2-12 (continued)

Name: Generating Unit Referencing File (GURF)

Compiler: Oak Ridge National Laboratory

Sponsor: DOE

Purpose: Power demand projections, future plant mixes, and fuel switching
             capabilities.

Extent: Pollutants: SO_x
             Geography: Nationwide
             Sources: Oil- and coal-fired power plants
             Time Frame: - Annual statistics
                           - 1978-79 represented

Comments: Data base is mainly FPC Form 67 data with some additional data from
             other FPC publications.

• In cooperating in the development of a new National-standard data base, states should adhere to a standard format for data gathering to eliminate large and expensive data conversion problems. Such a format would specify that essential data fields be mandatory and the more detailed fields be optional. This hierarchal design; i.e., "bare bones" information required for minor sources and detailed data on major facilities, would enable states to work efficiently within their budgets.

• Involved agencies should establish a standard set of quality assurance (QA) measures to ensure comparability of data among states. These computerized edit checks would consist of screening fields for valid data sets, ensuring that the data fall within acceptable limits, and comparing related fields for consistency.

• A standard procedure for updating data should be developed that specifies common updating time intervals by region.

• Modelers and other data base users should be strongly encouraged to document and communicate to the inventory agency, all refinements, updates, corrections, or other modifications made to the inventory. Information dissemination can be further improved by sponsoring frequent emission inventory workshops on a regional level, thereby promoting interaction among neighboring states and ensuring consistent, accurate interpretation of basic principles for inventory development.

OTHER SOURCES AFFECTING ACID RAIN FORMATION

Lesser Contributors

In addition to the principal sources, ammonia and chloride are also important in determining the acidity of precipitation. The roles of these atmospheric contaminants are discussed in the following sections.

Ammonia--

Ammonia generally exists as an alkaline vapor with the capacity to neutralize either sulfuric or nitric acid in the atmosphere.[116] It is readily soluble in water, dissociating to form ammonium (NH_4^+) and hydroxyl (OH^-) ions. Liljestrand and Morgan[117] and Munger[118] have suggested that the pH of precipitation is controlled by the interaction of ammonia and other bases (metal carbonates and oxides) with sulfuric and nitric acid, and the presence of ammonium has been found to increase the pH of rain and snow.[119]

Ammonia in the atmosphere can react directly with sulfuric acid to form ammonium sulfate [$(NH_4)_2SO_4$] particles, a component of photochemical smog.[120] In gas-phase reactions, Scott and Lamb[120] have shown that free SO_2 is removed by ammonia, which thereby decreases the available SO_2 that may otherwise be transformed into H_2SO_4. The National Center for Atmospheric Research (NCAR)[121] showed that the interaction of gaseous NH_3

and SO_2 in the presence of water produces ammonium sulfite and ammonium sulfate, thus suggesting that gaseous ammonia could help neutralize acid precipitation in the atmosphere. Gas-phase ammonia has also been found to increase the washout of SO_2 by raindrops.[122-124] Modeling studies have shown that the presence of NH_3 increases the pH of the drops and dramatically increases the capacity of the rain for sulfur. This mechanism of scavenging may be especially important near sources of SO_2, where the pollutant is still in the gas phase and has not undergone appreciable atmospheric transformation.

Although extensive studies on the neutralization of nitric acid (HNO_3) by ammonia in the atmosphere are not available, an equilibrium relationship between NH_3, HNO_3 and NH_4NO_3 does exist.[125] In atmospheric reactions with nitrogen oxides, ammonia acts both as a neutralizer of nitric acid and as a promoter of the precursor components of nitric acid. Ammonia may react with hydroxyl radicals to form NO_x at an estimated rate of 20 to 40 x 10^6 metric tons of NO_x-N per year.[45,126]

Recent studies on the chemical composition of atmospheric precipitation have shown generally high correlations between ammonium (NH_4^+) and sulfate ($SO_4^=$) and/or nitrate (NO_3^-).[118,124,127-129] These correlations may suggest common patterns of occurrence and abundance for the ions or they may be indicative of prior chemical relationships (i.e., the presence of ammonium sulfate and ammonium nitrate in precipitation). An analysis of 3 years of hourly sequential precipitation samples from central Long Island, New York showed that the correlation of NH_4^+ with $SO_4^=$ was statistically significant and was higher than for any other pair of ions measured.[129] However, the average $SO_4^=$ concentration in the samples was much greater than NH_4^+, suggesting that available atmospheric ammonia concentrations are too low for complete neutralization of particulate or dissolved acid sulfate. The correlation of NH_4^+ and NO_3^- in this study was slightly lower. Munger[118] analyzed precipitation pH and ion concentrations at three sites in Minnesota and North Dakota. Ammonium and sulfate ions were highly correlated and the ratio of NH_4^+:$SO_4^=$ increased with precipitation pH. These results suggest that precipitation acidity is at least partially controlled by the $SO_4^=$ fraction that is not neutralized by NH_4^+. The general consistency of the correlations reported supports the role of ammonia in the neutralization of acid precipitation.

Most ammonia emissions are released into the atmosphere by natural and biological processes, primarily through the decay and decomposition of organic matter (dead plants, animal and human excreta, etc.)[130,131] Other natural sources include emissions from forest fires and volatilization from land and ocean masses.[132] Decayed organic matter is converted into amino acids through proteolysis and then into ammonia. The ammonia in turn is oxidized by bacteria to form nitrites and nitrates, which are readily assimilated by plants or micro-organisms to produce necessary proteins.[133] In the overall flux of nitrogen between terrestrial and atmospheric biospheres, the process of ammonification is an essential one. Estimates of the natural global ammonia emissions range from 113 to 850 x 10^6 metric tons of N per year.[41] Table 2-13 lists the natural sources of global ammonia and their emission estimates.

TABLE 2-13.   NATURAL SOURCES OF AMMONIA AND
ESTIMATED EMISSIONS

Source	Global emission rate (10^6 metric tons/yr)
Biological decay	1054[a]
Volatilized from land	113 – 224 as N[b]
Volatilized from land and sea	165 as N[c] 860 as N[d]

[a]Wark and Warner (1976).[134]

[b]Söderlund and Svensson (1976).[41]

[c]Burns and Hardy (1975).[43]

[d]Robinson and Robbins (1975).[40]

Anthropogenic sources, shown in Table 2-14, account for a small
percentage of the total ammonia emissions. These sources are usually the
producers of ammonia or users of ammonia in the manufacture of other
materials. Approximately 80 percent of the ammonia manufactured in the United
States in 1977 was used to produce fertilizers.[137] The remainder of the
NH_3 was incorporated in the production of explosives, animal feed, nitric
acid, acrylonitrile and amines. The nitrogen fertilizer can be applied
directly as anhydrous ammonia or aqueous ammonia,[135] where the inefficient
handling and application of fertilizers can result in substantial ammonia
losses. The global loss of NH_3 from the handling and application of
fertilizer has been estimated at 7×10^6 metric tons per year.[138] The
United States uses one-quarter of all fertilizers produced[136] and therefore
may have the same proportion of global emissions. Ammonia is also generated
as a by-product of making coke from coal, ore refining, and fossil-fuel
combustion. Söderlund and Svensson[41] calculated that 4 to 12×10^6 metric
tons per year of NH_3 are emitted by coal combustion sources on a global
basis.

Urea nitrogen $[CO(NH_2)_2]$ may volatilize from feedlots where large
quantities of animal urine are generated. The National Research Council[139]
has estimated that as much as 50 to 100 percent of urea may be volatized and
hydrolyzed into NH_3 and CO_2, causing local odor and nuisance problems. An
estimated 2 to 4×10^6 metric tons of ammonia may be generated by
feedlots.[41]

Lau and Carlson[140] have estimated that atmospheric ammonia
concentrations vary geographically over the continental United States, with
the midwest region being the dominant source. The high level of agricultural

TABLE 2-14.   ANTHROPOGENIC SOURCES OF AMMONIA AND
ESTIMATED EMISSIONS

Source	U.S. emission rate (10^6 metric tons/yr)	Global emission rate (10^6 metric tons/yr)
Natural gas- and coal-based ammonia production	0.017[a]	NA
Application of anhydrous NH_3	0.153[a]	NA
Ammonium nitrate production	0.054[a]	NA
Petroleum refineries (all operations)	0.029[a]	NA
Sodium carbonate production	0.013[a]	NA
Diammonium phosphate production	0.009[a]	NA
Ammoniator-granulators	0.009[a]	NA
Urea production	0.004[a]	NA
Miscellaneous emissions from fertilizer production	0.002[a]	NA
Beehive coke oven	0.001[a]	NA
Coal combustion	NA	4-12[b]
Power generation	NA	1.09[c]
Industrial combustion	NA	1.64[c]
Refinery cracking operation	NA	0.018[c]
Fuel oil combustion	NA	0.73[c]
Natural gas combustion	NA	0.018[c]
Incineration	NA	0.073[c]
Wood combustion	NA	0.054[c]
Forest fires	NA	0.045[c]
Urea hydrolyzing (to NH_3 and CO_2)	NA	2-4[d]
Wastewater treatment	3.63[e]	NA

[a] EPA-600/1-77-054 (1977).[135]   [d] NRC (1978).[136]

[b] Söderlund and Svensson (1976).[41]   [e] Wark and Warner (1976).[134]

[c] Liptak (ed.) (1974).[116]   NA = Not available.

activity and the alkaline pH of the soils of this region are suggested as factors causing high NH_3 volatilization. Figure 2-14 shows the estimated atmospheric ammonia concentrations for the United States.[140] The figure indicates that there may be considerable regional differences in acid precipitation neutralization by NH_3. Raynor and Hayes[129] have indicated that values for ammonium (NH_4^+) ion concentration in precipitation are generally lower in the northeastern United States than those reported elsewhere. Further, in the eastern United States, aerosol samples taken in rural areas are reported to be more acidic than those from urban sampling sites.[141] In urban atmospheres, sulfate anions are usually present as neutralized ammonium sulfate or as partly neutralized ammonium bisulfite, with anthropogenic emissions concentrated in urban areas speculated to be the source of ammonia.[141]

While it is likely that ammonia can react with and neutralize the acidity in precipitation, the potential adverse effects may not be alleviated, since the ammonium ion (NH_4^+) can acidify soil through biological processes.[118] In addition, fertilizer applications may have an adverse impact on ground water, lakes, and streams, in terms of increasing acidity. Although research information on this topic is scarce, it has been noted that the acidification of soil can result from the application of nitrogen fertilizer (e.g., ammonium sulfates, nitrates, and phosphates).[142,143] It is plausible that rain water run-off into bodies of water at lower elevations than the fields where fertilizers were originally applied, can lower the pH of lakes and streams. With respect to the acidification of Adirondack lakes, such an event is unlikely, since the few agricultural tracts in that region are at lower elevations than the lakes themselves. In addition, since many lakes that are susceptible to damage from acid deposition (discussed in Section 6) are located in forested areas where fertilizers are not locally used, it is unlikely that fertilizer leachate run-off will be a significant component of acidity in these lakes and streams.

Chlorides--

Cogbill and Likens[144] calculated that hydrochloric acid (HCl) contributed 6 percent to the acidity of rain water in the northeastern United States. While this contribution is low compared to the contributions of sulfuric acid (62 percent) and nitric acid (32 percent), it is still significant. Although the sources of this strong acid have not been completely identified and the specific processes of HCl formation are not clearly understood, researchers have attempted to provide models to show the transformation of chlorine compounds or chlorine gas into hydrochloric acid, which is eventually absorbed by moisture and precipitated.

Yue et al.[145] used a theoretical model which showed that the formation of HCl is dependent on the interactions of SO_2, ammonia, CO_2, oxygen, and sulfuric acid. Another model[146] proposed that particulate chloride interacts with NO_2 to produce HCl. Robbins et al.[147] suggested that the reaction of aqueous HNO_3 with NaCl produces HCl in the atmosphere.

Cauer[148] suggested that salt spray oxidized by ozone and photochemically hydrolyzed into HCl is subsequently absorbed by moisture, resulting in acidic precipitation. However, Kohler and Bath[149] found that

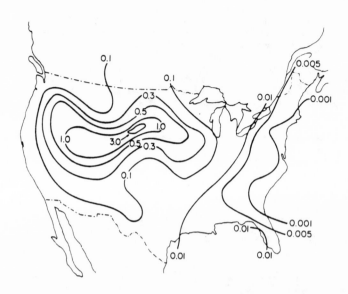

Figure 2-14.   Equilibrium partial pressure of atmospheric NH_3 over
the United States in ppb. Deduced from precipitation
chemistry.[140]

the sea salt (NaCl) to HCl conversion does not fully account for changes in the Na^+/Cl^- ratio in the air. Raynor and Hayes[150] measured Cl^-/Na^+ ion ratios in 3 years of hourly precipitation samples from a central Long Island, New York site. This ratio was highly variable and was often below the Cl^-/Na^+ ratio found in seawater. These authors suggested that the chlorine ion deficit might be due to the gas-phase reaction of 2 NaCl with H_2SO_4 to form Na_2SO_4 and 2 HCl.

Precursors of HCl acid precipitation in the atmosphere are generated from ground-level natural and anthropogenic sources. Table 2-15 provides a list of some of the major contributors of chlorides that may undergo reactions to form HCl.

Since the occurrence of chlorine gas in air is rare, owing to its highly reactive characteristics,[155,156] chloride compounds are more likely to be found. The natural sources of chloride include salt spray from the oceans,[119,157] volcanic gases,[155] and upper atmospheric reactions.[149] Concentrations of chlorides in noncoastal and coastal areas range from 0.02 mg/m^3 to 44 mg/m^3. Salt spray emissions estimated on a global scale are 600 to 1500 x 10^6 metric tons per year.[23,153,158] Nordlie[159] measured volcanic activity and found that chlorides are released in the magmatic gases. Bartel[154] estimated the global volcanic contribution of chloride to be 7.6 x 10^6 metric tons per year. Duce[146] estimated that 600 x 10^6 metric tons per year of HCl are produced through the interaction of trace gases and precipitation.

Anthropogenically-produced chlorine and chlorides are emitted in various manufacturing and process operations; primarily in the manufacturing, handling, and liquefaction of chlorine gas and HCl. Annual production rates of chlorine and HCl in the United States have been increasing since 1978.[160,161] Chlorine is used in a variety of industries including the production of solvents, pesticides, herbicides, chlorinated hydrocarbons, plastics, and bleaches. Other uses of chlorine compounds are in wastewater treatment, in pulp and paper mills, and in fluxing of ferrous and nonferrous metals.

The chlorine production facilities are located mainly in the eastern United States with a concentration of plants in the Gulf Coast region of Texas, Louisiana, and Alabama, which accounted for nearly 77 percent of the total chlorine output in 1975.[160] Other facilities are distributed throughout the remainder of the eastern United States, on the West Coast, and in the Midwest. Hydrochloric acid and chlorinated hydrocarbon production facilities are distributed in regions near chlorine production plants and are located mainly in the northeastern, south-central, and western United States.

The combustion of coal by power generating facilities also releases chlorides into the atmosphere. The chloride released and its subsequent dissolution in moisture can yield hydrochloric acid in precipitation.[162] The Tennessee Valley Authority has reported the presence of HCl in flue gases from coal combustion up to concentrations of 50 to 75 ppm.[143] In urban Britain, the deposition of chlorides was attributed to the chlorine contained

TABLE 2-15.   EMISSION OF CHLORIDE PRECURSORS TO THE ATMOSPHERE

Source	U.S. emission rate (10^3 metric tons)	Global emission rate (10^3 metric tons)
Anthropogenic Sources		
Chlorine gas and liquid manufacture	42.7[a] as Cl_2	NA
HCl acid manufacture	0.73[a] as Cl_2	NA
Chlorinated hydrocarbon manufacture	206.6[b] as HCl	NA
Pulp and paper mills	16[a] as Cl_2	NA
Ferrous metal fluxing	0.09[a] as Cl_2	NA
Nonferrous metal fluxing	1.72[a] as Cl_2	NA
Coal combustion	NA	NA
Water treatment	NA	NA
Natural Sources		
Ocean salt spray	NA	600,000[c]–1,500,000[d] as NaCl
Volcanic gases	NA	7,600[e,f]
Atmospheric reactions	NA	600,000[g] as HCl

[a]Sittig (1975).[151]
[b]Khan and Hughes (1979).[152]
[c]Junge (1963).[153]
[d]Eriksson (1959).[23]
[e]Bartel (1972).[154]
[f]Chloride form not stated.
[g]Duce (1969).[146]
NA = Not available.

in coals (up to 1 percent by weight)[163] because the high levels measured in precipitation in this region could not be accounted for by marine sources alone.[164] In the United States, coals mined in the midwestern and Appalachian regions contain 0.01 to 0.5 percent chlorine by weight[165] and are potential sources of chloride ions after combustion.

Synergistic Effects

Other pollutants that can potentially affect the formation and magnitude of acid precipitation and its precursors are emitted to and are present in the atmosphere. Although the potential synergistic reactions of these substances are largely a matter of speculation and hypothesis at this time, further research can be expected to reveal the extent of their contributions to the acid rain problem. Details on the atmospheric transformation and transport, scavenging, and removal of these pollutants and the precursors of acid rain are covered in Section 3.

Ozone and Other Photochemical Oxidants--
Ozone and other photochemical oxidants may play a role in the conversion of SO_x and NO_x to sulfates and nitrates. Chemical reactions leading to the formation of these acid rain precursors have been associated with gas-phase and heterogeneous (gas-liquid and gas-solid) processes related to photochemical smog. The major components of photochemical smog are NO_x and hydrocarbons which are produced in large part by transportation sources in urban population centers. Although hydrocarbon emissions directly contribute only minor amounts to acidic deposition, their participation in various photochemical reactions affecting the oxidation of SO_2 and NO_x may increase the acidity of precipitation.

Widespread regional exposure to ozone has been coupled with high concentrations of airborne sulfates. One study of summertime aerosol formation in urban plumes observed that the greatest rates of formation of $SO_4^=$ occurred when the plume was tracked through an ozone-laden air mass.[166] In addition, conversion rates of sulfur dioxide to sulfate have been observed to be higher in the daytime, suggesting a photochemical mechanism.[143,167-169] Tanner et al.[141] have reported pronounced diurnal patterns for acid aerosol levels at three sampling locations in the metropolitan New York City area. Highest acid levels occurred at midafternoon and lowest values were observed at night. At all three sampling sites, the diurnal acid aerosol pattern closely followed the observed diurnal ozone pattern.

Indirect photo-oxidation of SO_2 in the gas phase is a major route for conversion to $SO_4^=$. Direct collision of SO_2 with strong oxidizing radicals such as $HO\cdot$, $HO_2\cdot$, and $CH_3O_2\cdot$ results in the conversion. These radicals are intermediate products of the hydrocarbon-NO_x reactions that occur in photochemical smog. Marsh[124] has suggested that the reaction of SO_2 with hydroxyl ($HO\cdot$) radicals is the predominant photochemical oxidation mechanism. Both O_3 and hydrocarbons are seen as contributing to this process through their influence on $HO\cdot$ concentrations. Oxidation rates of SO_2 by gas-phase radicals may be as high as 10 percent per hour, depending on free radical concentrations.[170]

Oxidation of SO_2 by ozone in the liquid phase may also occur[171,172] and has been experimentally demonstrated at ambient O_3 concentrations.[173] Ozone absorbed in liquid droplets can promote oxidation to rates that exceed the conversion by indirect photo-oxidation. The reaction rates are relatively high at low pH levels in the aqueous phase, but the variability of existing rate data prevents an accurate assessment of this mechanism in the atmosphere.[167] Recent experimental[173] and modeling[174,175] studies of liquid-phase SO_2 oxidation have suggested that ozone may be more effective at higher pH levels and that oxidation by hydrogen peroxide (H_2O_2) may be favored at pH $\leq$ 5.5. Modeling results have also predicted that the presence of HNO_3 in the liquid phase will inhibit $SO_4^=$ formation due to oxidation of SO_2 by O_3.[175] Another factor that may decrease the importance of liquid-phase SO_2 oxidation is the scavenging of atmospheric ozone by NO in power plant plumes. Depression of ambient O_3 levels due to scavenging may result in only minor enhancement of SO_2 oxidation.[176]

Although ozone is formed by the photochemical reactions of hydrocarbons and NO_x, it may also play a role in the conversion of NO_x to nitrates. The major removal pathway for atmospheric NO_2 is by further oxidation to nitric acid, which is readily dry deposited, and NO_3^- aerosols, which are removed by precipitation. Oxidation rates depend on atmospheric photochemistry and the availability of atmospheric ozone.[170] A complex series of reactions is involved, and NO_x may be switched back and forth between various oxidation states over periods ranging from hours to days.[177]

In addition to the nitric acid that is formed directly in the photochemical reaction mix, the scavenging of ozone by NO in plumes from major fuel burning installations may lead to further nitric acid production. Ozone reacts readily with NO to form NO_2 and molecular oxygen. Additional ozone may react with NO_2 to form a transient symmetrical nitrogen trioxide species, which then reacts with NO_2 and water to form nitric acid. This reaction is known to occur homogeneously (in the gas phase) and heterogeneously, although the latter may predominate.[177] Nitric acid also may be produced by the reaction of NO_x with hydroxyl radicals in the vapor phase,[124] although free radical concentrations are expected to be lower in power plant plumes than in a photochemical reaction mix.

Carbon Dioxide--
   Pure distilled water has a pH level of 7. In the atmosphere, various gases are absorbed and dissolved in moisture because of atmospheric pressure, resulting in a gas-liquid equilibrium. Carbon dioxide is soluble in water as either aqueous CO_2 or as carbonic acid, H_2CO_3, a weak acid. Using a simplified model of water in equilibrium with atmospheric CO_2 at 25°C, the water will have a pH of 5.65.[178,179] However, this background or baseline pH level is a function not only of CO_2, but of other gases and soluble particles.[180] It can be expected that the extent to which SO_x, NO_x, ammonia, and chlorides contribute to the acidification of rainwater will vary according to the background pH. This synergism apparently disappears below a pH of 5. An experiment conducted by Galloway et al.,[180] found that carbonic acid, which is in equilibrium with the atmosphere, had no influence on the measured pH of any aqueous samples tested below a pH of 5. Atmospheric CO_2

at a concentration of 320 ppm was found by Adamowicz[123] to have a minimal effect on the washout of sulfur dioxide by falling raindrops.

In addition, the presence of dissolved carbonate species and the exchange of CO_2 with the atmosphere allows certain bodies of water to have a buffer mechanism with capacities for both acid and base neutralization. However, for lakes and other bodies of water having very little dissolved carbonates, the presence of carbon dioxide tends to acidify the water to the 5.65 level.[178]

Particulates--

Another factor in the formation or neutralization of acid precipitation is the presence of natural and anthropogenic dust. It has been suggested that alkaline dusts may react with and neutralize strong acids in the atmosphere.[181] Naturally-derived particles from soil erosion, agricultural activities, construction sites, unpaved roads, and volcanoes may play a large role in determining the acidity of precipitation. This may be particularly true in agricultural areas of the central and midwestern United States, where dust emissions from carbonaceous soils with high calcite and dolomite contents can act as buffers.[182] Natural dusts in the southwestern and central plains regions are characterized by both higher alkalinity (pH 7 to 8) and higher emissions.[182] Munger[118] has shown that alkaline soil dust can be a controlling factor in precipitation pH in the Midwest since increases in precipitation acidity were observed when airborne soil dust concentrations decreased. Natural dusts from the eastern United States are slightly acidic (pH 6 to 7).[182] In this area, dense forest cover, frequent precipitation events, and nonalkaline soil combine to reduce the potential neutralization capacity of natural dusts.

One recent analysis of the chemical composition of atmospheric precipitation found that sulfate ions were highly correlated with alkaline earth elements such as sodium (Na), potassium (K), and calcium (Ca).[128] These results suggest that atmospheric SO_2 may be adsorbed on particulate matter, reacting with soil-derived compounds such as $CaCO_3$, NaCl, and $NaCO_3$ to form sulfate aerosol. The author of this study concluded that particulate matter is very important in the mass removal of SO_2 from the atmosphere.

Adomaitis et al.[183] investigated the relationship between pH and the chemical composition of snow. Dusty snows, characterized by high soluble mineral content, were found to be alkaline, whereas clean snows with a lower soluble cation content were slightly acidic (pH of 5). Munger[118] found that falling snow was often more acidic than samples taken from the snowpack that had accumulated on the ground. He attributed this difference to neutralization of the snow, after it had fallen, by the uptake of alkaline dust. Winter inputs of acid in snow are often released during a short snow-melt period in the spring and may adversely affect the acid-sensitive juvenile stages of aquatic organisms. Thus, post-snowfall neutralization by alkaline dust may reduce the impact of acidic snow on aquatic ecosystems.

Shannon and Fine[184] have measured pH values of 9 to 11 from water extracts of fly ash. Lower concentrations of Na_2O and CaO in eastern coal fly ashes result in less alkaline ash from eastern coals.[185] Likens and

Borman have suggested that the removal of alkaline fly ash emissions by
industrial and utility electrostatic precipitators contributes to acid rain
formation.[186] On the other hand, Ananth et al.,[185] have indicated that
the removal of fly ash may not be a contributor because the particles removed
by the precipitator are probably larger in size than those remaining in the
plume and, thus, if left uncontrolled, would settle more rapidly, viz.,
reduced residence time in the plume. They further indicate that there are
insufficient data to determine whether the alkalinity of fly ash has a
significant effect on the neutralization of acid rain.

    Fly ash and other anthropogenically-generated carbon soot particles may
also enhance the formation of acid rain. Ananth et al.[185] investigated two
mechanisms by which the particulate matter from coal combustion may enhance
the oxidation of SO_2. Order-of-magnitude calculations indicate that both
absorption-oxidation and direct catalytic oxidation are plausible mechanisms
for the rapid formation of $SO_4^=$ in power plant plumes.[185]

    Absorption-oxidation of SO_2 involves catalysis by suspended fly ash or
soot particles in the presence of large amounts of water. Such conditions may
occur in the liquid phase, in cloud droplets, or during periods of
precipitation. A number of recent experimental investigations[187-190] have
looked at this process of sulfate formation. In all of these studies,
activated carbon or carbon soot particles in the presence of water were found
to increase the conversion of gaseous SO_2 to sulfates. The presence of
NO_2 at typical ambient concentration levels (a few ppm) dramatically
increased the conversion rate, in one case by an order of magnitude.[187] One
study reported SO_2 to $SO_4^=$ conversion rates as high as 58 percent per
hour when SO_2 and NO_2 were present at 100 ppm.[188] In two of the studies,
conversion continued at pH levels as low as 1.5.[188,189] Although there is
no doubt that absorption-oxidation of SO_2 by carbon particles can take
place, there is some debate about the significance of this mechanism in the
atmosphere. Some researchers feel that from the point of view of the overall
SO_2 oxidation process, heterogeneous reactions on soot or other particles
play a negligible role compared to photochemical mechanisms.[190] Others
speculate that heterogeneous conversion of SO_2 to sulfate on particle
surfaces may predominate over competitive gas-phase photo-oxidation.[187]

    A second mechanism occurs in the presence of small quantities of water.
This mechanism, direct catalytic oxidation, may rely on metallic constituents
of the fly ash acting as catalysts.[177] Although the catalytic activity of
many trace and minor elements has been demonstrated, the activity of vanadium
pentoxide is considered to be much higher than that of other metals.[185] One
recent study demonstrated that, in the presence of NO_2 or water, V_2O_5
greatly accelerated SO_2-to-sulfate conversion rates at ambient
temperatures.[191] Vanadium pentoxide is also formed in the combustion of
residual oil and, therefore, may influence the fate of SO_2 emitted from
oil-fired boilers.

    Atmospheric reactions that lead to the conversion of SO_x and NO_x to
sulfate and nitrate aerosols have important implications. The conversion of
acid rain precursors to these more stable particulate forms increases their

atmospheric lifetime, facilitates transport, and contributes to the regional nature of the acid rain problem.[192]

SUMMARY

The principal contributors to precipitation acidity are sulfuric and nitric acid. Although no direct quantitative relationship between pollutant emissions and the measured acidity of precipitation has been demonstrated, naturally- and anthropogenically-produced SO_x and NO_x are considered major acid rain precursors. The most recent estimates indicate that approximately 40 percent of global SO_x emissions are manmade, although in highly industrialized areas, anthropogenic sources may account for 90 percent of the total. Coal and oil combustion and various industrial processes are the major contributors. Estimates of the natural source contribution to global NO_x emissions vary considerably, although fossil fuel combustion and transportation sources account for most of the manmade emissions.

Emissions of SO_x and NO_x in the United States show no distinct trends for either pollutant from 1970 to the present. However, over the most recent 5-year period (NEDS date-of-record years 1977 and 1982), SO_x emissions decreased by 7.6 percent while NO_x emissions increased by 10.6 percent. Although it appears that transportation will continue to be a major source of NO_x emissions, future SO_x and NO_x emissions from fuel combustion will be influenced by a number of factors. The relative populations of old and new boilers are important. Coal cleaning, the use of low sulfur coal, the application of control technologies such as flue gas desulfurization systems, and the application of new combustion technologies, such as fluidized-bed combustion, will all play a role in determining fuel combustion SO_x and NO_x emissions.

In addition to SO_x and NO_x, other pollutants may directly or indirectly affect the acidity of precipitation. Hydrochloric acid, produced from atmospheric chlorine and chlorides, accounts for a small but significant percentage of rainwater acidity. Ammonia, because of its alkaline nature, is able to neutralize acidic components of precipitation. Less well understood are the roles of ozone, carbon dioxide, and particulate matter. Alkaline natural dusts and fly ash emissions may be capable of neutralizing precipitation acidity. However, certain metallic constituents of fly ash, such as vanadium pentoxide from the combustion of residual oil, may be involved in the catalytic oxidation of SO_2 to sulfates, leading to a possible increase in acidity.

A number of pollutants that may be involved in the formation or neutralization of acid rain have been identified. However, a number of uncertainties remain. Precise quantification of the contribution of each pollutant, the relative importance of their various sources, and determination of the factors affecting future emissions are all subjects for further investigation.

REFERENCES

1. Eriksson, E.   The Yearly Circulation of Chloride and Sulfur in Nature;
    Meteorological, Geochemical, and Pedological Implications. 2, Tellus,
    12:63, 1960.

2. Junge, C. E.   Sulfur in the Atmosphere. J. Geophys. Res., 68:3975-3976,
    1963.

3. Eriksson, E.   The Yearly Circulation of Sulfur in Nature. J. Geophys.
    Res., 68:4001-4008, 1963.

4. Robinson, E., and R. C. Robbins.   Sources, Abundance, and Fate of
    Gaseous Atmospheric Pollutants. Stanford Research Institute Final
    Proj. Rep. RP-6755, Menlo Park, California, 1968.

5. Robinson, E., and R. C. Robbins.   Emissions, Concentrations, and Fate of
    Gaseous Atmospheric Pollutants. In: Air Pollution Control, Part III.
    W. Strauss, ed., Wiley-Interscience, New York, 1972. pp. 1-93.

6. Kellogg, W. D., R. D. Cadle, E. R. Allen, A. L. Lazrus, and
    E. A. Martell.   The Sulfur Cycle. Science, 175:587-596, 1972.

7. Friend, J. P.   The Global Sulfur Cycle. In: Chemistry of the Lower
    Atmosphere, S. I. Rasool, ed. Plenum Press, New York, 1973. pp. 177-201.

8. Bolin, B. and R. J. Charlson.   The Role of the Troposopheric Sulfur
    Cycle in the Short-Wave Radiactive Climate of the Earth. Ambio.,
    5(47):54, 1976.

9. Hallberg, R. O.   A Global Sulfur Cycle Based on a Pre-industrial
    Steady-State of the Pedosphere. SCOPE Report No. 7. Ecol. Bull.
    (Stockholm), 22:93-101, 1976.

10. Granat, L.   A Global Atmospheric Sulfur Budget. SCOPE Report No. 7.
    Ecol. Bull. (Stockholm), 22:102-122, 1976.

11. Garland, J. A.   The Dry Deposition of Sulfur Dioxide to Land and Water
    Surfaces. Proc. R. Soc., A354:245-268, 1977.

12. Davey, T. R. A.   Anthropogenic Balance for Australia, 1976. Australian
    Mineral Industries Council Environmental Workshop. Hobart, October 1978.

13. Cullis, C. F., and M. M. Hirschler.   Atmospheric Sulphur: Natural and
    Man-Made Sources. Atmos. Environ., 14:1263-1278, 1980.

14. Aneja, V. P., A. P. Aneja, and D. F. Adams.   Biogenic Sulfur Compounds
    and the Global Sulfur Cycle. J. Air Pollution Control Assoc.,
    32(8):803-807, August 1982.

15. Gerlach, T. M., and B. E. Nordlie. Carbon-Oxygen-Hydrogen-Sulphur Gaseous Systems, I-III. Am. J. Sci., 275:353-376, 377-394, 395-410, 1975.

16. Ozawa, T. Chemical Analysis of Volcanic Gases III. Rapid Determination of Carbon Dioxide, Hydrogen Sulfide, Nitrogen and Sulphur Dioxide in Fumarolic and Hot Spring Gases Having Temperatures Near the Boiling Point of Water. J. Chem. Soc. Japan, 87:959-962, 1966.

17. Ross, J. B. Chemical Analysis of Naturally Occurring Gases in New Zeland. N. Z. Jl. Sci., 11:249-247, 1968.

18. Cadle, R. D. Volcanic Emissions of Halides and Sulfur Compounds to the Troposphere and Stratosphere. J. Geo. Phys. Res., 80:1650-1652, 1975.

19. Stoiber, R. E., and A. Jepsen. Sulfur Dioxide Contributions to the Atmosphere by Volcanoes. Science, 182:577-578, 1973.

20. Delmas, R. and C. Boutron. Sulphate in Antarctic Snow: Spatio-Temporal Distribution. Atmos. Environ., 12:723-728, 1978.

21. Delmas, R. Sulphate in Polar Snow and Ice. International Symposium on Sulphur Emissions and the Environment (London, May 1979). Society of Chemical Industry, 1979. pp. 72-76.

22. Sugawara, K. Exchange of Chemical Substances Between Air and Sea. Oceanogr. Mar. Biol. Ann. Rev., 3:59-77, 1965.

23. Eriksson, E. The Yearly Circulation of Chloride and Sulphur in Nature: Meteorological, Geochemical and Pedological Implications I. Tellus, 11:375-403, 1959.

24. Galloway, J. N., and D. M. Whelpdale. An Atmospheric Sulfur Budget for Eastern North America. Atmos. Environ., 14:409-417, 1980.

25. Rasmussen, R. A. Emission of Biogenic Hydrogen Sulphide. Tellus, 26:254-260, 1974.

26. Hitchcock, D. R. Microbiological Contributions to the Atmospheric Load of Particulate Sulfate. In: Environmental Biogeochemistry (Edited by J. O. Nriagu), Vol. 1, Chapter 24, pp. 351-367. Ann Arbor Science, Ann Arbor, MI, 1976.

27. Natusch, D. F. S., and B. J. Slatt. Hydrogen Sulphide as an Air Pollutant. In: Air Pollution Control (Edited by W. Strauss), Part 3, Chapter 9, pp. 459-518. John Wiley, New York, 1978.

28. Liss, P. S., and P. G. Slater. Flux of Gases Across the Air-Sea Interface. Nature (London), 247:181-184, 1974.

29. Hitchcock, D. R.   Dimethyl Sulfide Emissions to the Global Atmosphere. Chemosphere, 3:137-138, 1975.

30. Maroulis, P. J., an A. R. Bandy.   Estimate of the Contribution of Biologically Produced Dimethyl Sulfate to the Global Sulfur Cycle. Science, 196:647-648, 1977.

31. Jaeschke, W., and W. Haunold.   New Methods and First Results of Measuring Atmospheric H_2S and SO_2 in the ppb Range.   In: Special Environmental Report No. 10 - Air Pollution Measurement Techniques, WMO No. 460, 1977.   pp. 193-198.

32. Hansen, M. H., K. Ingvorsen, and B. B. Jorgensen.   Mechanisms of Hydrogen Sulfide Release from Coastal Marine Sediments to the Atmosphere.   Limno. Oceanogr., 23:68-76, 1978.

33. Adams, D. F., M. R. Pack, W. L. Bamesberger, A. E. Sherrard, and S. O. Farwell.   Measurement of Biogenic Sulfur-Containing Gas Emissions from Soils and Vegetation.   In: 71st Annual Meeting of the Air Pollution Control Assoc., Houston, Texas, Paper No. 78-7.6, 1978.

34. Aneja, V. P., J. H. Overton, L. T. Cupitt, J. L. Durham, and W. E. Wilson.   Direct Measurements of Emission Rates of Some Atmospheric Biogenic Sulfur Compounds.   In: 174th American Chemical Society Meeting, Miami, Florida, 1978.

35. Delmas, R., J. Bandet, J. Servant, and R. Baziard.   Emissions and Concentration of Hydrogen Sulfide in the Air of the Tropical Forest of the Ivory Coast and of Temperate Regions in France.   Presented at the Fourth International Conference of the Commission of Atmospheric Chemistry and Global Pollution, University of Colorado, Boulder, CO, 1979.

36. Adams, D. F., S. O. Farwell, F. Robinson, and M. R. Pack.   Biogenic Sulfur Emissions in the SURE Region.   Washington State University, Pullman (U.S.A.), Report No. EPRI-EA-1516, September 1980.   pp. 170.

37. Rice, H., D. H. Nochumson, and G. M. Hidy.   Contribution of Anthropogenic and Natural Sources to Atmospheric Sulfur in Parts of the United States.   Atmos. Environ., 15:1-9, 1981.

38. Szabo, M., M. Esposito, and P. Spaite.   Acid Rain: Commentary on Controversial Issues and Observations on the Role of Fuel Burning. Report No. DOE/MC/19170-1168, Dept. of Energy, March 1982.

39. Robinson, E., R. B. Husar, and J. N. Galloway.   Sulfur Oxides in the Atmosphere.   In: Sulfur Oxides, National Academy of Sciences, Washington, D.C., 1978.

40. Robinson, E., and R. C. Robbins. Gaseous Atmospheric Pollution from Urban and Natural Sources. In: The Changing Global Environment, S. F. Singer, ed. D. Reidel Publ. Co., Dardrecht-Holland, Boston, 1975. pp. 111-123.

41. Söderlund, R., and B. H. Svensson, The Global Nitrogen Cycle. In: Nitrogen, Phosphorus, and Sulfur - Global Cycles. SCOPE Report No. 7, B. H. Svensson and R. Söderlund, eds. Ecol. Bull. (Stockholm), 22:23-73, 1976.

42. Delwiche, C. C. The Nitrogen Cycle. Scientific American, 223(3):137-146, 1970.

43. Burns, R. C., and R. W. F. Hardy. Nitrogen Fixation in Bacteria and Higher Plants. Springer-Verlag, Berlin-Heidelberg-New York, 1975.

44. Liu, S. C., R. J. Cicerone, R. M. Donahue, and W. L. Chameides. Sources and Sinks of Atmospheric N_2O and the Possible Ozone Reduction Due to Industrial Fixed Nitrogen Fertilizers. Tellus, 29:251-263, 1977.

45. Chameides, W. L., D. H. Stedman, R. R. Dickerson, D. W. Rusch, and R. J. Cicerone. NO_x Production in Lighting. J. Atmos. Sci., 34:143-149, 1977.

46. Crutzen, P. J., and D. H. Ehhalt. Effects of Nitrogen Fertilizers and Combustion in the Stratospheric Ozone Layer. Ambio., 6(2-3):112-117, 1977.

47. Noxon, J. F. Atmospheric Fixation by Lightning. Geophys. Res. Lett., 3:463-465, 1976.

48. Griffing, G. W. Ozone and Oxides of Nitrogen Production During Thunderstorms. J. Geophys. Res., 82:943-950, 1977.

49. Noxon, J. F. Tropospheric NO_2. J. Geophys. Res., 83:3051-3057, 1978.

50. Crutzen, P. J., I. S. A. Isaksen, and J. R. McAfee. The Impact of the Chlorocarbon Industry on the Ozone Layer. J. Geophys. Res., 83:345, 1978.

51. U.S. Environmental Protection Agency. 1977 National Emissions Report. In: National Emissions Data System of the Aerometric and Emissions Reporting System. EPA-450/4-80-005, 1980.

52. Sellars, F. M. Availability and Frequency of Emission Inventories for Regional Scale Air Quality Modeling. In: Proceedings of an APCA Specialty Conference On: Emission Inventories and Air Quality Management. Kansas City, MO, April 27-30, 1982, pp. 97-106.

53. U.S. Environmental Protection Agency. National Air Quality, Monitoring and Emissions Trends Report, 1977. EPA-450/2-78-052, 1978.

54. Bureau of the Census, Statistical Abstract of the United States, 1981. U.S. Department of Commerce. 102nd Edition, 1981.

55. Department of Health, Education, and Welfare National Emission Standards Study. Appendix – Volume 3, Appendix F (Part 2), 1970.

56. U.S. Environmental Protection Agency. National Air Pollutant Emission Estimates, 1940–1976. EPA-450/1-78-003, 1978.

57. Hendrey, G. R., and F. W. Lipfert. Acid Precipitation and the Aquatic Environment. Brookhaven National Laboratory. Presented to the Committee on Energy and Natural Resources, United States Senate, May 28, 1980.

58. Environmental Trends to the Year 2000: A Supplement to the National Energy Policy Plan. U.S. Department of Energy, DOE/EP-0021, July 1981.

59. Lin, K., and J. Dotter. Steam Electric Plant Factors 1979. National Coal Association, 1979.

60. Esposito, M. P., M. F. Szabo, T. W. Devitt, and P. Spaite. Acid Rain: The Impact of Local Sources. Prepared by PEDCo Environmental for U.S. DOE, Morgantown Energy Research Center, Contract No. DE-AC-21-81MC14787, November 1980.

61. Squires, A. Query: Is There a Connection Between the Expansion of Acid Rain and a Shift from Coal to Oil for Small-Scale Heat Needs? In: Workshop Proceedings on Primary Sulfate Emissions from Combustion Sources, Volume 2 Characterization. EPA-600/9-78-020b, August 1978.

62. Ando, J. SO_2 Abatement for Stationary Sources. EPA-600/7-78-210, November 1978.

63. Tanaka, S. et al. Sulfur and Associated Elements and Acidity in Continental and Marine Rain from North Florida. J. Geophys. Res., 85(C8):4519-4526, August 20, 1980.

64. Voldner, E. C., Y. Shah, and D. M. Whelpdale. A Preliminary Canadian Emissions Inventory for Sulfur and Nitrogen Oxides. Atmos. Environ., 14(4):419-428, 1980.

65. Environment Canada. A Nation-wide Inventory of Air Contaminant Emissions - 1974. Report EPS 3-AP-78-2, Air Pollution Control Directorate, 1978. Augmented and updated by P. J. Choquette, 1979.

66. Altshuller, A. P., and G. A. McBean. The LRTAP Problem in North America: A Preliminary Overview. Prepared by the United States - Canada Research Consultation Group on the Long-Range Transport of Air Pollutants.

67. Battelle Memorial Institute. The Federal R&D Plan for Air Pollution Control by Combustion Processes Modification. Contract No. CPA-22-69-147, 1971.

68. Locklin, D. W., et al. An Overview of Research Needs for Air Pollution Control by Combustion Process Modification. AICHE Symp. Series, 68(126):1, 1972.

69. Commission on Natural Resources. Air Quality and Stationary Source Emission Control. National Academy of Sciences, March 1975.

70. Demeter, J., and D. Bienstock. Sulfur Retention in Anthracite Ash. Report of Investigation 7160, U.S. Bureau of Mines, 1968.

71. Sondreal, E. A., W. R. Kube, and J. L. Elder. Analysis of the Northern Great Plains Province Lignites and Their Ash: A Study of Variability. U.S. Bureau of Mines Report of Investigation 7158, 1968.

72. Ode, W. H., and F. H. Gibson. Effect of Sulfur Retention on Determined Ash in Lower-Rank Coals. U.S. Bureau of Mines Report of Investigation 5931, 1962.

73. Walden Research Corporation. Final Report on Sulfur, Mercury, and Other Materials Studies at Neil Simpson Station. Cambridge, Massachusetts, 1973.

74. Gronhovd, G. H., P. H. Tufte, and S. J. Selle. Some Studies on Stack Emissions from Lignite-Fired Powerplants. In: 1973 Lignite Symposium, Grand Forks, North Dakota, 1973.

75. Homolya, J. B., and J. L. Cheney. An Assessment of Sulfuric Acid and Sulfate Emissions from the Combustion of Fossil Fuels. In: Workshop Proceedings on Primary Sulfate Emissions from Combustion Sources, Volume 2, Characterization. EPA-600/9-78-020b, 1978. pp. 3-11.

76. Bennett, L., and K. T. Knapp. Sulfur and Trace Metal Particulate Emissions from Combustion Sources. In: Workshop Proceedings on Primary Sulfate Emissions from Combustion Sources, Volume 2, Characterization. EPA-600/9-78-020b, 1978. pp. 165-183.

77. Cheney, J. L. and J. B. Homolya. Sampling Parameters for Sulfate Measurement and Characterization. Env. Sci. and Tech., 13:584, 1979.

78. Dooley, A. and G. Whittingham. The Oxidation of Sulfur Dioxide in Gas Flames. Trans. Faraday Soc., 42:344, 1946.

79. Homolya, J. B., and S. Lambert. Characterization of Sulfate Emissions from Nonutility Boilers Firing Low-S Residual Oils in New York City. J. Air Pollution Control Assoc., 31(2):139-143, February 1981.

80. Homolya, J. B., H. M. Barnes, and C. R. Fortune. A Characterization of the Gaseous Sulfur Emissions from Coal and Oil-Fired Boilers. In: Energy and the Environment, Proceedings of the 4th National Conference, October 3-7, 1976.

81. Dietz, R. N. An Extensive Study of an Oil-Fired Power Plant. Final Report, Volume I. Brookhaven National Laboratory, 1980.

82. Harlow, W. F. Causes of High Dew-Point Temperatures in Boiler Flue Gases. Proc. Inst. Mech. Engrs., 151:293, 1944.

83. Bueters, K. A., and W. W. Habect. NO_x Emissions from Tangentially Fired Utility Boilers - Theory. In: 66th Annual AICHE Meeting. Philadelphia, Pennsylvania, November 1973.

84. Crawford, A. R., E. H. Manny, and W. Bartok. Field Testing: Application of Combustion Modifications to Control NO_x Emissions from Utility Boilers. Exxon Research and Engineering Company, 1974.

85. Compilation of Air Pollutant Emission Factors (with supplements). EPA Publication AP-42, U.S. Environmental Protection Agency, 1975.

86. Surprenant, N., R. Hall, S. Slater, T. Susa, M. Sussman, and C. Young. Preliminary Emissions Assessment of Conventional Stationary Combustion Systems: Vol. II. EPA-600/2-76-046b, 1976.

87. Blakeslee, C. E., and H. E. Burbach. NO_x Emissions from Tangentially-Fired Boilers - Practice. Presented at the 66th Annual AICHE Meeting, Philadelphia, PA, November 1973.

88. U.S. Environmental Protection Agency. Steam Electric Generating Units: Background Information for Proposed SO_2 Emission Standards. EPA-450/2-78-007a, July 1978.

89. Battelle Memorial Institute, 1977. Evaluation of Physical Coal Cleaning as an SO_2 Emission Control Technique. EPA-600/7-78-034, February 1978.

90. Makansi, J., and B. Schweiger. Fluidized-Bed Boilers. Power, 126(8), August 1982.

91. Aulisio, C., and W. Howe. AFBC Development: R&D Status Report of the Coal Combustion Systems Division. EPRI Journal, March 1982.

92. New Stationary Source Performance Standards; Electric Utility Steam Generating Units. Federal Register, 44(113):33594, June 11, 1979.

93. Rivers, M. E., and K. W. Riegel. Work Group 3B: Emissions, Costs and Engineering Assessment. Memorandum of Intent on Transboundary Air Pollution. Final Report No. 3B, June 15, 1982.

94. Dickerman, J. C., and K. L. Johnson. Technology Assessment Report for Industrial Boiler Applications: Flue Gas Desulfurization. EPA-600/7-79-178i, November 1979.

95. Homolya, J. B., and J. C. Cheney. A Study of Primary Sulfate Emissions from a Coal-Fired Boiler with PCB. J. Air Pollution Control Assoc., 29:1000-1004, 1979.

96. McCurley, W. R., and D. G. DeAngelis. Measurement of Sulfur Oxides from Coal-Fired Utility and Industrial Boilers. In: Workshop Proceedings on Primary Sulfate Emissions from Combustion Sources, Vol. 2, Characterization, EPA-600/9-78-020b, 1978. pp. 67-85.

97. Hilst, G. R. SURE Findings and Conclusions: R&D Status Report of the Energy Analysis and Environment Division. EPRI Journal, July/August 1982.

98. Lim, K. J., R. J. Milligan, and H. I. Lips. Technology Assessment Report for Industrial Boiler Applications: NO_x Combustion Modification. EPA-600/7-79-178f, December 1979.

99. Jones, G. D., and K. L. Johnson. Technology Assessment Report for Industrial Boiler Applications: NO_x Flue Gas Treatment. EPA-600/7-79-178g, December 1979.

100. U.S. Environmental Protection Agency. Electric Utility Steam Generating Units: Background Information for Proposed NO_x Emission Standards. EPA-450/2-78-005a, July 1978.

101. U.S. Environmental Protection Agency. Field Testing: Application of Combustion Modifications to NO_x Emissions from Utility Boilers. EPA-650/2-74-066, June 1974.

102. Martin, G. B. Field Evaluation of Low NO_x Coal Burners on Industrial and Utility Boilers. In: Proceedings of the Third Stationary Source Combustion Symposium. EPA-600/7-79-050a, February 1979.

103. Mobley, J. D. Assessment of NO_x Flue Gas Treatment Technology. In: Proceedings of the Joint Symposium on Stationary Combustion NO_x Control. EPRI WS-79-220, 1981.

104. U.S. Department of Energy. Energy Data Reports. EIA-0049/1, 1976.

105. California Board of Air Sanitation. The Oxides of Nitrogen in Air Pollution. California Department of Public Health, 1966.

106. Ashby, H. A., R. C. Stahman, B. H. Eccleston, and R. W. Hurn. Vehicle Emissions - Summer to Winter. SAE Paper 741053, SAE Automobile Engineering Meeting, Toronto, Canada, 1974.

107. Federal Highway Administration. Traffic Volume Trends, Tables 5A, 5B,
      and 9A. November–December 1978. Highway Statistics Division,
      Washington, D.C.

108. Lavery, T. F., G. M. Hidy, R. L. Baskett, and P. K. Mueller. The
      Formation and Regional Accumulation of Sulfate Concentrations in the
      Northeastern United States. Prepared for the Proceedings of the
      Symposium on Environmental and Climatic Impact of Coal Utilization, 1979.

109. U.S. Environmental Protection Agency. Background Information for New
      Source Performance Standards: Primary Copper, Zinc, and Lead Smelters,
      Vol. I, Proposed Standard. EPA–450/2–74–002a, 1974.

110. Klemm, H. A., and R. J. Brennan. Emission Inventory on the SURE
      Region. GCA/Technology Division, EPRI Contract No. TP 862–5, 1980.

111. Dykema, O. W., and V. E. Kemp. Inventory of Combustion–Related
      Emissions from Stationary Sources (First Update). EPA–600/2–77–066a,
      1977.

112. Clark, T. L. Gridded Annual Air Pollutant Emissions East of the Rocky
      Mountains. EPA–600/4–79–030, 1979.

113. GCA/Technology Division. Unpublished data from the development of the
      SURE Emissions Inventory, 1977.

114. Environmental Research & Technology, Inc. The Sulfate Regional
      Experiment (SURE) Final Report, Volume 2. Project No. EPRI RP 862, 1980.

115. Bosch, J. C. Emission Inventories for Acid Rain Studies. In
      Proceedings of an APCA Specialty Conference on: Emission Inventories
      and Air Quality Management. Kansas City, MO, April 27–30, 1982.
      pp. 298–306.

116. Liptak, B. G., ed. Environmental Engineer's Handbook, Vol. 2, Air
      Pollution. Chilton Book Co., Radnor, Pennsylvania, 1974.

117. Liljestrand, H. M., and J. J. Morgan. Chemical Composition of Acid
      Precipitation in Pasadena, CA. Env. Sci. and Tech., 12(12), 1978.

118. Munger, J. W. Chemistry of Atmospheric Precipitation in the
      North–Central United States; Influence of Sulfate, Nitrate, Ammonium and
      Calcareous Soil Particulates. Atmos. Environ., 16(7):1633–1645, 1982.

119. Likens, G. E., R. F. Wright, J. N. Galloway, and T. J. Butler. Acid
      Rain. Scientific American, 241(4), 1979.

120. Scott and Lamb. J. of Am. Chem. Soc., 92:3943, 1970.

121. National Center for Atmos. Res., unpublished results. (See
      Reference 111).

122. Adewuji, Y. G., and G. R. Carmichael. The Effects of Simultaneous
      Absorption of SO_2, NH_3, and HNO_3 on Precipitation Acidity.
      Presented at AICHE National Meeting. New Orleans, LA, November 8-12,
      1981.

123. Adamowicz, R. F. A Model for the Reversible Washout of Sulfur Dioxide,
      Ammonia and Carbon Dioxide from a Polluted Atmosphere and the Production
      of Sulfates in Raindrops. Atmos. Environ., 13(1):105-121, 1979.

124. Marsh, A. R. W. Sulfur and Nitrogen Contributions to the Acidity of
      Rain. Atmos. Environ., 12:401-406, 1978.

125. Doyle, G. J., et al. Simultaneous Concentrations of NH_3 and HNO_3 in
      a Polluted Atmosphere and Their Equilibrium Relationship to Particulate
      Ammonium Nitrate. Env. Sci. and Tech., 13:1416, 1979.

126. McConnell, J. C. Atmospheric Ammonia. J. Geophys. Res., 78:7812-7820,
      1973.

127. Raynor, G. S. and J. V. Hayes. Acidity and Conductivity of
      Precipitation on Central Long Island, New York in Relation to
      Meteorological Variables. Water, Air and Soil Pollution, 15(2):229-245,
      February 1981.

128. Sequeira, R. Chemistry of Precipitation at High Altitudes:
      Interrelation of Acid-Base Components. Atmos. Environ., 16(2):329-335,
      1982.

129. Raynor, G. S., and J. V. Hayes. Sulfate, Nitrate Plus Nitrite and
      Ammonium Ion Concentrations in Central Long Island, New York
      Precipitation in Relation to Meteorological Variables. Brookhaven
      National Laboratory, Upton, New York, July 1980.

130. Stanford, G., and J. O. Legg, et al. Denitrification and Associated
      Nitrogen Transformation in Soils. Soil Sci., 120:147-152, 1975.

131. Denmead, O. T., J. R. Simpson, and J. R. Freney. Ammonia Flux into the
      Atmosphere from Grazed Pasture. Science, 185:609-610, 1974.

132. Bouldin, D. R., et al. Losses of Inorganic Nitrogen from Aquatic
      Systems. J. Env. Qual., 3(2):107-114, 1974.

133. Pelczar, M. J., Jr., R. D. Reid, and E. C. S. Chan. Microbiology.
      Fourth Edition. McGraw-Hill Book Company, New York, 1977.

134. Wark, K., and C. F. Warner. Air Pollution, Its Origin and Control.
      Harper and Row Publishers, Inc., New York, 1976.

135. Health Effects Research Laboratory. Ammonia. U.S. Environmental
      Protection Agency. EPA-600/1-77-054, 1977.

136. National Research Council. Ammonia. Subcommittee on Ammonia, Committee
      on Medical and Biological Effects of Environmental Pollutants, Assembly
      of Sciences, National Academy of Science, 1978.

137. Rawlings, G. D., and R. B. Reznik. Source Assessment: Synthetic
      Ammonia Production. Monsanto Research Corp., EPA-600/2-77-107m, 1977.

138. Council for Agricultural Science and Technology. Effect of Increased
      Nitrogen Fixation on Stratospheric Ozone. In: CAST Report No. 53, 1976.

139. National Research Council. Nitrates: An Environmental Assessment.
      National Academy of Sciences, 1978.

140. Lau, N., and R. J. Carlson. On the Discrepancy Between Background
      Atmospheric Ammonia Gas Measurements and the Existence of Acid Sulfates
      as a Dominant Atmospheric Aerosol. Atmos. Environ., 11:475-478, 1977.

141. Tanner, R. L., B. P. Leaderer, and J. D. Spengler. Acidity of
      Atmospheric Aerosols. Env. Sci. and Tech., 15(10):1150-1153, October
      1981.

142. Frank, C. R., and G. K. Voight. Potential Effects of Acid Precipitation
      on Soils in the Humid Temperature Zone. In: Proceedings of the First
      International Symposium on Acid Precipitation and the Forest Ecosystem.
      Columbus, Ohio, May 12-15, 1975.

143. Gorham, E. Acid Precipitation and Its Influence Upon Aquatic
      Ecosystems—An Overview. In: Proceedings of the First International
      Symposium on Acid Precipitation and the Forest Ecosystem, USDA Forest
      Service, Ohio State University, Columbus, Ohio, May 12-15, 1975.

144. Cogbill, C. V., and G. E. Likens. Acid Precipitation in the
      Northwestern United States. Water Resources Res., 10(6):1133-1137, 1974.

145. Yue, G. K., V. A. Mohen, and C. S. Kiang. A Mechanism for Hydrochloric
      Acid Production in Clouds. In: Proceedings of the First International
      Symposium on Acid Precipitation and the Forest Ecosystem, USDA Forest
      Service, Ohio State University, Colubmus, Ohio, May 12-15, 1975.

146. Duce, R. A. On the Source of Gaseous Chlorine in the Marine Atmosphere,
      J. Geophys. Res., 74:4597-4599, 1969.

147. Robbins, R. C., R. D. Cadle, and D. L. Eckhart. The Conversion of NaCl
      to Hydrogen Chloride in the Atmosphere. J. of Meteorology, 16(53), 1959.

148. Cauer, H. Einiges uber dan Einpluss des Meeres aur den Chemisus der
      Luft, der Balneologes, 5:409-415, 1938.

149. Kohler, H., and M. Bath. Qualitative Chemical Analysis of Condensation
      Nuclei from Sea Water. Nova Acta Regiol. Soc. Scient., 15(7):24, 1953.

150. Raynor, G. S. and J. V. Hayes. Chloride and Sodium Ion Concentrations
     in Central Long Island, New York Precipitation in Relation to
     Meteorological Variables. Brookhaven National Laboratory, Upton, New
     York, March 1980.

151. Sittig, M. Environmental Sources and Emissions Handbook. Noyes Data
     Corp., Park Ridge, New Jersey, 1975.

152. Kahn, Z. S. and T. W. Hughes. Source Assessment: Chlorinated
     Hydrocarbons Manufacture. Monsanto Research Corp. EPA-600/2-79-019,
     1979.

153. Junge, C. E. Atmospheric Chemistry and Radioactivity. Academic Press,
     New York, New York, 1963.

154. Bartel, O. G. Health Phys., 22:387, 1972.

155. Stahl, Q. L., and Litton Systems, Inc. Preliminary Air Pollution Survey
     of Chlorine Gas. APTD 69-33, U.S. Department of Health, Education, and
     Welfare, 1969.

156. Barton, L. V. Toxicity of Ammonia, Chlorine, Hydrogen Cyanide, Hydrogen
     Sulfide, and Sulfur Dioxide Gases. Contrib. Boyce Thompson Inst.,
     11(5)357, 1940.

157. Laird, A. R., and R. W. Miksad. Observations on the Particulate
     Chlorine Distribution in the Houston-Galveston Area. Atmos. Environ.,
     12:1537-1542, 1978.

158. Seinfeld, J. H. Air Pollution, Physical and Chemical Fundamentals.
     McGraw-Hill, Inc., New York, 1975.

159. Nordlie, B. E. Amer. J. Sci., 271:417, 1971.

160. Kirk and Othmer. Encyclopedia of Chemical Technology, 3rd Ed., 1(800)
     J. Wiley & Sons, New York, 1978.

161. USDC. Survey of Current Business, 60(6), 1980.

162. Babich, H., D. L. Davis, and G. Stotzky. Acid Precipitation. Envir.,
     24(4):6, 1980.

163. Meetham, A. R. Natural Removal of Pollution from the Atmosphere.
     Quart. J. Roy. Meteor. Soc., 76:359-371, 1950.

164. Parker, A. The Investigation of Atmospheric Pollution, 27th Report of
     the Standing Conference of Cooperating Bodies. HMSO, London, 1955.

165. Coal Research Center. Pollution by Chlorine in Coal Combustion. In:
     Sect. V of Air Pollution Research Progress Report for Quarter Ended
     December 31, 1966. BM/41-BM/50, U.S. Bureau of Mines, 1966.

166. Loiy, P. J., and T. J. Kneip. Aerosols: Anthropogenic and Natural
      Sources and Transport - Summary of a Conference. J. Air Pollution
      Control Assoc., 30:358-361, 1980.

167. Committee on Sulfur Oxides. In: Sulfur Oxides, National Academy of
      Sciences, 1978.

168. Roberts, D. B., and D. J. Williams. The Kinetics of Oxidation of
      Sulphur Dioxide Within the Plume from a Sulphide Smelter in a Remote
      Region. Atmos. Envion., 13:1485, 1979.

169. Hegg, D. A., and P. V. Hobbs. Measurement of Gas-to-Particle Conversion
      in the Plumes from Five Coal-Fired Electric Power Plants. Atmos.
      Environ., 14:99, 1980.

170. Barnes, R. A. The Long Range Transport of Air Pollution. A Review of
      European Experience. J. Air Pollution Control Assoc., 29:1219-1235,
      1979.

171. Beilke, S., and G. Gravenhorst. Heterogeneous SO_2-Oxidation in the
      Droplet Phase. Atmos. Environ., 12:231-239, 1978.

172. Eggleton, A. E. J., and R. A. Cox. Homogeneous Oxidation of Sulphur
      Compounds in the Atmosphere. Atmos. Environ., 12:227-230, 1978.

173. Penkett, S. A., B. M. R. Jones, K. A. Brice, and A. E. J. Eggleton. The
      Importance of Atmospheric Ozone and Hydrogen Peroxide in Oxidizing
      Sulphur Dioxide in Clouds and Rainwater. Atmos. Environ., 13:123-137,
      1979.

174. Chang, S. G., R. Brodzinski, S. Oblath, S. Maskowitz, R. Toosi and T.
      Novakov. Role of Soot Particles and NO_x in the Oxidation of SO_2 in
      Aqueous Solution. LBL-10886, Lawrence Berkeley Lab, CA, 1980.

175. Overton, J. H. Jr. Acidification of Rain in the Presence of SO_2,
      H_2O_2, O_3 and HNO_3. PB82-167206, Northrop Services, Inc.,
      January 1982. p. 27.

176. Drewes, D. R., J. M. Hales, and C. Hakkarinen. SO_2 Oxidation in
      Precipitation Falling Through a Power Plant Plume. In: The Commission
      on Atmospheric Chemistry and Global Pollution Symposium on the Budget
      and Cycles of Trace Gases and Aerosols in the Atmosphere, University of
      Colorado, Boulder, Colorado, 1979.

177. Haagen-Smit, A. J., and L. G. Wayne. Atmospheric Reactions and
      Scavenging Processes. In: Air Pollution (Third Ed.), Volume I, Ch. 6,
      A. C. Stern, ed. Academic Press, New York, 1976.

178. Stumm, W., and J. J. Morgan. Aquatic Chemistry. Wiley Interscience,
      New York, 1970.

179. Glass, N. R., G. E. Glass, and P. J. Rennie. Effects of Acid Precipitation. Env. Sci. and Tech., 13(11), 1979.

180. Galloway, J. N., G. E. Likens, and E. S. Edgerton. Hydrogen Ion Speciation in the Acid Precipitation of the Northeastern United States. In: Proceedings of the First International Symposium on Acid Precipitation and the Forest Ecosystem. USDA Forest Service, Ohio State University, Columbus, Ohio, 1975.

181. Winkler, E. M. Natural Dust and Acid Rain. In: Proceedings of the First International Symposium on Acid Precipitation and the Forest Ecosystem, USDA Forest Service, Ohio State University, Columbus, Ohio, 1975.

182. Smith, R. M., P. C. Twiss, R. K. Krauss, and M. J. Brown. Dust Deposition in Relation to Site, Season, and Climatic Variables. Proc. Sci. Soc. Am., 34(11), 1970.

183. Adomaitis, V. A., H. A. Kantrud, and T. A. Shoesmith. Some Chemical Characteristics of Aeolian Deposits of Snow-Soil on Prairie Wetlands. Proc. North Dakota Acad. Sci., 21:65-69, 1967.

184. Shannon, D. G., and L. O. Fine. Cation Solubilities of Lignite Fly Ashes. Env. Sci. and Tech., 8:1026-1028, 1974.

185. Ananth, K. P., J. B. Galeski, L. J. Shannon, F. I. Honea, and D. C. Drehmel. Impact of Particulates and SO_2 from Coal-Fired Power Plants on Acid Rain. In: Proceedings of The Fourth Clean Air Congress, the Japanese Union of Air Pollution Prevention Association, 1977.

186. Likens, G. E., and F. H. Bormann. Acid Rain: A Serious Regional Environmental Problem. Science, 184:1176-1179, 1974.

187. Schryer, D. R., R. S. Rogowski, and W. R. Cofer III. A Study of the Influence of Airborne Particulates on Sulfate Formation. In: Environmental and Climatic Impact of Coal Utilization. J. J. Singh, and A. Deepak (eds.). Academic Press, 1980. pp. 275-290.

188. Rogowski, R. S., D. R. Schryer, W. R. Cofer, III, R. Edahl, and S. Munaralli. Carbon-Catalyzed Oxidation of SO_2 and NO_2 in Air. NASA Technical Paper 2014, Langley Research Center, WV, April 1982.

189. Cofer, W. R., D. R. Schryer, and R. S. Rogowski. The Enhanced Oxidation of SO_2 by NO_2 on Carbon Particulates. Atmos. Environ., 14:571-575, 1980.

190. Britton, L. G., and A. G. Clarke. Heterogeous Reactions of Sulfur Dioxide and SO_2/NO_2 Mixtures With a Carbon Soot Aerosol. Atmos. Environ., 14:829-839, 1980.

191.   Barbaray, B., J-P. Contour, and G. Mouvier.   Effects of Nitrogen Dioxide and Water Vapor on Oxidation of Sulfur Dioxide Over V_2O_5 Particles. Env. Sci. and Tech., 12(12):1294-1297, November 1978.

192.   Hidy, G. M., J. R. Mahoney, and B. J. Goldsmith.   International Aspects of the Long Range Transport of Air Pollutants.   Document P-5252, U.S. Department of State, 1978.

3

Atmospheric Transport, Transformations, and Deposition Processes

INTRODUCTION

Manmade pollutants are injected into the atmosphere at heights ranging from a few feet, as is the case with auto exhaust, to more than 1000 feet in the case of tall stacks. Significant quantities of many of these same substances are also emitted over a wide range of heights from natural sources, for example, decaying vegetation and volcanoes. Once introduced into the atmosphere, the fate of all such substances depends on the physical processes of dispersion, transport, and deposition, and on complex chemical transformations that take place between the point of emission and the time of delivery to ground-level receptors. The residence time within the atmosphere of these emitted substances may be brief or may extend over several days, weeks, or even years, depending upon such properties as their reactivity and solubility in water and, in the case of particles, their physical size. Related determining factors include the height of release, amount of solar radiation, presence of precipitation, and the nature of the underlying earth's surface.

This section briefly discusses the processes affecting substances from the time of entry into the atmosphere until deposition under three major headings: transport and diffusion, chemical transformations during transport, and deposition processes.

TRANSPORT AND DIFFUSION

Once substances are in the atmosphere, they are subject to natural processes of dilution and bulk or advective transport. Dilution is efficiently accomplished by random fluctuations in the wind, i.e., by atmospheric turbulence. These fluctuations are generated mechanically in regions of wind shear and particularly by interaction of the wind with the roughness elements of the earth's surface, e.g., houses, trees, and mountains. They are also generated thermally when solar radiation heats the earth's surface producing convective motions, some of which grow to large cells and result in vigorous vertical mixing through depths of several kilometers.

Advection is the bulk transport of material by the mean wind. It occurs over a wide range of temporal and spatial scales. On a small scale, the mean wind near an industrial plant calculated over the period of an hour may

correctly define the average direction in which substances emitted from a
stack move during that hour. On a larger scale, the transport flow will be
controlled by synoptic-scale weather systems covering geographical regions
that extend several thousands of kilometers horizontally and through the
troposphere vertically. Atmospheric processes that occur over time periods of
several days determine transport flow over these distances.

The pollutants to be considered in the acid deposition problem may
intersect the earth's surface close to its source if the source is near ground
level, or if daytime convection is distributing pollutants throughout the
mixing layer regardless of source height; on the other hand, pollutants
emitted above a nocturnal inversion layer may remain aloft until daytime
convection is established through solar heating and not reach the surface for
several hundred kilometers. Pollutants can be brought to the surface at any
distance by the onset of precipitation, which is an efficient cleansing
mechanism. Figure 3-1, taken directly from Reference 1, provides perspective
on the length of time that various constituents remain in the atmosphere and
the corresponding distances they may be transported. Transport distances
(source to receptor) relevant to the acid deposition problem can be bounded at
the upper end by considering the combined residence times of acid precursors
and their acidic end products, a period estimated to be from 3 to 5 days, but
one that is highly dependent upon the amount of precipitation experienced
en route. During this time interval, material would travel from one to two
thousand kilometers if the transport wind speed were to average 16 km/hr,
a value that is frequently exceeded.

Although the meteorological factors associated with a particular
pollutant release govern the diffusion and transport for that event,
climatological features of the area control the longer-term distribution of
any acidic deposition that may result from continuous or frequent releases.
Some of the more significant of these climatological features are summarized
for North America in the discussion that immediately follows. A few comments
concerning the probable effect of stack height on the transport of emissions
from power plants and large industrial sources of pollutants are also included.

Seasonal Changes in Mean Flow

Except for southern Florida and the Gulf Coast, the contiguous United
States lies in the belt of the prevailing westerlies. Thus, on the average,
relatively clean air enters the continent from the west and receives
pollutants while traversing toward the east coast. However, this flow is
impeded by mountain ranges, has day-to-day weather patterns superimposed, and
undergoes significant seasonal changes.

Seasonal differences in prevailing low-level wind fields are suggested by
Figures 3-2 and 3-3, which show the mean resultant surface winds at principal
reporting stations during January and July, the months with maximum seasonal
difference. During both seasons, air enters the west coast from the Pacific;
flow through the mountain states, although rather ill-defined near the surface
because of topographical influences, shows an average movement from the south

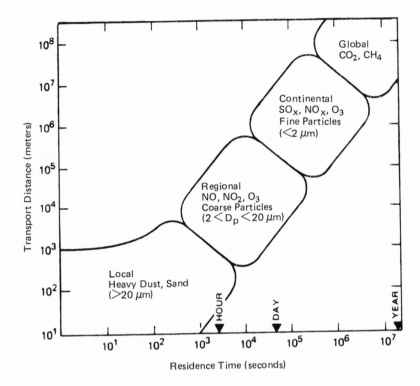

Figure 3-1.   Dispersion of pollutants introduced into the atmosphere as
determined by residence time. Man-made sulfur compounds,
including fine particles, are distributed on a continental
scale. Source: R. B. Husar and D. E. Patterson, Center
for Air Pollution Impact and Trend Analysis, Washington
University, St. Louis, Missouri (National Research Council[1]).

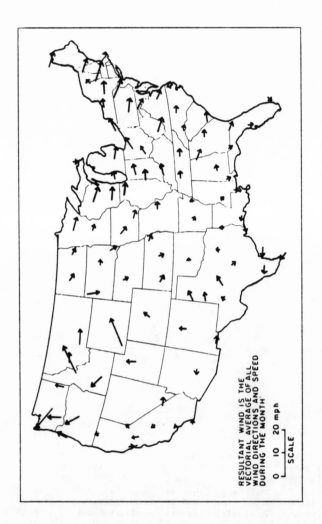

Figure 3-2.   Mean resultant surface winds for January (resultant winds taken from Climatological Atlas of the United States[2]).

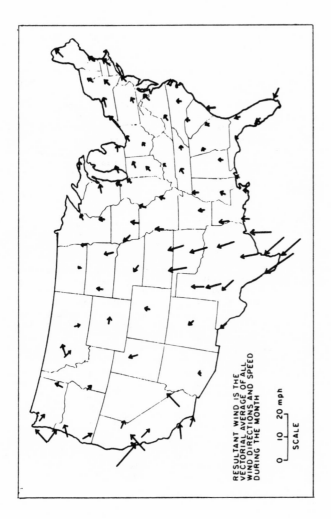

RESULTANT WIND IS THE
VECTORIAL AVERAGE OF ALL
WIND DIRECTIONS AND SPEED
DURING THE MONTH

0   10   20 mph
SCALE

Figure 3-3.   Mean resultant surface winds for July (resultant winds taken from Climatological Atlas of the United States[2]).

and west. Very marked seasonal differences occur east of the Rockies,
however. During January, major inflow from Canada dominates the pattern over
the north central and northeastern states. In the far south, flow from the
Gulf of Mexico moves north over Texas, and air from the Atlantic crosses
southern Florida.

In July, in the mean, all of the states east of the Rockies are dominated
by southerly flow, which is particularly steady and strong over the central
states and becomes southwesterly over the northeastern states. During the
summer, incursions of Canadian air are less frequent than in winter and
penetrate less deeply into the United States. Figures 3-3 and 3-4, which
depict surface flow over the North American continent schematically for the
month of July, are representative of mean surface flow during the summer when
the highest seasonal values of sulfate and acidity are observed in the eastern
and northeastern regions of the United States (see Reference 4 and Section 4).

Storm Tracks and Precipitation Patterns

Some of the most frequent routes of low pressure (cyclonic) weather
systems are sketched in Figure 3-5. These paths give a general picture of the
movement of low pressure centers and do not refer to the exact movement of
individual storms. This figure shows that, regardless of their origin, many
storms pass over the eastern states. In the development of storms moving from
the west, moisture is supplied principally from the Gulf of Mexico or Atlantic
Ocean, and the combination of this moisture supply and preferred storm paths
leads to high annual precipitation amounts in the southern and eastern states,
as shown in Figure 3-6. The second area with high annual amounts of
precipitation lies along the coastal region of Washington and Oregon where
storm activity from the Pacific is frequent, particularly during the winter
and early spring. Figure 3-6 was prepared from mean precipitation amounts
given for state climatic divisions, and precipitation amounts at specific
locations may differ substantially from those indicated by the figure. Air
masses moving in from the Pacific drop much of their moisture during passage
over the western mountain ranges. This loss of moisture is reflected in the
extensive areas in the West with less than 20 inches of annual precipitation.

The effectiveness of precipitation in cleansing the atmosphere depends
not only on the total amount of precipitation that falls during a year, but
also on its temporal distribution. The most readily available climatological
statistic bearing on this distribution is the number of days in a year with
measurable precipitation (i.e., >0.01 inches). Figure 3-7 gives the
geographic distribution of this information. The number of days with
precipitation and the annual precipitation have similar geographic patterns;
the principal difference is in the eastern part of the country where total
precipitation amounts are greatest in the south and the number of days with
precipitation is greatest in the North.

Figures 3-6 and 3-7 were prepared from average precipitation amounts for
a 10-year period, 1951 through 1960. Large variations do occur from year to
year, however. At many locations there are also large seasonal differences.

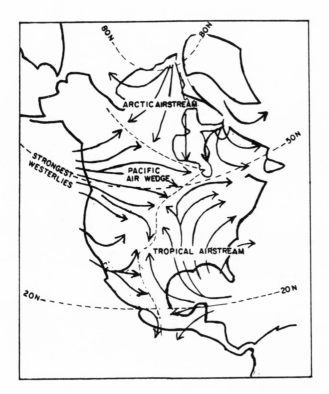

Figure 3-4.   Schematic representation of the surface
flow across North America based on July
resultant surface winds (Bryson et al.[3]).

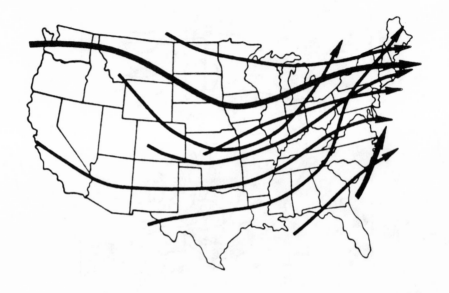

Figure 3-5. Average tracks of low pressure systems
(Klein[5]).

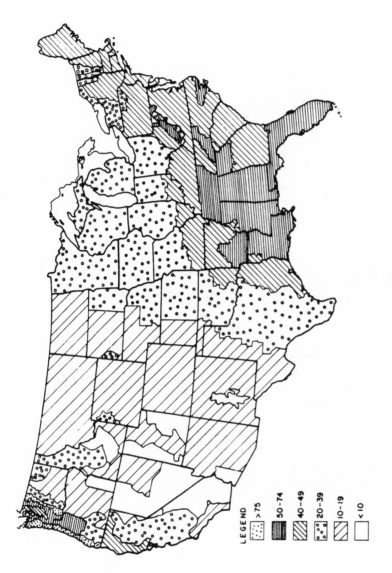

Figure 3-6. Mean annual precipitation in inches (Prepared from data in Climatic Atlas of the United States[2]).

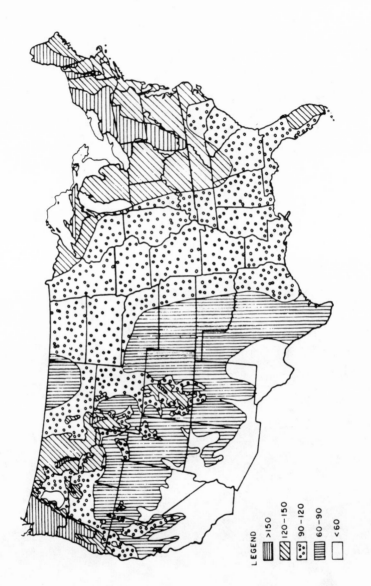

LEGEND

▦ >150
▨ 120-150
⬚ 90-120
▤ 60-90
▢ <60

Figure 3-7. Mean number of days with 0.01 inches or more of precipitation in 1 year (prepared from data in Climatic Atlas of the United States[2]).

The extent of seasonal differences in precipitation at selected cities within the United States can be seen in Figure 3-8 which shows average monthly amounts during a 30-year period.

When considered together, Figures 3-6, 3-7, and 3-8 show that the northeastern United States experiences frequent precipitation, generally totaling over 40 inches per year but exceeding 50 inches per year at some of the higher locations, and that this precipitation is distributed quite uniformly throughout the year. This is a region that both produces acid rain precursor pollutants and is subject to an influx of acidic pollutants from neighboring regions.

Occurrence of Stagnant Conditions

Warm high-pressure systems that are slow moving or stagnant favor the accumulation of sulfate compounds and other pollutants. The accompanying clear skies favor smog-producing photochemical reactions, and temperature inversions in the lower atmospheric layers limit the depth of vertical mixing. In addition, because of the absence of rain, depletion of the pollutant cloud is minimal. In an analysis of particulate matter, Hidy, Mueller and Tong[7] found that the highest ambient concentrations of sulfate were found under summertime conditions when a synoptic-scale high pressure system stalled for more than 2 days over a region of high SO_2 emissions, such as the Ohio River Valley.

Korshover[8] studied the frequency and persistence of stagnating anticyclones east of the Rockies during a 30-year period. He found that the number of cases per year when a stagnating anticyclone lasted for 4 or more days ranged from 4 to 16 and that the maximum frequency in both number of cases and number of days stagnation occurred in an area covering parts of Georgia, South Carolina, and North Carolina. Seasonally, the frequency of occurrence peaks in October and has a secondary maximum in May. One of the consequences of having an anticyclone with its clockwise circulation and light winds stagnate over the southeastern United States is an enhancement of the flow of highly polluted air northeastward from industrialized areas. This results in part from the accumulation of pollutants within the air mass, coupled with weak anticyclone surface flow, and in part from steady southwesterly winds typically found at heights of a few thousand feet to the west of the surface anticyclone as a result of the associated upper air pressure pattern. Such a stagnant weather pattern over the southeastern United States is frequently ended by the approach of a cold front from the north or northwest. This intensifies the flow of air parallel to the front typically carrying pollutants toward the Northeast. In addition, frontal precipitation can remove significant amounts of pollutants. More detailed discussion of the accumulation and disposition of pollutants associated with stagnating high pressure cells has been given by Vukovich,[9] Whelpdale,[10] and LaFleur and Whelpdale.[11]

Figure 3-9, sketched from data in a figure presented by Korshover, shows the geographic distribution of the average annual number of stagnation days from 1936 through 1965. Stagnation days are least likely to occur during the winter; a secondary minimum occurs in July.

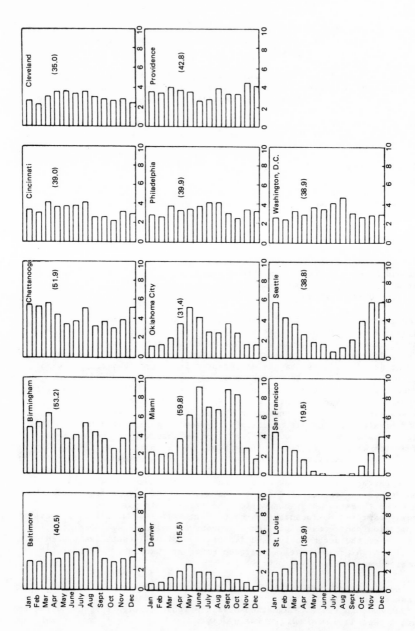

Figure 3-8. Normal monthly precipitation in 14 cities (inches). Annual averages are given in parentheses (Record et al.[6]).

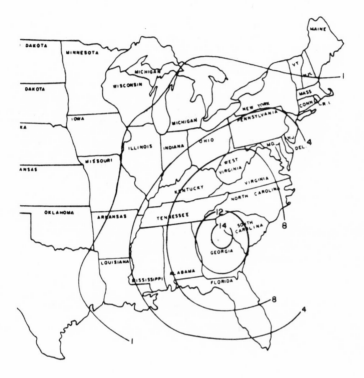

Figure 3-9.   Average annual number of stagnation days,
1936 to 1965 (see Korshover[8]).

Topographic Impacts

Topographic features such as the existence of bodies of water and the presence of mountain ranges may affect wind patterns and the amount of precipitation, and consequently influence the distribution and amount of wet and dry deposition. Because many of the effects of acid rain are cumulative, the total annual precipitation is important as well as its average acidity. The frequent occurrence of snow immediately south of the Great Lakes when cold northerly winds flow over open water in the early part of winter is a well-known illustration of the influence of a moisture source on local precipitation patterns. Orographic precipitation is produced when moisture-laden air rises and cools while passing over a topographic barrier. It is an important factor in intensifying rainfall on windward slopes. Precipitation on the leeward side of a range tends to be diminished or absent because of downslope motion and the resulting warming of the air mass. Additionally, orographic barriers hinder the passage of storms and frontal systems and promote convection by differential heating along the slopes.

The rugged north-south mountain ranges along the west coast of North America prevent the moderately warm and humid Pacific air masses from entering the central portion of the continent without major modification. The prevailing westerly winds and the impact of storms from the Pacific result in heavy orographic precipitation along the coast, particularly north of 40° latitude, and lesser amounts east of the mountains. The Rocky Mountains play a similar but less marked role in determining precipitation patterns because of the lower average moisture content of the air masses. They also provide a barrier to the occasional storm systems that move against the mountains from the south and east. Although the mountains near the east coast are not a very effective climatic barrier, they do have an important influence on the weather under certain meteorological regimes. For example, the Adirondacks, being centrally located with respect to storm tracks, are subject to relatively large amounts of precipitation, the acidity of which would presumably be controlled by the emission and transformation of precursor pollutants from upwind sources.

An illustration of the extent to which a mountain range can remove acidic pollutants from an air mass has been given by Likens et al.[12] In this example, the pH of precipitation from air masses arriving from the British Isles increased from an average of 4.2 at the Norwegian coast to 4.6 or 4.7 after passing over mountainous areas with an elevation of 1000 meters (3280 feet) or so. Presumably, precipitation on the leeward side of the mountains was being produced within an airmass already partially cleansed by earlier precipitation on the windward side.

The Role of Tall Stacks

For a period of years, one of the most popular methods for reducing the ground-level concentration of pollutants in the vicinity of power plants and industrial complexes has been the use of tall stacks. For example, the average height of stacks built for coal-burning power plants increased from 243 feet to 609 feet over the period 1960 to 1969, and numerous stacks as high as 1000 feet exist today. Although the tall stack by itself does not reduce the amount of pollutants introduced into the atmosphere, the additional dilution experienced by the pollutants under most meteorological conditions is frequently sufficient to keep ground-level concentrations below ambient standards. The overall effect of using a tall stack on atmospheric chemistry and the ground-level concentrations of transformed pollutants is not yet completely clear. Nonetheless, it is probable that the contribution to regional-scale pollution problems is enhanced by the use of tall stacks.

With increasing stack height, the frequency at which effluents are emitted above a stable layer that prevents or inhibits downward vertical mixing increases. This is largely a nighttime phenomenon, but emissions released at night may travel many miles before the increased vertical mixing brought about by the sun's heating destroys the stable layer and brings the pollutants into contact with the earth's surface. Although the pollutants may experience chemical changes during this period of transport, they are not subject to the substantial losses by dry deposition that low-level emissions experience close to the source. Additionally, plume studies conducted in the Midwest[13,14] have confirmed the rather frequent existence of a summertime, nocturnal "jet-stream" (i.e., a bulge in the vertical profile of wind speed) at about the usual tall stack plume height. During these particular studies, the wind speed in the low-level jet-stream averaged 12 m/sec (27 mi/hr).

An attempt to estimate the effect of stack height on the far field wet and dry deposition of sulfur over Europe by modeling has been reported by Fisher.[15] Two calculations were performed: the first assumed that half the sources in Europe are at a height of approximately 300 meters (984 feet) and that the remaining sources were at approximately 30 meters (98 feet); the second calculation assumed that all of the sources were low-level sources. The effect of changes in source height on wet deposition was found to be less than about 10 percent. The effect on dry deposition was not reported. Fisher's model takes a statistical approach to obtain the long-term deposition pattern. The model is being developed to provide a fairly rapid and efficient method of determining the pattern of total and wet annual deposition of sulfur over Europe. The results are considered no more accurate than a factor of two, but have been found to be in good agreement with the results of models based on trajectory computations.

The 1977 amendments to the Clean Air Act recognize the limitations of the tall stack approach to the control of pollution. Section 123 states that the stack height must not exceed good engineering practice requirements. Good engineering practice is interpreted to mean "the height necessary to insure that emissions from the stack do not result in excessive concentrations of any air pollutant in the immediate vicinity of the source as a result of atmospheric downwash, eddies and wakes which may be created by the source itself nearby structures or nearby terrain obstacles"--and is usually taken to be two and a half times the height of the source.

CHEMICAL TRANSFORMATIONS DURING TRANSPORT

Investigators agree that the phenomenon of acid precipitation, as measured by pH, is caused by the presence of the three strong acids: H_2SO_4, HNO_3, and HCl.[16,17,18] Of these three, H_2SO_4 and HNO_3 are by far the most important. The relative contribution of H_2SO_4 and HNO_3 within the United States, however, varies with geographical area and with season. After comparing the absolute concentrations of the sulfate, nitrate, and chloride ions in precipitation, Cogbill and Likens[19] concluded that H_2SO_4 was the dominant acid in the northeastern United States, making an average contribution of 62 percent, followed by HNO_3 with 32 percent, and HCl with 6 percent. Farther south, recent measurements of precipitation at Gainesville, Florida, showed average contributions of the three acids to be: H_2SO_4, 69 percent; HNO_3, 23 percent; and HCl, 8 percent.[20] In the Los Angeles basin precipitation study, Liljestrand and Morgan[21] found HNO_3 to be 32 percent more prevalent than H_2SO_4, while a study by Johnson reported by Dethier[22] indicates that sulfate is the dominant anion in western Washington. Although monitoring programs are generally less extensive in the west, the available evidence supports an H_2SO_4 to HNO_3 ratio of about 1 to 1 or 1.4 to 1 west of the Mississippi River in contrast to a ratio of about 2 to 1 to the east.[23]

As reported in Section 2 of this document, it is also agreed that the two principal anthropogenic sources of atmospheric acidity are emissions of sulfur oxides and nitrogen oxides which, after participating in a variety of chemical reactions, are chiefly responsible for the observed high concentrations of sulfate, nitrate, and hydrogen ions found in precipitation. The burning of distillate and residual oils may also produce significant amounts of sulfate within the furnace which are released into the atmosphere as primary pollutants.[24] What are not known yet in verifiable detail, however, are many of the chemical pathways followed from source emission to acidic end product and the associated reaction rates, plus the way these reactions are controlled by the atmospheric environment. Important clues, helpful in the attempt to establish quantitative relationships between anthropogenic emissions and the acidity of precipitation, are being discovered, nonetheless. However, it will be necessary to understand the mechanisms by which SO_2 is oxidized to sulfates in much greater detail before the extent of sulfate reduction that would be brought about by a given reduction in SO_2 emissions will be known, or whether perhaps indirect strategies for sulfate control, such as altering the initial pollutant mix in plumes, might be more effective.[25] The pathways followed during the transformation of NO_x to nitrates are even less well understood.

A qualitative discussion of some of the chemical interactions taking place in the lower atmosphere was given near the end of Section 2. This section concentrates on probable transformation rates of SO_2 and NO_x to sulfates and nitrates, since these rates directly affect the regional distribution of the acidic end products. A short discussion of the neutralization of acidic products by substances found in the atmosphere is also included.

Formation of Sulfates

The oxidation of SO_2 in the atmosphere may take place while all of the involved substances are in the gaseous state (i.e., by homogeneous reactions) or by heteorogeneous reactions in which gas molecules become attached to liquid or solid aerosols. The heterogeneous reactions are particularly complex and their details are incompletely understood. More is known about homogeneous gas phase reactions[26] and laboratory and field evidence accumulated over the past decade has been frequently interpreted to indicate that photochemical gas phase oxidation is the most important oxidation route for SO_2.[27] During the past few years, however, heterogeneous reactions have been suspected of being at least equally important.[28]

Direct photo-oxidation of sulfur dioxide in pure air is believed to be negligible. If it occurs at all, the rate is probably slower than 0.03 percent per hour.[29] In polluted atmospheres, homogeneous oxidation of sulfur dioxide proceeds at a more rapid rate after gas-phase collision with strong oxidizing radicals such as HO, HO_2, and CH_3O_2. The source of these radicals is hydrocarbon-NO_x emission, which through daytime photo-oxidation produces oxidizing radicals as intermediate products.[30] The rate of oxidation is believed to depend on the initial ratio of hydrocarbons to NO_x, temperature, dewpoint, solar radiation, and the absolute concentrations of the reactive pollutants. The direct observations of reactive transients under a variety of atmospheric conditions needed to confirm details of the oxidation mechanism, however, are not available. Table 3-1 prepared from estimates presented by Barnes,[31] summarizes probable homogeneous oxidation rates for a variety of conditions. Other information compiled by the National Academy of Sciences[30] suggests rates ranging from 0.5 to 5 percent per hour for sunny summer days. Wintertime rates are expected to be lower by a factor of 2 to 5 or more because of reduced sunlight intensity.

TABLE 3-1.   ESTIMATED HOMOGENEOUS OXIDATION RATES FOR SULFUR DIOXIDE

Degree of pollution	Oxidation rate (%/hour)
Pure air	Negligible (<0.03)
Natural background	<0.1
Urban mixture (containing both NO_x and olefinic hydrocarbons)	1-10

Three heterogeneous mechanisms are believed to be important in the atmospheric conversion of SO_2. They are: (1) catalytic oxidation in water droplets by transition metals, (2) oxidation in the liquid phase by strong oxidants such as ozone and hydrogen peroxide originating from the gas-phase photo-oxidation of hydrocarbon-NO_x mixtures, and (3) surface-catalyzed oxidation of sulfur dioxide on collision with solid particles, paticularly elemental carbon (soot). Oxidation rates for these heterogeneous reactions in the atmosphere are not known. Although the relative importance of homogeneous and heterogeneous reactions is uncertain, it is agreed that both types of reaction occur and that both are affected by environmental conditions.

Laboratory simulations and chemical kinetic model calculations have played a key role in providing estimates of potential reaction rates among various constituents of the atmosphere, and in identifying the most probable controlling environmental factors. The results have guided field experiments to confirm and explore these reactions in the atmosphere by studying elevated plumes from major SO_2 sources. Different initial mixes of pollutants have been achieved by selecting plumes from both coal-fired and oil-fired power plants and from smelters. An overview of recent findings from these studies has been published by Newman[32] who concludes that the diurnal average oxidation rate of sulfur dioxide to sulfate is probably less than 1 percent per hour with little or no oxidation occurring from early evening to early morning, but with the rate sometimes reaching as high as 3 percent per hour during the daytime. Newman found little concensus, however, concerning details of the reactions.

In an attempt to discover common features of SO_2 conversion related to basic and readily available environmental information, Wilson[33] assembled a broad data base from 13 plume studies conducted by 8 organizations. In these studies, measurements were made in plumes from 8 coal-fired power plants, 1 oil-fired power plant, and 1 metal smelter (copper, lead, silver, and zinc). One study was carried out in Australia, one in Canada, and the remaining 11 in the United States (see Reference 14 and References 34 through 42). The measurement periods included both diurnal and seasonal cycles, and a number of different measurement techniques were used. In combining the data, Wilson used the rato S_p/S_T, where S_p is the amount of particulate sulfur and S_T is the amount of total sulfur (both reduced by background levels), as a measure of the extent of conversion. This ratio, divided by the age of the plume at the sampling distance, ΔT, was used to represent the average conversion rate. Figures 3-10 and 3-11 show two of Wilson's summary data plots. In Figure 3-10, the average conversion rate during the period of plume transport is plotted against the mid-point of this period. In Figure 3-11, the percent sulfate in particulate form is plotted against the solar radiation dose. An approximate conversion between solar radiation dose and plume age can be made from the two abscissa scales. In the composite data set, plume age ranged from an arbitrary 1-hour cutoff at the low end to a maximum age of 14.8 hours. A relationship between conversion rate and time of day is apparent in Figure 3-10. The correlation coefficient of 0.64 for the data in Figure 3-11 indicates that 41 percent of the observed variance in the extent of conversion is accounted for by solar radiation dose. Wilson concludes "that environmental factors linked to solar radiation strongly influence the rate and extent of sulfur-conversion in point-source plumes." He points out, however, that because of diurnal and seasonal covariance of insolation-related factors, it is difficult to determine the relative importance of specific environmental factors or conversion pathways. He further states that without

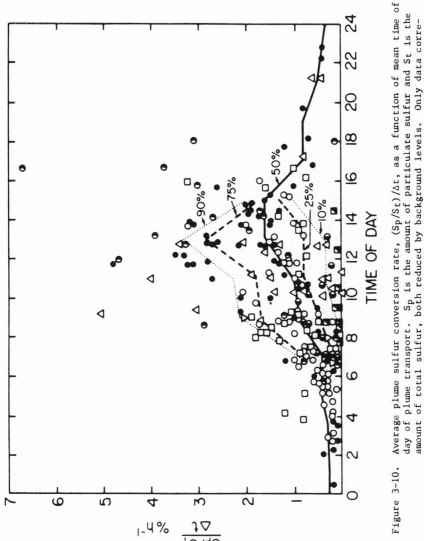

Figure 3-10.   Average plume sulfur conversion rate, $(S_p/S_t)/\Delta t$, as a function of mean time of day of plume transport. S_p is the amount of particulate sulfur and S_t is the amount of total sulfur, both reduced by background levels. Only data corresponding to plume age greater than 1.5 h are plotted. Data points are keyed by symbol to each of the eight reporting agencies. For details see Wilson, Reference 33.

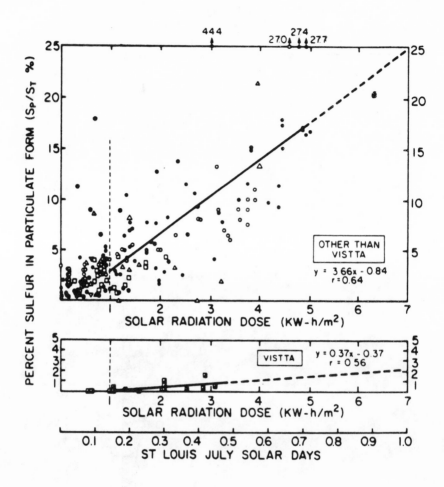

Figure 3-11. Extent of plume sulfur conversion, S_p/S_t, vs solar radiation
dose during the period of plume transport. Only data
corresponding to plume age greater than 1.5 h are plotted.
Data points are keyed by symbol to each of the eight reporting
agencies. For details see Wilson, Reference 33.

more sophisticated analyses of existing data and more comprehensive documentation of the environmental conditions under which plume measurements are made, it cannot be concluded that solar radiation is involved directly or that photochemical pathways are the dominant route of conversion.

Figure 3-12, an example of results from one of the United States studies, shows the conversion rates determined by nine summertime sampling missions into the plume from the 2400 MW coal-fired Labadie power plant near St. Louis, Missouri. When plotted against time of day, the rates show a very strong diurnal variation with daytime rates varying between 1 and 4 percent per hour, and nighttime rates consistently below 0.5 percent per hour.

A second approach to estimate conversion rates uses a regional model in which rate constants for the conversion and removal of sulfur dioxide are included as unknowns and are determined from a best-fit comparison between calculated and observed values. From a practical point of view, this regional approach has the advantage of providing rate constants that are averages over all sources included in the emission inventory and over the spatial-temporal scales of interest. Application of this technique in Europe lead to a year-round average conversion rate of SO_2 to $SO_4^=$ of 1 to 2 percent per hour.[43]

Formation of Nitrates

The chemistry of nitrogen oxides in the atmosphere is complex and the details are not well understood. Of the various processes involved, those by which nitric oxide (NO) and nitrogen dioxide (NO_2) are converted to acidic end products are of principal concern in the formation of acid rain. Other oxides of nitrogen occur only in very low concentrations. The conversion of NO_x to nitric acid takes place through a series of complicated reactions during which participating nitrogen oxides switch back and forth between various stages of oxidation and eventually end up as nitrates.

NO, formed during high temperature combustion, is easily oxidized to NO_2 by a number of reactions including:

$$2 \text{ NO} + O_2 \longrightarrow 2 \text{ } NO_2$$

The rate of oxidation by this reaction, however, is highy dependent upon concentration. This reaction may be important during initial dilution with air, but for typical ambient levels of nitric oxide, the reaction proceeds very slowly. For example, at 0.1 ppm, its half-life is approximately 1000 hours.[44]

In contrast, conversion may take place rapidly (within a matter of seconds) in a polluted atmosphere exposed to solar radiation, as it does in the formation of smog. The key to this rapid conversion lies in sequences of reactions between transient species and other reactive molecules such as carbon monoxide, hydrocarbons, and aldehydes. During daytime conversion, an important photochemical cycle takes place in which both the production and destruction of ozone occurs. As part of this process NO_2 is converted to

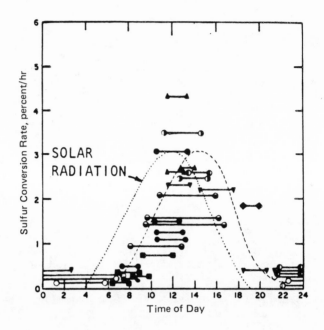

Figure 3-12.   Sulfur conversion rates for the Labadie power plant for nine aircraft sampling flights. The points to the left of each bar are the release times and to the right, the sampling times (Husar et al.[14]).

nitric acid vapor and NO, and NO_2 may be absorbed into existing particles. Many of the same oxidizing agents in the atmosphere that are involved in the formation of sulfates are also involved in the oxidation of NO_x. Among these, the hydroxyl radical (HO), produced by the photolysis of ozone, is considered to be one of the most active.

Most of our understanding of the oxidation processes and photochemical reactions involving nitrogen oxides that take place in the atmosphere has come through laboratory studies involving chemical and kinetic modeling. Key information needed to tie these studies firmly to reactions within the atmosphere is still missing.[45] Furthermore, it will be very difficult to obtain this information directly because many of the reacting substances are transient, secondary pollutants that occur only in very small concentrations. There are also numerous possible paths by which nitrate salts may be formed from gaseous nitric acid. Some of these involve homogeneous processes such as the direct capture of gaseous nitric acid by gaseous ammonia, which leads to the formation of ammonium nitrate. Others, also believed to be of importance, include heterogeneous reactions occurring during the absorption and accumulation of acids and other substances by aerosol droplets and cloud water.

Because of the complexity of the chemical processes involved in the production of acidic products from nitrogen oxides in the atmosphere and the spatial and temporal variations of key parameters controlling these processes, rates of conversion of nitrogen oxides to nitrates can be expected to vary greatly. Thus, Haagen-Smit and Wayne[44] state that these processes may take hours or days. Barnes[46] reports that precise conversion rates are not known but are thought to vary with season. Barnes further states that the atmospheric lifetime of nitrogen compounds is greater than that for sulfur oxides.

Figure 3-13 shows results from a series of smog chamber experiments conducted by Spicer et al.[47] to identify variables influencing NO_x chemistry in diluted power plant plumes. The independent variables tested for possible effects were: (1) hydrocarbon concentration, (2) hydrocarbon composition, (3) relative humidity, (4) SO_2 concentration, and (5) presence of H_2SO_4. These semilog plots of NO_x (i.e., NO + NO_2) concentration versus reaction time illustrate the extremes in reactivity likely to be experienced in diluted plumes as a result of environmental conditions. Irradiation and dilution rates were maintained constant for all experiments.

Only a few field studies have attempted to measure the reaction rates of NO_x. The results of one such study in which measurements were made in the coal-fired Cumberland Steam Plant of TVA have recently been reported by Forrest et al.[48] Figure 3-14 shows the rate of nitrate formation plotted against time of day. Late night and early morning conversion rates ranged from approximately 0.1 to 6 percent per hour. Late morning and afternoon rates ranged from approximately 3 to 12 percent per hour with outlying values of 0.6 and 22 percent per hour. For comparison, the rate of sulfate formation found during these tests showed a similar diurnal variation with rates varying from 0.1 to 7 percent per hour.

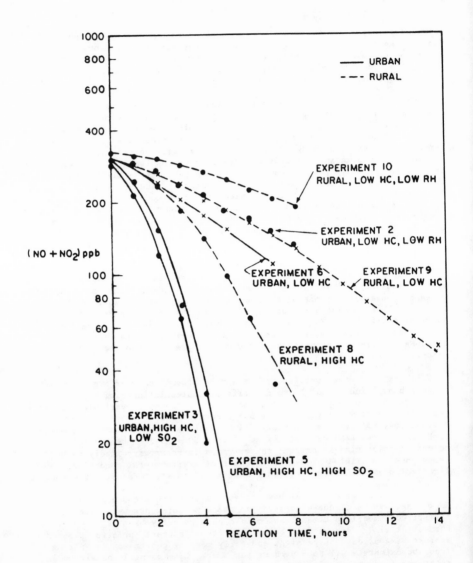

Figure 3-13.   Semilog plot of (NO + NO₂) for
               selected experiments (Spicer, et al.[47]).

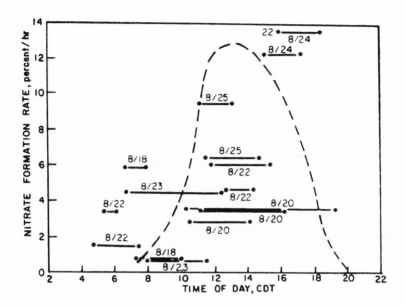

Figure 3-14.   Conversion rate of NO → NO$_3^-$ as a function
of time of day (Forrest et al.[48]).

The development of chemical models based on laboratory studies in which reaction rates among atmospheric pollutants can be determined under controlled conditions can also provide insight into transformation processes occurring within the atmosphere. The following example is an application of such a model.

Rodhe, Crutzen, and Vanderpol[49] formulated a chemical model describing the basic photochemical transformation of SO_2 and NO_x into the acids H_2SO_4 and HNO_3 and combined it with a simple transport and deposition model operating over time scales of a few days. Nineteen chemical reactions with appropriate reactive and dissociation rates were selected to represent the transformation processes. In addition to the most important reactions describing the transformation of SO_2 and NO_x to their corresponding acids, reactions were included which were believed to determine concentrations of the oxidizing agents OH and H_2O_2. The liquid-phase transformation of SO_2 occurring in cloud droplets and rain plus the exchanges of the reacting species between droplets and surrounding air, and the frequency of occurrence of clouds and precipitation, were included in the representation. Estimates of total removal rates by precipitation and dry deposition were used. The model was then run with input data representative of summertime conditions in northern Europe to establish reference concentration changes with time for pollutants of concern. This was followed by runs to investigate the effect of changes in initial concentrations of key reactants, including one to simulate changes resulting from recent European trends in SO_2 and NO_x emissions.

Comparison of the model results with European data encouraged the modelers to suggest a number of tentative conclusions. The following model results and conclusions are of particular note: (1) In a coupled chemical system one may not assume a proportional dependence of concentrations on emission rates. (2) The formation of HNO_3 takes place significantly faster than the formation of H_2SO_4. Under similar scavenging rates, nitrate in precipitation would, therefore, be of a more local origin than sulfate. (3) Other things being equal, an increase in the emission rate of hydrocarbons will enhance the rate of production of both H_2SO_4 and HNO_3. (4) Changes in NO_x emissions may affect the formation of both HNO_3 and H_2SO_4 through their effect on the concentration of oxidants. If NO_x emissions are increased, more OH is used up initially in the formation of HNO_3 so that the formation rate of H_2SO_4 is decreased. The net effect is that less H_2SO_4 is formed in the atmosphere and that relatively more SO_2 is removed by deposition. Doubling the NO_x emission rate in the model led to a decrease in the total amount of H_2SO_4 formed by about 45 percent.

Computer simulations of chemical reactions are also being used to understand the formation of secondary pollutants within plumes and the scavenging of gases and formation of acids during precipitation. For example, Meagher and Luria[50] modeled the plume from a 300 MW coal-fired power plant located in rural southeastern United States to explore the influence of environmental conditions (wind speed, atmospheric stability, solar intensity, and concentration of background gases) and initial plume concentrations on the rate of formation of sulfate, ozone, and nitrate. They describe the production of secondary pollutants in terms of three reaction zones, with the rate of production greatest during the second zone where the ratio of hydrocarbons to NO_x becomes more balanced due to plume dilution and the entrainment of background air. The model calculations also showed that the production of secondary pollutants was reduced by reducing the emission of either NO_x or SO_2 but that the decrease in secondary pollutants production was only a small fraction of the primary emission reduction.

As an example of a somewhat different type of modeling, Durham, Overton, and Aneja[51] used a physio-chemical subcloud model to simulate the effect of gaseous HNO_3 and NO_x on pH and $SO_4^=$ production below a precipitating cloud. Ambient gases considered were SO_2, NO, NO_2, HNO_3, O_3 and CO_2. This work represents a part of a continuing effort to model acidification during the precipitation process. With the mechanisms considered, absorption of gaseous HNO_3 controlled the acidification in the initial stages of a rain event, and inhibited the production of $SO_4^=$. NO and NO_2 played no direct role in the acidification or formation of NO_3^- or $SO_4^=$, and preacidified raindrops were further acidified only by absorbing HNO_3.

NEUTRALIZATION OF ACIDITY

The acidity (pH) of precipitation is determined by the chemical nature and relative proportion of acids and bases in solution. Major cations and anions present typically include hydrogen (H^+), ammonium (NH_4^+), potassium (K^+), sodium (Na^+), calcium (Ca^{++}), magnesium (Mg^{++}), nitrate (NO_3^-), sulfate ($SO_4^=$), chlorine (Cl^-), and phosphate ($PO_4^=$),[23] but the concentrations of the individual ions that determine the ionic balance and resultant acidity sometimes vary greatly from one geographic area to another, and from season to season. Thus, as pointed out by Sequeira,[52] sulfate and nitrate are not quantitative indicators of acid deposition unless the relative alkali deposition is negligible or corrected for neutralization. In principle, changes in pH can be brought about as well by changes in the concentrations of neutralizing substances as by changes in the concentrations of the strong acids. Substances recognized for their ability to neutralize the atmosphere's acidic load include fine wind-blown soil particles and ammonia. Additionally, it has been hypothesized that fly ash from coal combustion historically played a major role in reducing atmospheric acidity,[53] but consideration of the relative sizes of fly ash and sulfate particles, and the chemical composition of fly ash from midwestern and eastern coals, and the change from stoker-fired coal boilers to pulverized coal boilers suggests that the neutralizing effect would have been confined to the immediate locality of a few heavy fly ash emitters.[54]

Evidence of the neutralizing effect of airborne soil particles was found by Thornton and Eisenreich[55] in a study of the impact of land use on the chemical composition of precipitation in the north central United States. Event precipitation and snow core samples were taken along a transect extending from southeastern North Dakota to northeastern Minnesota for a period of approximately 1 year. Land use along the transect changed from prairie-agricultural in the west to forested in the east. The study indicated that soil and anthropogenic sources each contributed importantly to the composition of both rain and snow, with soils being more important in the west and anthropogenic sources in the east. After studying elemental and component ratios, the investigators concluded that sulfate and nitrate at the western sites appeared to be primarily soil-derived, whereas this was not the case at the eastern forested sites. They also concluded that the major influence of wind-blown soil on precipitation chemistry disappeared only a short distance east of the prairie-forest transition, being associated chiefly with particles of short atmospheric residence times. (The possibility that arid soils are a major contributor of sulfates and nitrates in precipitation in the Southwest as well has also been pointed out.)[52]

As further evidence of the neutralizing effect of soil particles in the Midwest, an analysis of precipitation data collected by the Illinois State Water Survey reported by Semonin[56] showed that the drop in pH from 5.6 to 4.7 that occurred between 1954 data and 1960 data was associated with a decrease in the concentration of calcium and magnesium (from 65 to 37 microequivalents per liter) and not with an increase in sulfates or nitrates. Semonin notes that 1954 was a year of severe drought in both the northeastern and midwestern states and that dust storms were a common occurrence. Sequeira[52] has also observed that recent levels of alkaline dust in United States precipitation are considerably lower than those observed during the 1955 to 1956 or 1959 to 1963 periods and that this change may be the cause of the observed lower pH values.

Ammonia is produced from a variety of natural and anthropogenic sources, and is able to neutralize both sulfuric and nitric acids. In urban atmospheres, the sulfate anion is usually present as neutral ammonium sulfate or partially neutralized ammonium bisulfate.[57] The effect of ammonia in precipitation may be complicated by its dissolving to form the ammonium ion NH_4^+, the presence of which may increase the conversion rate of SO_2 to sulfurous and then to sulfuric acid.[58]

DEPOSITION PROCESSES

The processes by which pollutants are transferred from the atmosphere to the earth's surface are conveniently divided into two categories called wet and dry deposition. Wet deposition encompasses those processes that remove gases, liquids, or solids by precipitation. Dry deposition includes those processes that do not involve precipitation, namely: (1) the absorption or adsorption of gases by exposed surfaces such as vegetation, soil, water, and manmade structures; (2) gravitational settling of relatively coarse particles; and (3) impaction of fine particulate on vegetation and other surfaces. The effectiveness of the various deposition processes is a function of the physical and chemical characteristics of the particular substance, the nature of the receiving surface, and meteorological factors.

Removal by Precipitation

The processes by which pollutants are removed from the atmosphere during cloud growth and precipitation are frequently separated into two groups. Processes that occur within the cloud are referred to as rainout and begin with the condensation of water vapor on cloud condensation nuclei (CCN). Many of these nuclei are believed to be sulfate particles that have been formed as a result of the gas-to-aerosol conversion of natural and manmade sulfur dioxide emissions. Condensation is followed by droplet growth, during which various pollutants dissolve in the droplets, undergo chemical changes, and begin their descent to the ground in falling precipitation. The removal of pollutants below the cloud base by this precipitation is called washout. Of the two processes, rainout is the more complex, and no adequate quantitative theory covering all aspects of it exists.[59] However, an appreciation of its complexity can be gained by considering the process of cloud formation.

Clouds are dynamic systems within which water vapor is condensing, evaporating, and recondensing. During these cycles large volumes of air are processed by the clouds, but it has been estimated that even in large storms, only about half of the water vapor passing upward through the cloud base is returned to the ground as precipitation. The initial condensational growth on CCN can produce droplets about 10 μm in radius in 5 to 10 minutes; thereafter, growth by condensation is extremely slow.[60] Growth of droplets to precipitable size occurs principally by the collison and coalescence of smaller cloud droplets. Within the clouds, pollutants are absorbed by droplets, participate in chemical reactions, and frequently return to cloud-free air at higher elevations following droplet evaporation. Thus the acidity of droplets depends not only on the ionic species present within the droplet but also on their dilution within the droplet. This is a function of where the droplet is in its condensation-evaporation cycle. Pollution may be cycled through the aqueous phase many times before being deposited on the ground by precipitation.[61] Cloud systems vary in horizontal and vertical dimensions and in internal vertical motions. Also, the life history of individual droplets varies greatly from cloud type to cloud type as well as from drop to drop within the same cloud.

Attempts have been made to calculate the relative importance of rainout and washout to the concentration of ionic species in precipitation. The general approach followed has been to calculate the contribution produced by washout and to ascribe the remaining species found in the precipitation to in-cloud scavenging processes. To a large extent, the research effort to date has concentrated on the physical processes and chemical reactions leading to the formation of sulfates. As pointed out by Marsh,[59] the washout of SO_2 by rain falling through a uniform concentration of SO_2 is a function of: (1) the size spectrum of droplets and hence the rate of precipitation, (2) the initial pH of the rain, (3) the height of the SO_2 concentration, and (4) the absolute magnitude of the SO_2 concentration. Furthermore, the joint washout of SO_2 with other pollutants differs from that of SO_2 alone. In particular, the presence of NH_3 hastens the absorption of SO_2 and its conversion to sulfate.[62] Calculations by Marsh[59] suggest that the scavenging of SO_2 gas and particulates below cloud base and in-cloud scavenging contribute about equally to the concentration of sulfates in precipitation. Also of interest are network data from MAP3S that indicate that sometimes as much as 30 percent of the total sulfur in rainwater may be a result of direct scavenging of SO_2.

Although the major source of H_2O_2 is suspected to be gas-phase reactions, calculations recently performed by Chameides and Davis[63] suggest that aqueous-phase chemical reactions within cloudwater may play an important role in the production of H_2O_2 leading to the rapid oxidation of sulfur species. That the production of sulfate in the atmosphere through cloud reactions can proceed at a very rapid rate has been demonstrated by Hobbs, who has reported a doubling of the sulfate content of air during its passage through a cloud.[64]

The amount of a substance deposited by precipitation within a specified area can be estimated directly from the amount and chemical content of precipitation falling within the time period of interest, after taking into account temporal and spatial variations by appropriate averaging procedures.

Dry Deposition

Since the amount of a substance deposited by dry deposition is dependent both upon its physical state and the characteristics of the surface with which it is interacting, direct dry deposition information of general application is very difficult to obtain, and no accurate methodology for doing so has been developed to date.[65] Estimates of dry deposition over complex surfaces are, therefore, inherently less accurate than estimates of wet deposition.

Calculations of deposition rate are usually performed either by multiplying the air concentration at a specified height by an experimentally derived parameter called the deposition velocity, V_d, or in cetain situations by a mass balance approach. Deposition velocities have most frequently been obtained by eddy-correlation or concentration gradient measurement techniques. Deposition velocities have been published for a few typical locations, but since the deposition process depends on many factors and the observational techniques are inherently difficult it is not surprising that the range of suggested values covers more than an order of magnitude. Dry deposition rates are particularly susceptible to atmospheric parameters such as stability, turbulence, and wind speed, and to surface parameters such as physical roughness, type of vegetation, and chemical characteristics. An appreciation for the wide range of deposition velocities possible over various types of vegetation and soil can be gained from the estimates for SO_2 presented in Table 3-2, a and b. These tables were developed during the workshop at the International Symposium on Sulfur in the Atmosphere.[66] Dry deposition velocities for sulfate particles are usually assumed to be about 0.1 cm s^{-1}, but some observations have indicated that values five times as great might be more appropriate in light and moderate winds over natural grassland.[67] On the other hand, Slinn[68] expects that the deposition of sulfate, most of the mass of which is in the 0.1 to 1 μm diameter range, in a vegetative canopy falls in the 0.01 to 0.1 cm s^{-1} range.

Relative Contributions of Wet and Dry Deposition

Until recently, wet deposition was considered to be the chief mechanism by which acidic substances are removed from the atmosphere and deposited on the surface of the earth. Within the last few years, however, consideration of more extensive observations, modeling results, and mass balance

TABLE 3-2a.   DEPOSITION VELOCITIES FOR SO_2 OVER VEGETATION

Vegetation		Height (m)	Range of V_d (cm s^{-1})	Typical V_d[a] (cm s^{-1})
Height	Example			
Short	Grass	0.1	0.1 to 0.8	0.5
Medium	Crops	1.0	0.2 to 1.5	0.7
Tall	Forest	10.0	0.2 to 2.0	Uncertain

[a]These values were obtained in a humid climate. Much smaller values are likely in arid climates.

TABLE 3-2b.   DEPOSITION VELOCITIES FOR SO_2 OVER SOIL

Soil type	pH	State	Range of V_d (cm s^{-1})	Typical V_d (cm s^{-1})
Calcareous	≥ 7	Dry	0.3 to 1.0	0.8
Calcereous	≥ 7	Wet	0.3 to 1.0	0.8
Acid	~ 4	Dry	0.1 to 0.5	0.4
Acid	~ 4	Wet	0.1 to 0.8	0.6

Note: As yet no information is available to assess V_d on desert sand or lateritic soils.

calculations has led to the view that dry deposition may be of equal importanc over western Europe and North America. At any given site, however, the relative contributions could be quite different. Because of early interest in sulfur dioxide and sulfates and the consequent existence of substantial data bases, most of the estimates carried out to date have been for sulfur compounds. Although preliminary, these estimates are useful in bringing to attention the role played by dry deposition. Many of these results have been expressed in terms of total sulfur rather than as separate sulfur dioxide and sulfate constituents, which are of greater interest in evaluating contribution to acid deposition. To illustrate the results obtained by current techniques, results determined by three different approaches are presented below.

Calculations recently carried out by Shannon[69] using the ASTRAP model permit wet and dry sulfur deposition amounts to be compared. The calculations covered three periods: July to August 1974, January to February 1975, and July to August 1975. The model was run twice--once with emissions from the eastern United States only and once with emissions from eastern Canada only. The relative contributions of the two deposition processes are shown in Table 3-3. In both model runs, wet deposition was slightly more effective than dry deposition in removing sulfur from the atmosphere over the United States (1.3 to 1). Over Canada, however, wet deposition proved to play a considerably greater part, particularly for emissions entering from the United States (3 to 1).

TABLE 3-3.   RELATIVE CONTRIBUTIONS OF WET AND DRY DEPOSITION
(BASED ON ASTRAP MODEL--SHANNON[69])

Period	United States		Canada	
	Dry	Wet	Dry	Wet
U.S. Emissions Only				
July to August 1975	1	1.1	1	2.6
July to August 1974	1	1.2	1	3.3
January to February 1975	1	1.7	1	3.1
Average	1	1.3	1	3.0
Canada Emissions Only				
July to August 1975	1	1.1	1	1.7
July to August 1974	1	1.2	1	1.9
January to February 1975	1	1.5	1	1.4
Average	1	1.3	1	1.7

A second example is provided by Galloway and Whelpdale,[70] who have developed an atmospheric sulfur budget for eastern North America. Their estimates of wet deposition were made from observations throughout the eastern United States and Canada. Dry deposition was calculated from representative air concentrations of SO_2 and $SO_4^=$ and deposition velocities. The authors estimate the accuracy of their dry deposition estimates to be approximately ± 90 percent for both Canada and the United States. Using their results, the ratios of wet to dry deposition over the two regions are: for the eastern United States, 0.76 to 1; and for eastern Canada, 2.5 to 1. Consideration of possible errors introduced into the wet deposition estimates by the use of monthly collections led Galloway and Whelpdale to suspect that their estimates of wet deposition might be high by up to 30 percent. According to their estimates, the dry deposition of sulfur as SO_2 exceeds that as $SO_4^=$ by a factor of about four in Canada and by a factor of about five in the United States.

Finally, a simplified model employed by Garland[71] led him to conclude that about one half of the SO_2 emitted to the atmosphere is removed by dry deposition, and that the remainder is oxidized to sulfate and removed in precipitation. He concluded further that the residence time for sulfur within the atmosphere is about 5 days.

A table of representative annual average wet and dry deposition rates for various parts of the world was prepared during the workshop held at the time of the International Symposium on Sulfur in the Atmosphere held in Dubrovnik, Yugoslavia, in September 1977.[66] This table is reproduced here as Table 3-4. Ranges represent spatial variations for each area.

SUMMARY

The spatial and temporal distributions of acid precipitation in North America are strongly influenced by large-scale climatological features. Of particular importance are the prevailing wind patterns that transport pollutants from major industrial areas, and the location of preferred storm tracks. In combination, those two features make the acid rain phenomenon of special concern to the northeastern United States and the neighboring parts of Canada. In addition, precipitation is enhanced when moisture-laden air is forced to ascend topographic barriers, such as the Adirondacks.

Pollutants are removed from the atmosphere not only by wet deposition, which includes all processes involving precipitation, but also by dry deposition, which includes the absorption and adsorption of gases by exposed surfaces, the impaction of fine particles upon such surfaces, and gravitational settling of relatively coarse particles. The relative importance of wet and dry deposition of acidic products and precursor gases is dependent upon the characteristics of receptor surfaces and the frequency, rate, total amount, and form of precipitation. Over western Europe and much of North America, wet and dry deposition are believed to be about equally effective in removing SO_2 and its oxidized end products from the atmosphere. However, the relative importance of these processes in producing acidity in watersheds is not yet fully understood.

TABLE 3-4.   REPRESENTATIVE ANNUAL AVERAGE WET AND DRY DEPOSITION RATES[66]

Location		Excess sulfate in precipitation ($mg\ S\ \ell^{-1}$)	Wet deposition rate ($g\ S\ m^{-2}y^{-1}$)	Dry deposition rate ($g\ S\ m^{-2}y^{-1}$)
Heavy industrialized areas	North America	3-?	0.1^a-3	?
	Europe	3-20	2-4	3-15
Rural	North America	0.5-2	0.1-2	0.2-2.6
	Europe	0.5-3	0.2-2	0.5-5.0
	North Atlantic	0.2-0.6	0.1-0.3	0.04-0.4
Remote	Other Oceans	0.04	0.01^a-0.2	0.1
	Continents	0.1	0.01^a-0.5	0.4

^{a}Low deposition rates result from low precipitation.

The chemical and physical processes acting during transport and deposition are exceedingly complex. Transformation processes involve both gas-phase, homogeneous reactions and heterogeneous reactions between gas molecules and liquid or solid aerosols. The chemical pathways followed and the rates of transformation appear to be highly dependent upon the composition of the polluted air and the presence of solar radiation. Other environmental factors such as temperature and humidity are also believed to be important. Some reactions are completed very quickly while others proceed over several days or weeks. Neutralization by substances introduced into the atmosphere by both natural processes and manmade activities may be significant. At the present time, only a relatively few of the many possible complex interactions among pollutants are considered when modeling chemical transformations within the atmosphere. One of the most complete attempts to represent the formation of sulfuric and nitric acids by modeling used 19 reactions, as discussed on page 3-26. The development and validation of source-receptor relationships by which the acid deposition problem can be most effectively managed and controlled requires better knowledge of all these processes.

There is general agreement that a reduction in SO_2 emissions would bring about a reduction in the production of sulfate aerosol and, probably to a lesser extent, the acidity of precipitation. However, recent studies have led some investigators to conclude that the resulting reduction in the sulfuric component of acid rain will be smaller than that indicated by a one-to-one relationship. On the other hand, it is thought that the reduction in the dry deposition of sulfur components would approximate reductions made in SO_2 emissions. The supporting theoretical argument is that oxidizing agents are a limiting factor in the formation of acids. In addition, some reactions are slowed as pH drops. Confirmation of this hypothesis could lead to a sophisticated control strategy based on concurrent changes in reactive hydrocarbon and nitrogen oxide emissions as well as a reduction in SO_2 emissions.

Better techniques for identifying contributions from specific sources or source categories would be helpful in developing control strategies that could be tuned to the needs of known sensitive areas. Promising techniques include the use of tracers, either added to individual sources, as suggested by Chamberlain et al.,[28] or by associating ambient trace element ratios with source types, as being done by Rahn[72] and others. Such techniques may prove to be useful additions to the more traditional modeling and trajectory approaches.

REFERENCES

1. National Research Council. Atmospheric-Biosphere Interactions: Toward a Better Understanding of the Ecological Consequences of Fossil Fuel Combustion. Committee on the Atmosphere and the Biosphere, Board on Agriculture and Renewable Resources, Commission on Natural Resources. National Academy Press, Washington, D.C., 1981.

2. Environmental Science Services Administration. Climatic Atlas of the United States. U.S. Department of Commerce, Environmental Data Services, 1968.

3. Bryson, R. A., and F. K. Hare. World Survey of Climatology, Vol. 11, Climates of North America. Elsevier Scientific Publishing Company, New York, New York, 1974.

4. Tong, E. Y. and R. B. Batchelder. Aerometric Data Compilation and Analysis for Regional Sulfate Modeling. Project Report, EPA Contract No. 68-01-1921 and University of Illinois (Ohio River Basin Energy Study), 1978.

5. Klein, W. H. Principal Tracks and Mean Frequencies of Cyclones and Anticyclones in the Northern Hemisphere. U.S. Weather Bureau. Research Paper No. 40, 1957.

6. Record, F. A., D. A. Lynn, G. L. Deane, R. C. Galkiewicz, and R. M. Bradway. National Assessment of the Urban Particulate Problem. Vol. 1, Summary of National Assessment. EPA-450/3-76-024. GCA/Technology Division, 1976.

7. Hidy, G. M., P. K. Mueller, and E. Y. Tong. Spatial and Temporal Distributions of Airborne Sulfate in Parts of the United States. Atmos. Environ., 12(1-3):735-752, 1978.

8. Korshover, J. Climatology of Stagnating Anticyclones East of the Rocky Mountains, 1936-1965. P.H.S. Publication No. 999-AP-34, U.S. Department of Health, Education, and Welfare, National Center for Air Pollution Control, Cincinnati, Ohio, 1967.

9. Vukovich, T. A Note on Air Quality in High Pressure Systems. Atmos. Environ., 13(2):255-265, 1979.

10. Whelpdale, D. M. Large Scale Atmospheric Sulfur Studies. Atmos. Environ., 12(1-3):661-670, 1978.

11. LaFleur, R. J. and D. M. Whelpdale. Spatial Distribution of Sulfates Over Eastern Canada During August 1976. Presented at the 70th Annual Meeting of the Air Pollution Control Association, June 20-24, Toronto, Ontario, 1977.

12. Likens, G. E., R. F. Wright, J. N. Galloway, and T. J. Butler. Acid Rain. Scientific American, 241(4):43-51, 1979.

13. Smith, T. B., D. L. Blumenthal, J. A. Anderson, and A. H. Vanderpol. Transport of SO_2 in Power Plant Plumes: Day and Night. Atmos. Environ., 12(1-3):605-611, 1978.

14. Husar, R. B., D. E. Patterson, J. D. Husar, N. V. Gillani, and W. E. Wilson, Jr. Sulfur Budget of a Power Plant Plume. Atmos. Environ., 12(1-3):549-568, 1978.

15. Fisher, B. E. A. The Calculation of Long Term Sulfur Deposition in Europe. Atmos. Environ., 12(1-3):489-501, 1978.

16. Galloway, J. N., G. E. Likens, and E. S. Edgerton. Acid Precipitation: pH and Acidity. Science, 194:722, 1976.

17. Likens, G. E., N. M. Johnson, J. N. Galloway, and F. H. Bormann, Acid Precipitation: Strong and Weak Acids. Science, 194:643, 1976.

18. Semb, A. Measurement of Acid Precipitation in Norway. Water, Air and Soil Pollution, 6:231, 1976.

19. Cogbill, C. V. and G. E. Likens, Acid Precipitation in the Northeastern United States, Water Resources Res., 10(6):1133-7, 1974.

20. Hendry, C. D. and P. Brezonik. Chemistry of Precipitation at Gainesville, Florida. Env. Sci. and Tech., 14(7):843-849, July 1980.

21. Liljestrand, H. M. and J. J. Morgan. Chemical Composition of Acid Precipitation in Pasadena, California. Env. Sci. and Tech., 12:1271, 1978.

22. Dethier, D. P. Atmospheric Contribution of Stream Water Chemistry in the North Cascade Range, Washington. Water Resource Research, 15(4):787-794, August 1979.

23. Cowling, E. B. and R. A. Linthurst. The Acid Precipitation Phenomenon and Its Ecological Consequences. BioScience, 31(9):649-653, October 1981.

24. Esposito, M. P., M. E. Szabo, T. W. Devitt, and P. Spaite. Acid Rain: The Impact of Local Sources. Prepared for Dept. of Energy, Morgantown Energy Research Center, Contract No. DE-AC-21-81MC14787, November 24, 1980.

25. Wilson, W. E. Sulfates in the Atmosphere: A Progress Report on Project MISTT. Atmos. Environ., 12(1-3):537-547, 1978.

26. Calvert, V. G., F. Su, J. W. Bottenheim, and O. P. Strausz. Mechanism of the Homogeneous Oxidation of Sulfur Dioxide in the Troposphere. Atmos. Environ., 12(1-2):197-226, 1978.

27. Chemical Transformations, Workshop 1B. Proceedings of the International Symposium on Sulfur in the Atmosphere, Dubrovnik, Yugoslavia, September 1977. Atmos. Environ., 12(1-3):10, 1978.

28. Chamberlain, J., H. Foley, D. Hammer, G. MacDonald, O. Rothas, and M. Ruderman. The Physics and Chemistry of Acid Precipitation. JASON/SRI International Technical Report No. JSR-81-25, 1981.

29. Cox, R. A. Particle Formation from Homogeneous Reactions of Sulfur Dioxide and Nitrogen Dioxide. Tellus, 26:235, 1974.

30. Committee on Sulfur Oxides. Sulfur Oxides. National Research Council, National Academy of Sciences, Washington, D.C., 1978.

31. Barnes, R. A. The Long Range Transport of Air Pollution - A Review of European Experience. J. Air Pollution Control Assoc., 29(12):1219-1235, 1979.

32. Newman, L. Atmosphere Oxidation of Sulfur Dioxide: A Review as Viewed from Power Plant and Smelter Plume Studies. Atmos. Environ., 15(10/11):2231-2239, 1981.

33. Wilson, W. E. Sulfate Formation in Point Source Plumes: A Review of Recent Field Studies. Atmos. Environ., 15(12):2573-2581, 1981.

34. Lusis, M. A., K. G. Anlauf, L. A. Barrie, and H. A. Wiebe. Plume Chemistry Studies at Northern Alberta Power Plan. Atmos. Environ., 12(12):2429-2437, 1978.

35. Battelle. Pacific Northwest Laboratories Plume Conversion Rates in the SURE Region. Final Report EA-1498. Vol. 1. Electric Power Research Institute, 1980.

36. Forrest, J., R. W. Garber, and I. Newman. Conversion Rates in Power Plant Plumes Based on Filter Pack Data. Part I. The Coal-Fired Cumberland Plume Preprints from the Symposium on Plumes and Visibility. Measurements and Model Components. Grand Canyon, AZ, November 10-14, 1980. Atmos. Environ., 15(10/11):2273-2282, 1981.

37. Newman, L., J. Forrest, and B. Manowitz. The Application of an Isotopic Ratio Technique to a Study of the Atmospheric Oxidation of Sulfur Dioxide in the Plume from an Oil-Fired Power Plant. Atmos. Environ., 9(11):959-968, 1975.

38. Roberts, D. B. and D. J. Williams. The Kinetics of Oxidation of Sulphur Dioxide Within the Plume from a Sulphide Smelter in a Remote Region. Atmos. Environ., 13(11):1485-1499, 1979.

39. Richards, I. W., J. A. Anderson, D. L. Blumenthal, A. A. Brandt, J. A. McDonald, N. Waters, E. S. Macias, and P. S. Bharadwaja. The Chemistry, Aerosol Physics, and Optical Properties of a Western Coal-Fired Power Plant Plume Preprints from the Symposium on Plumes and Visibility Measurements and Model Components. Grand Canyon, AZ, November 10-14, 1980. Atmos. Environ., 15(10/11):2111-2134, 1981.

40. Dittenhoefer, A. C. and R. G. dePena. Sulfate Aerosol Production and Growth in Coal-Operated Power Plant Plumes. J. Geophys. Res., 85:4499-4506, 1980.

41. Meagher, J. F., L. Stockburger, E. M. Bailey, O. Huff. The Oxidation of Sulfur Dioxide to Sulfate Aerosols in the Plume of a Coal-Fired Power Plant. Atmos. Environ., 12(11):2197-2203, 1978.

42. Gillani, N. V. and W. F. Wilson. Formation and Transport of Ozone and Aerosols in Power Plant Plumes. Ann. N.Y., Acad. Sci., 338:276-296, 1980.

43. OECD Programme on Long Range Transport of Air Pollutants, Measurements and Findings, Paris: Organization for Economic Cooperation and Development, 1977.

44. Haagen-Smit, A. J. and L. G. Wayne. Atmospheric Reactions and Scavenging Processes. In: Air Pollution, 3rd Edition, Vol. 1. A. C. Stern, ed., 1976.

45. The National Research Council. Nitrogen Oxides. National Academy of Sciences, Washington, D.C., 1977.

46. Barnes, R. A. The Long Range Transport of Air Pollution - A Review of European Experience. J. Air Pollution Control Assoc., 29(12):1219-1235, 1979.

47. Spicer, C. W., G. M. Sverdrup, and M. R. Kuhlman. Smog Chamber Studies of NO_x Chemistry in Power Plant Plumes. Atmos. Environ., 15(10/11):2353-2365, 1981.

48. Forrest, J., R. W. Garber, and L. Newman. Conversion Rates in Power Plant Plumes Based on Filter Pack Data: The Coal-Fired Cumberland Plume. Atmos. Environ., 15(10/11):2273-2282, 1981.

49. Rodhe, H., P. Crutzen, and A. Vanderpol. Formation of Sulfuric and Nitric Acid in the Atmosphere During Long-Range Transport. Tellus, 33:132-141, 1981.

50. Meagher, J. F. and M. Luria. Model Calculations of the Chemical Processes Occurring in the Plume of a Coal-Fired Power Plant. Atmos. Environ., 16(2):183-195, 1982.

51. Durham, J. L., J. H. Overton, Jr., and V. P. Aneja. Influence of Gaseous Nitric Acid on Sulfate Production and Acidity in Rain. Atmos. Environ., 15(6):1059-1068, 1981.

52. Sequeira, R. Acid Rain: An Assessment Based on Acid-Base Considerations. J. Air Pollution Control Assoc., 32(3):241-245, 1982.

53. Frohlinger, J. O., and R. Kane. Precipitation: Its Acidic Nature. Science, 189:455-457, 1975.

54. Smith, L. The Acidity Problem - Its Nature, Causes, and Possible Solutions. Presented at the Symposium on Effects of Air Pollutants on Mediterranean and Temperate Forest Ecosystems, Riverside, California, June 22-27, 1980.

55. Thornton, J. D., and S. J. Eisenreich. Impact of Land-Use on the Acid and Trace Element Composition of Precipitation in the North Central U.S. Atmos. Environ., 16(8):1945-1955, 1982.

56. Siebel, E. P. Acid Rain: What Do We Know? State Water Survey Division, Illinois Institute of Natural Resources, 1981.

57. Tanner, R. L., B. P. Leaderer, and J. D. Spengler. Acidity of Atmospheric Aerosols. Env. Sci. and Tech., 15(10):1150-1153, 1981.

58. Interagency Task Force on Acid Precipitation. National Acid Precipitation Assessment Plan. Washington, D.C., 1982.

59. Marsh, A. R. W. Sulfur and Nitrogen Contributions to the Acidity of Rain. Atmos. Environ., 12(1-3):401-406, 1978.

60. Hobbs, P. V. A Reassessment of the Mechanisms Responsible for the Sulfur Content of Acid Rain. In: Proceedings, Advisory Workshop to Identify Research Needs on the Formation of Acid Precipitation, Alta, Utah. Electric Power Research Institute, Palo Alto, California, 1978.

61. Pack, D. H. Acid Precipitation - The Physical Systems. In: Proceedings, Advisory Workshop to Identify Research Needs on the Formation of Acid Precipitation, Alta, Utah. Electric Power Research Institute, Palo Alto, California, 1978.

62. Scott, W. D., and P. V. Hobbs. The Formation of Sulfate in Water Droplets. J. of Atmos. Sci., 24:54-57, 1967.

63. Chameides, W. L., and D. D. Davis. The Free Radical Chemistry of Cloud Droplets and Its Impact Upon the Composition of Rain. J. Geophys. Res., 87(C7):4863-4877, 1982.

64. Peterson, I. To Catch a Cloud. Science News, 122:138-140, August 28, 1982.

65. Still Waters. Report of the Subcommittee on Acid Rain of the Standing Committee on Fisheries and Forestry. House of Commons, Canada. 1981.

66. Dry and Wet Deposition, Workshop 2. Proceedings of the International Symposium on Sulfur in the Atmosphere, Dubrovnik, Yugoslavia, September 1977. Atmos. Environ., 12(1-3):14, 1978.

67. Wesely, M. L., B. B. Hicks, W. P. Dannevik, S. Frisella, and R. B. Husar. An Eddy-Correlation Measurement of the Particulate Deposition from the Atmosphere. Atmos. Environ., 11(6):561-563, 1977.

68. Slinn, W. G. N. Predictions for Particle Deposition to Vegetative Canopies. Atmos. Environ., 16(7):1785-1794, 1982.

69. Shannon, J. D. A Model of Regional Long-Term Average Sulfur Atmospheric Pollution, Surface Removal, and Net Horizontal Flux. Atmospheric Physics Section, Radiological and Environmental Research Division, Argonne National Laboratory, Argonne, Illinois, 1980.

70. Galloway, N. J., and D. M. Whelpdale. An Atmospheric Sulfur Budget for North America. Atmos. Environ., 14(14):409-417, 1980.

71. Garland, J. A. Dry and Wet Removal of Sulphur from the Atmosphere. Atmos. Environ., 13:349-362, 1978.

72. Kerr, R. A. Tracing Sources of Acid Rain Causes Big Stir. Research News, Science, 215:881, February 12, 1982.

4

Monitoring Programs and Results

Measurement of acid deposition is critical to the determination of the magnitude and extent of the phenomenon, the understanding of its causes, the resolution of its severity, and the development of control strategies to mitigate its effects. Although it is unquestionable that acid rain is falling, conflicting conclusions[1-5] as to whether or not there is a trend toward increasing acidity have been drawn based on the interpretation of composite data gathered by different sampling networks operated over different time periods and sometimes with different sampling methods. As a result, some investigators[6,7] insist the data are inconclusive. Resolution of this issue will require long-term operation of a comprehensive monitoring network or set of networks that incorporate the use of uniform sampling and analytical procedures. This section provides a review of the monitoring networks currently or recently operated and a discussion of current interpretations of some of the monitoring results.

SUMMARY OF MONITORING PROGRAMS

Researchers have noticed that the pH of rainwater in many areas is lower than would be expected for a solution of carbon dioxide dissolved in pure water (i.e., pH ~5.6). In the context of this report, and throughout the literature, the term "acid rain" actually encompasses all forms of atmospheric deposition of acids, which include, in addition to atmospheric precipitation (rain and snow), dry deposition, and other meteorological phenomena such as fog, frost, and dew. While wet precipitation of acids and their precursors has been studied intensively, a considerably lesser emphasis has been placed on dry deposition, fog, dew, and frost.[7] While this section covers monitoring activities associated with precipitation, dry deposition, and the other meteorological phenomena, emphasis is placed on monitoring of wet deposition, since most current monitoring activities focus on this area.[7]

Historical Development

In the mid-1800's Robert Angus Smith first discovered many features of the phenomenon of acid rain. A report published by Smith in 1852 called attention to changes in precipitation chemistry as a function of distance from a polluted city.[8] It was Smith who, some 20 years later, first coined the phrase "acid rain" in a clairvoyant book titled "Air and Rain: The Beginnings of a Chemical Climatology"[9] in which he proposed procedures for the collection and analysis of precipitation.[8]

One of the first 20th-century monitoring networks was set up by Hans Egner, a Swedish soil scientist, in the mid 1940's.[8] Precipitation acidity was one of the parameters measured regularly each month. This network was gradually expanded from Sweden to Norway, Denmark, Finland, and finally throughout all of Western Europe when it became known as the European Air Chemistry Network.[8,10] Consisting of more than 100 bulk collection monitoring stations, the European Air Chemistry Network has remained in continuous operation for nearly three decades, providing a unique opportunity to examine changes in precipitation chemistry. One such early analysis (1966) identified an area centered on the Low Countries with precipitation below pH 4.0 and showed that the affected area had expanded during the data collection period.[11] Oden[12] has presented an overview of the changing chemistry of precipitation and surface waters in Europe during this period. For a short period during the 1950's, precipitation monitoring was undertaken in the United States, and then was practically abandoned due to difficulties in measurement and lack of support.[13]

Concern over acidic precipitation spread to the United States in the early-to-mid 1970's. Likens and Bormann[14] noted the high acidity of New Hampshire lakes, particularly those of the Hubbard Brook watershed, a 75,000-acre experimental forest. Because no direct pH measurements had been taken in that area before the 1960's, no firm trend could be established. However, they made the supposition that precipitation had been much less acidic before 1930 based on the fact that the concentration of carbonate measured in rain at that time was higher than that which would be expected if strong acids were also present. Because the problem in Europe has been linked to long-range transport of air pollutants, they suggested that part of the problem could be emissions from midwestern stationary sources. Since that time, acidic precipitation has also been documented throughout the northeastern United States,[2,15-18] in northern Minnesota,[19] near the Continental Divide in Colorado,[20] in California,[21-23] in Hawaii,[24] in areas of the Northwest,[25] in Florida,[26-29] and in areas of Canada.

Current Monitoring Practices

The historical precipitation data have been sparse and not readily comparable. Recent concern over the possible effects of acid precipitation has resulted in a resurgence of interest in precipitation monitoring. Recent studies[7,30] have surveyed acid rain-related monitoring activities in North America. One major difference noted in comparing acid precipitation monitoring networks is the type of collector used. There are three general types of collectors currently in use. Bulk collection utilizes an open container which collects wet and dry deposition together and can be as simple as an open bucket. Others are more complex and include heaters for collecting snow samples and refrigerated containers to help maintain the integrity of the samples. Wet deposition samplers are equipped with moisture-sensing devices which open the sample container only during precipitation events. Finally, the wet/dry collector captures wet and dry deposition separately. Like the wet sampler, the wet/dry collector is equipped with a moisture sensor, but has two containers only one of which is open at any time, depending on the weather.

Galloway and Likens[31] present data which indicate that differences in collector design can result in significant differences in measured chemical compositions of dry and bulk deposition samples. No reliable standardized procedures are available for monitoring nor analyzing dry deposition,[7,32] which affects bulk sample results as well. While dry deposition collectors capture acidic particles deposited by gravitational settling, they do not adequately simulate impaction of particles on natural surfaces nor absorbtion and adsorbtion of gases by them. Therefore, data on dry deposition are believed to correlate poorly with actual dry deposition.[7,13,31,32] Lack of a good monitoring method for dry deposition has made the relative importance of dry deposition versus wet deposition uncertain. Estimates have included: from one-third to three times as much acidity as wet deposition,[33] from less than 1 up to 8-12 times as great,[34] and approximately equal contributions.[13] Recent improvements in dry deposition monitoring should result in better understanding of the role of this process.

Wet deposition monitoring results are believed to be much more reliable.[7,13,32] A recent comparison of wet deposition samples obtained from two wet deposition collectors and a wet/dry deposition collector revealed good correlation among the three instruments.[7,35]

Acid deposition by frost, dew, and fog are largely unstudied. Additional research is required to assess the relative importance of these meteorological phenomena on acid deposition.[7]

Major Current Monitoring Programs

Wisniewski and Kinsman[7] have prepared a comprehensive overview of current monitoring programs in the United States, Canada, and Mexico. Tables 4-1 through 4-3 present summaries of more than 70 networks detailed in this overview.[7] A few of the major networks now in operation are briefly discussed below.

National Atmospheric Deposition Program (NADP)--
Funded by a host of government and private sponsors, the NADP was established in May 1978 to provide data on pollutant deposition and its subsequent impact on the environment.[7,13,36,37] In early 1982, five additional sites were established, bringing the network total to 97 locations scattered across the continental United States, Alaska, Hawaii, and American Samoa. All sites are equipped with wet/dry collectors. Wet deposition samples have been collected weekly at some sites since July 1978,[13] while dry samples are collected bimonthly.[7]

NOAA/WMO Precipitation Chemistry Network--
Jointly sponsored by the National Oceanic and Atmospheric Administration (NOAA), the World Meteorological Organization (WMO), and originally the Environmental Protection Agency (EPA), this network consists of approximately 130 sites worldwide, 10 of which are located in the continental United States.[7,13,37] The network began operation in 1972,[7] and the United States sites became part of the NADP in 1979.[7,13] Wet deposition is sampled weekly and dry deposition is measured bimonthly.[7]

TABLE 4-1.   UNITED STATES ACID RAIN MONITORING STUDIES—NATIONAL, REGIONAL, STATE, LOCAL, AND RECENTLY COMPLETED.[7]

Study/Network	Funding organization	Parameters monitored	Extent and location	Period of operation	Sampling and analysis	Contact
NATIONAL:						
National Atmospheric Deposition Program (NADP)	A consortium of government (USDA, NOAA, USGS, EPA, DOE, U.S. Forest Service, National Park Service, Bureau of Land Management, State Agricultural Experiment Stations), educational and private sector entities.	pH, conductivity, SO_4, NO_3, NH_4, Cl, PO_4, Na, K, Ca, Mg	As of 1 January 1982, the NADP consisted of 92 operating stations, with five more expected in early 1982. At its inception, the NADP was concentrated in the east but now a more balanced distribution exists from coast to coast, including sites located in Alaska, Hawaii and American Samoa.	The network was established in May 1978.	Each site utilizes an Aerochem Metrics 201 wet/dry deposition collector. Wet deposition samples are collected on a weekly basis and dry deposition is collected bimonthly. All samples are analyzed at the Illinois State Water Survey.	J. H. Gibson Natural Resources Laboratory Colorado State University Ft. Collins, Colo. 20910
NCA/BCR Precipitation Quality Network	The network is funded by the National Coal Association (NCA) and managed by Bituminus Coal Research, Inc. (BCR).	pH, conductivity, acidity, SO_4, NO_3, NH_4, Cl, Ca, Na, K, Mg (in order of priority in event of sample with small volume)	The NCA network will exist nationwide, with most sites east of the Mississippi. The network will be especially concentrated in the coal-producing regions of Illinois, Ohio, Pennsylvania, and West Virginia. Forty sites were in operation as of January 1982. Approximately 10 more sites will begin monitoring in 1982.	Initial sites began collection in early 1981.	Aerochem Metrics 201 wet/dry samplers will be used to collect weekly wet and biweekly dry samples. Analyses will be performed at laboratories located at each site. If no laboratory is available, analyses will be performed at Bituminus Coal Research, Inc.	James F. Boyer Manager, Environmental Research Bituminus Coal Research, Inc. 350 Hochberg Rd. Monroeville, Pa. 15146
National Urban Runoff Program (NURP)	Environmental Protection Agency (EPA), U.S. Geological Survey (USGS)	pH, conductivity, SO_4, NO_3, NH_4, Cl, P, PO_4, Na, K, Ca, Mg, Cd, Cu, Pb, Zn. Also, some multi-element trace metal scans, carbonate, bicarbonate, TOC and DIC.	The network consists of up to nine precipitation collectors in each of 28 cities nationwide.	The earliest sites have been in operation since summer 1978. Three-year data collections are in progress at most sites.	The network uses Aerochem Metrics 201 wet/dry precipitation collectors principally, along with two other very similar models. Wet deposition is collected on an event basis and dry deposition collection is monthly or bimonthly. Analyses are performed at the EPA laboratory in Kansas City, at the USGS laboratories in Denver and Atlanta, and at various universities and private firms.	Dennis N. Athayde WH554, EPA 401 M St., S.W. Washington, D.C. 20460 Ernest D. Cobb USGS-WRD, Mail Stop 415 Reston, Va. 22092
Utility Acid Precipitation Study Program (UAPSP)	The network is funded by 34 electric utilities in the eastern U.S. Technical management is provided by EPRI.	pH, conductivity, SO_4, NO_3, NH_4, Cl, P, Na, K, Ca, Mg	The network consists of 19 sites, extending from eastern South Dakota south to eastern Texas and east to Maine. The network includes five stations from the recently completed EPRI Eastern Regional Chemistry Network.	The six sites from the EPRI Eastern Regional Chemistry Network have been in operation since September 1978. The other 13 sites include two sites initiated in April 1981 and 11 sites initiated in October 1981.	Aerochem Metrics samples are used to collect wet-only precipitation daily. Analyses are performed by Rockwell International. Acidity is measured at the site.	Chuck Hakkarinen Energy Analysis and Environment Division Electric Power Research Institute P.O. Box 10412 3412 Hillview Ave. Palo Alto, Calif. 94303

TABLE 4-1 (continued)

Network	Sponsor	Parameters	Description	History	Collection/Analysis	Contact
EPA/NOAA/WMO[a] Precipitation Chemistry Network	Environmental Protection Agency (EPA), National Oceanic and Atmospheric Administration (NOAA), World Meteorological Organization (WMO)	pH, conductivity, SO_4, NO_3, NH_4, Cl, PO_4, Na, Ca, Mg	The network consists of 12 stations. Ten sites are located within the continental U.S. with one site each on Mauna Loa, Hawaii, and American Samoa. All sites in this network are also members of the NADP network since 1979.	The network began operation during 1972.	The network switched to Aerochem Metrics 201 wet/dry deposition collectors in mid-1979. Sampling is performed weekly for wet deposition and bimonthly for dry deposition. All samples are analyzed at the Illinois State Water Survey.	John M. Miller[b] NOAA-Air Resources Laboratories 8060 13th St. Silver Spring, Md. 20910

REGIONAL:

Network	Sponsor	Parameters	Description	History	Collection/Analysis	Contact
EPA Great Lakes Atmospheric Deposition Network	Environmental Protection Agency (EPA)	pH, conductivity, alkalinity, acidity, SO_4, NO_3, NO_2, NH_4, total N, Cl, total P, Na, K, Ca, Mg, Si, TOC, and 23 metals. Thirteen toxic organics will be analyzed in the bulk collections at all sites and 12 sites will be selected for annual complete toxic organic scans.	The network is to encompass the area along the 8045 km U.S. shoreline of the Great Lakes, from Minnesota to the St. Lawrence River. Approximately 30 monitoring sites were active as of mid-August 1981. The network is expected to be fully operational with 41 sites.	This program replaces and includes several sites from the Atmospheric Pollutants Loading Study of EPA Region V, which was initiated in 1977.	Two types of collectors are currently used: an Aerochem Metrics 201 wet/dry sampler and a regular bulk collector. Later in the project a special bulk collection will be used, which separately collects nutrients, metals, and organics. Wet and dry deposition samples are collected weekly and bulk samples monthly. Analyses are performed at the EPA Region V Central Regional Lab in Chicago.	David Lueck U.S. EPA-GLNPO-SRS 536 S. Clark St. Chicago, Ill. 60605
University of Nevada Study	Bureau of Reclamation, Department of Interior; State of Nevada	pH, Na, K, Ca, Mg, Ag, Cr, Fe, I, In, Mn, Rb	The network has included collection of precipitation samples at various sites in the Sierra-Nevada Mountains, northeastern Colorado and Antarctica since its inception. Currently, samples are collected at approximately 30 sites in the Truckee-Tahoe, Carson-Walker, and Spring Mountain catchment basins in Nevada.	Initial sampling took place in 1966.	Since the majority of samples are in the form of snow, mechanical devices used for coring and profile analysis are used in sample collection. Analyses are performed at the Desert Research Institute Laboratory in Reno.	J. A. Warburton Desert Research Institute University of Nevada System Reno, Nev. 89506
Tennessee Valley Authority (TVA) Network	Tennessee Valley Authority (TVA), Electric Power Research Institute (EPRI)	pH, conductivity, weak acidity, strong acidity, SO_4, NO_3, NH_4, Cl, F, PO_4, Na, K, Mg, Ca	The TVA network currently consists of 11 monitoring sites; including trend stations, watershed collection sites and sites located in the vicinity of coal-fired power plants.	Some monitoring has been conducted since 1971 in connection with various studies. Calendar year 1979 marked the first full year of operation for all 11 stations.	Collection sites employ TVA wet/dry precipitation collectors similar to the Aerochem Metrics 201. The majority of sampling is biweekly wet and bimonthly dry. Samples are shipped to the TVA laboratory at Chattanooga, Tenn. for analyses.	W. J. Parkhurst Tennessee Valley Authority Air Resource Program River Oaks Bldg. Muscle Shoals, Ala. 35660
Multi-State Atmospheric Power Production Pollution Study/Research in Acidity from Industrial Emissions (MAP3S/RAINE)	Environmental Protection Agency (EPA), Department of Energy (DOE)	pH, conductivity, SO_4, SO_2, NO_3, NH_4, Cl, PO_4, Na, K, Ca, Mg	The network consists of nine stations, mostly in the northeast.	The initial four stations began operating in 1976 and an additional four began in 1978. Oak Ridge National Laboratory was added as the ninth site in early 1981.	Modified wet-only Battelle precipitation collectors are being replaced by HASL automatic wet-only collectors. Samples are collected on a modified-event basis defined by the operator and are shipped to Pacific NW Laboratories for analyses.	M. Terry Dana Battelle, Pacific NW Laboratories P.O. Box 999 Richland, Wash. 99352

[a] No longer sponsored by EPA.   [b] New address is 6010 Exec. Blvd., Rockville, MD 20857.

TABLE 4-1 (continued)

Network	Agency	Parameters	Description	Period	Methods	Contact
Great Smoky Mountains National Park Precipitation Network	U.S. Forest Service	pH, conductivity, SO_4, NO_3, turbidity	The network consists of four sites at lower elevation (610 to 730 m): two in Tennessee and two in North Carolina. A fifth site is located at Clingman's Dome, North Carolina (1830 m).	Monitoring began in early 1979.	The Elkmont site is part of the NADP network and utilizes an Aerochem Metrics 201 wet/dry collector. All sites also collect wet precipitation with TVA collectors. Dry deposition is sampled bimonthly at the Elkmont site. Wet deposition is sampled weekly at all sites. Analyses are performed at the Uplands Field Research Laboratory.	Lab Director, Uplands Field Research Laboratory, Route 2, Gatlinburg, Tenn. 37738

State:

Network	Agency	Parameters	Description	Period	Methods	Contact
Clemson University Experiment	Clemson University	Sulfur in air and precipitation at 15 sites; pH, conductivity, SO_4, NO_3, Cl, PO_4, Na, K, Ca, and Mg at the NADP site.	The sulfur network consists of 15 sites throughout South Carolina, three of which are the same as operated during a 1953 to 1955 monitoring effort. Clemson also operates one NADP station.	Clemson has monitored sulfur from 1953 to 1955, and from 1973 to present. The NADP site was initiated in 1979.	Each site in the sulfur network collects precipitation in three liter plastic bulk buckets and sulfur in air using PbO_2 candles. Sampling occurs every 30 days to replicate 1953-55 sampling conditions. The NADP site collects weekly wet samples and bimonthly dry samples with an Aerochem Metrics 201 wet/dry precipitation collector. NADP analyses are performed at the Illinois State Water Survey.	U.S. Jones, Department of Agronomy & Soils, 277 P & AS Building, Clemson University, Clemson, S.C. 29631
Florida Acid Deposition Study	Florida Electric Power Coordinating Group	pH, conductivity, SO_4, NO_3, NO_2, NH_4, Cl, PO_4, Na, K, Ca, Mg	The network includes 14 sites throughout Florida.	Collection started at all sites in July 1981 and will continue for three years.	The study utilizes Aerochem Metrics 301 wet/dry collectors, with all sites having weekly collection and two sites having colocated daily collection. Analyses will be performed by Environmental Science and Engineering, Inc.	Bill Palmer, Florida Electric Power Coordinating Group, 402 Reo St., Suite 214, Tampa, Fla. 33609
USGS New York State Precipitation Monitoring Network	U.S. Geological Survey (USGS)	pH, conductivity, SO_4, NO_3, NO_2, NH_4, organic N, Cl, total N, P, Na, K, Ca, Mg, Pb, bicarbonate when the pH is greater than 4.5	The network began with nine stations, of which five are still in existence. The network currently includes 12 stations.	The network was established in October 1964.	The network collects bulk precipitation monthly but is in the process of converting six stations to Aerochem Metrics 301 wet/dry samplers, which will sample on the event basis whenever an event is greater than 1.27 cm.	Roy Schroeder, USGS, P.O. Box 1350, Albany, N.Y. 12201

TABLE 4-1 (continued)

Program	Organization	Parameters	Network	History	Methods	Contact
Minnesota/Wisconsin Power Supply Group Precipitation Monitoring Program	Minnesota/Wisconsin Power Supply Group	The following parameters are measured for wet precipitation: pH, SO_4, NO_3, NO_2, NH_4, Br, Cl, F, I, PO_4, Na, K, Ca, Mg, Al, B, Cu, Fe, Mn, Ni, Pb, and Zn. Dry deposition samples are analyzed for SO_4, NO_3, NO_2, Br, Cl, F, I, PO_4, K, Ca, Al, As, Ba, Fe, Hg, Mn, Pb, S, Si, V, and Zn.	This summer-sampling network consisted of six sites distributed throughout Minnesota and one site in southwest Wisconsin during 1981.	Various acid rain-related monitoring activities have been conducted by the University of Minnesota since 1973. The first year of funding by the Minnesota/Wisconsin Power Suppliers Group was in 1981.	Each site is equipped with a wet/dry precipitation collector designed by the University of Minnesota. Wet samples are collected sequentially on a sub-event (0.25 cm) basis from mid-April to the end of October. Samples are picked up within 48 h of collection and analyses are performed at the University of Minnesota. Dry deposition is collected for 24 h every sixth day, using virtual impaction dichotomous air samplers.	S. V. Krupa, Department of Plant Pathology, 1515 Gortner Ave., University of Minnesota, St. Paul, Minn. 55108
Texas Air Control Board Precipitation Chemistry Network	Texas Air Control Board	pH, SO_4, NO_3, NH_4	The network began with three sites across Texas, with a fourth site added later.	The initial three sites began sampling in mid-1979 and the fourth site was added six months later. Two NADP sites will be added in early 1982.	Sampling is done with a funnel collector on the event basis, with a pH electrode used at the site to determine sample pH.	T. H. Porter, Texas Air Control Board, 6330 Highway 290 East, Austin, Tex. 78723
Wisconsin Acid Deposition Monitoring Project	Wisconsin Utilities Association	pH, conductivity, total acidity, strong acidity, SO_4, NO_3, NH_4, Cl, Na, K, Ca, Mg, Al, PO_4, and alkalinity (in order of priority in the case of small sample volume).	The network will consist of three sites: one each in northwest, central, and southeast Wisconsin.	The network is scheduled to begin operation in late March 1982 and to continue for 24 months.	Wet deposition will be collected daily using an Aerochem Metrics 301 sampler. Drydall will be collected biweekly at the northwest site. pH and conductivity will be measured at the site and the remainder of the sample will be shipped to Pacific NW laboratories for analyses.	John Flickinger, Wisconsin Power and Light Company, 222 West Washington Ave., P.O. Box 192, Madison, Wis. 53701
Precipitation Chemistry in North Dakota Study	Water Resources Division, U.S. Geological Survey (USGS); North Dakota State Health Department	pH, conductivity, alkalinity, SO_4, NO_3, NH_4, Cl, F, PO_4, Na, K, Ca, Mg, Al, Ag, As, Cd, Cr, Cu, Fe, Hg, Mn, Mo, Ni, Pb, Se, V, Zn	Currently the North Dakota State Health Department operates two sites (Dunn Center and Woodworth). The USGS operated three additional sites (Wibaux, Beulah, and Gascoyne) until October 1981.	The North Dakota State Health Department sites, Dunn and Woodworth, were initiated in October 1980 and June 1981, respectively, and are funded through the end of 1986. The USGS sites began collection in May 1981. Several or all of the USGS sites may resume operation in 1982.	The North Dakota State Health Department sites use Aerochem Metrics collectors, sampling wet deposition on the event basis and dry deposition monthly. Analyses are performed by the North Dakota State Health Department. The USGS sites used colocated Aerochem Metrics and Leonard Mold and Die collectors, sampling wet deposition on the event basis and dry deposition monthly. Analyses were performed by the USGS laboratory in Denver.	Robert L. Houghton, USGS, WRD, 821 E. Interstate Ave., Bismarck, N.D. 58501. Robert Angelo, North Dakota State Health Department, Division of Environmental Research, 1200 Missouri Ave., Bismarck, N.D. 58505

TABLE 4-1 (continued)

LOCAL

Name	Organization	Parameters	Network	Status	Contact
Wet Deposition in Southern California Study	Southern California Edison Company	pH, conductivity, alkalinity, acidity, SO_4, NO_3, NO_2, NH_4, Cl, Na, K, Ca, Mg, Al, Fe, Ni, Pb, V	The network consists of 13 stations within a 80 km radius of Los Angeles and two stations in the east central California desert.	The Los Angeles area stations began collection during the 1979–80 winter rainy season. The two desert sites began collection in 1981 and will continue to collect all wet deposition through at least 1983.	Wet-only precipitation is collected on the event basis using a rain-triggered funnel arrangement, which separates the sample into an initial 0.1 inch increment and a "rest of event" sample. Measurements are performed by Global Geochemistry Corporation in Canoga Park, Calif. pH, acidity, conductivity, and NH_4 are measured within 12 h after collection.	E. C. Ellis, Southern California Edison Co. Research and Development, P.O. Box 800, Rosemead, Calif. 91770
McDonald's Branch Watershed Network	University of Pennsylvania, Yale University	pH, conductivity, NO_3, NH_4, total P, Na, K, Ca, Mg, Al, Cd, Cr, Cu, Fe, Mo, Mn, Ni, Pb, Zn	Ten precipitation collectors are located within a 6 km² area in the McDonald's Branch Watershed, which is situated in the Lebanon State Forest of the south New Jersey pine barrens.	Initial sampling began in May 1978 and the status of the network will be reviewed after the initial three-year sampling period.	Funnel-type bulk collectors with evaporation traps are located at nine of 10 stations. A project-designed wet-only precipitation collector is located at the tenth site. Sampling has varied from event to biweekly to monthly (currently). Analyses are performed at the University of Pennsylvania and Yale University.	Arthur H. Johnson, Department of Geology, University of Pennsylvania, 240 South 33rd St., Philadelphia, Pa. 19104
Tesuque Watershed Precipitation Network	University of New Mexico	pH, conductivity, NO_3, NH_4, organic N, Cl, Na, K, Ca, Mg, Cu, Fe, Pb	The network consists of nine monitors in the Tesuque Watershed of the Santa Fe National Forest.	The network is part of a study conducted by the University of New Mexico since 1971.	Samples are collected using funnel-and-bottle bulk collection devices for rain. Snow is collected in open, exposed containers. Summer sampling is weekly or more frequently. Winter samples are collected once containers are full of snow. Samples are analyzed at the University of New Mexico.	James R. Gosz, Department of Biology, Room 173, University of New Mexico, Albuquerque, N.M. 87131
Monongahela National Forest Study	U.S. Forest Service	pH, conductivity, total alkalinity, total acidity, SO_4, NO_3, NO_2, Cl, PO_4, Na, K, Mg, Al, Cu, Mn, Pb, Zn	initially the network included 24 sites statewide but currently only eight sites exist.	The first site began monitoring in 1972. Since late 1981, only pH and conductivity analyses have been performed.	Wet and bulk deposition samples are collected on a variety of time schedules (event, weekly, biweekly and monthly) with Belfford rain gages. Analyses are conducted at the Monongahela National Forest hydrology laboratory.	Forest Hydrologist, Monongahela National Forest, U.S. Forest Service, P.O. Box 1548, Elkins, W. Va. 26241

TABLE 4-1 (continued)

Network	Organization	Parameters measured	Sites	Dates	Methods	Contact
NASA/Kennedy Space Center Network	National Aeronautics & Space Administration (NASA)	pH, conductivity, H, excess SO_4, marine SO_4, NO_3, NH_4, Cl, F, Na, K, Ca, Mg	The network consists of seven sites within a 400 km^2 area in central Florida. At one time, 14 sites covering 700 km^2 were in operation.	The network was initiated in July 1977.	Aerochem Metrics model 201 precipitation collectors are used to sample wet precipitation weekly at six sites and daily at one site. Samples are analyzed at the J. F. Kennedy Space Center.	W. Knott MD-RSB-2 J. F. Kennedy Space Center Cape Canaveral, Fla. 32899
Washington, D.C. Precipitation Network	National Oceanic and Atmospheric Administration (NOAA)	pH, conductivity, and occasionally a full chemical analysis for major ions	The study presently includes six sites in the Washington, D.C. area.	The network began operation in April 1974.	Bulk samples are collected daily, with pH and conductivity measured within 48 h at the NOAA Air Resources Laboratory in Silver Spring. Occasionally, a full chemical analysis for major ions is performed at the University of Virginia.	John M. Miller NOAA-Air Resources Laboratory 8060 13th St. Silver Spring, Md. 20910
Maryland Geological Survey Acid Precipitation Project	U.S. Geological Survey (USGS), Environmental Protection Agency (EPA)	pH, conductivity, acidity, SO_4, NO_3, NO_2, NH_4, Br, Cl, F, P, PO_4, Na, K, Ca, Mg, Be, C, Cd, Cr, Cu, Fe, Ni, Pb, Si, Zn, anthropogenic organic compounds, filtratable solids	Six samplers are located on the Maryland portion of the Chesapeake Bay: three each on the western and eastern sides.	Sampling began in March 1981.	Wet and dry samples are collected in automatic collectors. Wet events of one inch or greater over a 24 h period are collected. Dryfall samples are allowed to accumulate for at least three months. Analyses are performed by the Maryland Geological Survey, except anthropogenic organic compounds (Virginia Institute of Marine Science) and trace metals in particulates (National Bureau of Standards).	Robert D. Conkwright Maryland Geological Survey 2100 Guilford Ave. Baltimore, Md. 21218
Tahoe Monitoring Program	University of California at Davis, California Air Resources Board, California State Water Resources Control Board	pH, conductivity, alkalinity, SO_4, NO_3, NH_4, DON, Cl, PO_4, Na, K, Ca, Mg	Five sites are located in the Tahoe Basin, approximately 260 km northeast of the San Francisco Bay.	Monitoring has existed since November 1978, initially as a member of the UC/CARB network, which ended in May 1979. At least three more years of funding are expected.	The network now operates three wet/dry stations and two bulk deposition stations. The wet/dry sites use Aerochem Metrics 201 wet/dry collectors, sampling on the event basis. Tipping bucket bulk deposition collectors are used at all five sites. Dry samples are collected concurrently with wet samples, or at least weekly during dry periods. Analyses are performed at the University of California laboratories at Tahoe and Davis.	Robert C. Leonard Director, Tahoe Monitoring Program P.O. Box 1125 Tahoe City, Calif. 95730
Integrated Lake Watershed Acidification Study (ILWAS)	Electric Power Research Institute (EPRI)	pH, conductivity, SO_4, NO_3, NH_4, Cl, Na, K, Ca and Mg, Al, DOC, total P, and total acidity analyses were performed in the past.	ILWAS currently consists of four watershed sites on the western slope of the Adirondack Mountains in New York state near Old Forge. The network operates up to seven samplers.	Sampling began in March 1978 and should continue through the end of 1981.	All sites employ Aerochem Metrics 201 wet/dry samplers. Wet deposition is collected on an event basis and dry deposition is collected weekly. Bulk samplers also are located at each site, with collection on the event basis. Analyses are conducted at the Rensselaer Polytechnic Institute.	A. H. Johannes Department of Environmental Engineering Rensselaer Polytechnic Institute Troy, N.Y. 12181

TABLE 4-1 (continued)

Study	Agency	Parameters measured	Description	Time established	Method	Contact
EML Deposition Chemistry Study	Department of Energy (DOE), Environmental Measurements Laboratory (EML)	pH, conductivity, SO_4, NO_3, NH_4, Cl, PO_4, Na, K, Ca, Mg, bicarbonate. Trace metals (Al, As, Cd, Cr, Fe, Mn, Ni, Pb, V, Zn) are measured in samples from each site every three months.	The network included seven stations nationally from its inception until June 1981. Sampling outside the New York–New Jersey region ended in June 1981, but additional sampling sites are being set up within that smaller region. Currently four sites exist, two each in New York city and New Jersey.	The network was established in July 1976.	The network collects bulk, wet and dry samples monthly; event samples also are collected HASL and Aerochem Metrics collectors are used to obtain the wet and dry samples. Analyses are performed by Rockwell International, Inc.	Herb Feely, DOE-EML, 376 Hudson St., New York, N.Y. 10014
Effects of Energy Production Emissions on Colorado Lakes	U.S. Geological Survey (USGS)	pH, acidity, SO_4, NO_3, NO_2, NH_4, organic N, Br, Cl, F, PO_4, Na, K, Ca, Mg	The network consists of four sites in northwestern Colorado.	Sampling began at one site in December 1980.	Wet and dry deposition is sampled with variable frequency using Leonard Mold and Die collectors. Samples are analyzed at the USGS lab in Denver, Colorado.	John T. Turk, USGS, Building 53, Mail Stop 415, Denver Federal Center, Lakewood, Colo. 80225
Atmospheric Inputs to the Chesapeake (AITC) Study	Environmental Protection Agency (EPA)	pH, conductivity, SO_4, NO_3, NO_2, NH_4, Cl, F, PO_4, Na, K, Ca, Mg, Br, Cd, Cr, Cu, Fe, Mn, Ni, Pb, Si, Zn, TOC, TIC, hydrocarbons	The network consists of four stations on the lower Chesapeake Bay in Virginia.	Sampling was initiated in December 1980. Present funding ends in March 1982.	Aerochem Metrics 301 wet/dry collectors are used to sample wet events, which are collected as soon as possible after the event. Analyses are conducted at the Department of Oceanography, Old Dominion University.	Terry L. Wade or George T. Wong, Old Dominion University, Department of Oceanography, Norfolk, Va. 23508
Chemical Quality of Atmospheric Deposition in Alabama Study	U.S. Geological Survey (USGS)	pH, conductivity, alkalinity, SO_4, NO_3, NH_4, Na, K, Ca, Mg, Al, Cd, Cu, Fe, Mn, Pb, Zn	This network will consist of three sites in central Alabama.	Initial sampling will begin in January 1982.	Wet samples are collected both after major rainfall events and weekly. The first three parameters are measured in the field. All other analyses are made at the Geological Survey of Alabama laboratory.	Ira A. Giles, USGS, 1317 McFarland Boulevard, East Tuscaloosa, Ala. 35405
West Point Area Study	Environmental Protection Agency (EPA), Army Research Office	pH, SO_4, NO_3, NH_4, Cl, PO_4, Na, K, Ca, Mg	Two sites are located 10 km apart on the U.S. Military Academy Reservation in West Point, New York.	Collection has occurred intermittently since 1976 at one site. A second site, to be colocated with a NADP site, will be activated in spring 1982.	Collection is on the event basis. Collection is by intensity-weighted wet-only samplers that break a storm into 0.01 inch "increments." pH is measured in the field and other analyses are conducted in the Science Research Laboratory.	Major John K. Robertson, Science Research Laboratory, U.S. Military Academy, West Point, N.Y. 10996

TABLE 4-1 (continued)

Network	Sponsor	Parameters	Description	History	Methods	Contact
Orange County Network	Environmental Management Agency, County of Orange, California	pH, conductivity, SO_4, NO_3 plus NO_2, NH_4, TKN, PO_4, Pb, Zn, TDS.	This network consisted of 11 sites from 1974 to 1978 in Orange County, approximately 60 km southwest of Los Angeles. The network was reduced to two sites in 1979	This network was established with two sites in 1973.	The network uses a self-designed wet-only precipitation collector and sampling is on the event basis. Analyses are performed by a contractor laboratory under a quality control program administered by the Environmental Research Laboratory of Orange County.	Chief of Environmental Management Agency, Environmental Management Agency, Environmental Resources Section, P.O. Box 4048, Santa Anna, Calif. 92702
University of Colorado Study	U.S. Forest Service (through the Eisenhower Consortium), University of Colorado	pH, conductivity, H, SO_4, NO_3, NO_2, NH_3, organic N, Cl, P, Na, K, Ca, Mg, DOC, and DON Also, C, H, N and P in dry particulate matter.	One site with two stations one kilometer apart is operated in the Como Creek Watershed, Boulder County, Colorado.	Sampling began in the spring of 1975	Bulk deposition is collected weekly and analyses are generally performed within six hours of collection at the University of Colorado laboratory. A dry-only fraction was collected and analyzed for five and one-half years.	Michael C. Grant, Department of Environmental, Population & Organismic Biology, University of Colorado, Boulder, Colo. 80309
Shenandoah Watershed Acidification Study,	Air Quality Office, National Park Service	pH, conductivity, SO_4, NO_3, NH_4, Cl, Na, K, Ca, Mg, Si	The study includes two watersheds centered 32 km northwest of Charlottesville, Va	The network began operation during November 1979	The study utilizes Hubbard Brook-type funnel collectors. Analyses are performed at the Department of Environmental Sciences, University of Virginia.	James N. Galloway, Dept. of Environmental Sciences, University of Virginia, Charlottesville, Va. 22903
Hubbard Brook Ecosystem Study	National Science Foundation	pH, conductivity, SO_4, NO_3, NH_4, Cl, P, Na, K, Ca, Mg and SiO_2. Occasionally Al, DOC, and DON are tested for. Trace metal sampling existed from 1975 to December 1979 and has recently been resumed	Two to four sites are located within the 3035 hectare watershed near West Thornton, N.H. The number of sites depends on the number of projects in operation.	Precipitation samples have been collected since 1963.	Weekly bulk precipitation is collected in Hubbard Brook-type funnel collectors. One NADP site is located within the Hubbard Brook Experimental Forest, with collection performed using an Aerochem Metrics 201 wet/dry collector. At this site, the study also maintains a similar wet/dry sampler. pH and conductivity are measured at the site. Samples are shipped to Cornell University for chemical analysis.	G. E. Likens, Section of Ecology & Systematics, Langmuir Lab, Cornell University, Ithaca, N.Y. 14850
University of Arkansas Site	Office of Water Resources Research, U.S. Department of the Interior	pH, conductivity, SO_4, NO_3, NH_4, PO_4, Cl, K, Na, Ca, Mg, Fe, Mn, Zn	The single station is located at Fayetteville, Ark.	Current collection and analysis procedures have been in use since April 1980. Other monitoring efforts have existed for several years. The site is also a member of the NADP network since May 1980	The site is equipped with an Aerochem Metrics 201 wet/dry sampler. A second wet/dry collector collects wet deposition episodically and dry deposition bimonthly. Trace metal analyses are performed at the University of Arkansas laboratory, with other analyses performed at the Illinois State Water Survey.	George H. Wagner, Geology Department, University of Arkansas, Fayetteville, Ark. 72701

TABLE 4-1 (continued)

Program	Sponsoring agency	Parameters measured	Site description	History	Methods	Contact
Oak Ridge National Laboratory (ORNL) Site	Department of Energy (DOE), Electric Power Research Institute (EPRI)	pH, conductivity, SO_4, NO_3, NH_4, Cl, PO_4, Na, K, Ca, Mg, Cd, Mn, Pb, Zn, strong and weak acidity	Currently one centralized monitoring site is used for the collection of data for both the NADP and MAP3S networks. Previously, up to five permanent stations existed in the Walker Branch Watershed. Temporary sites occasionally operate to satisfy various research projects.	The ORNL monitoring effort has existed since 1967 for hydrological monitoring and since 1976 for precipitation chemistry monitoring.	The permanent site utilizes an Aerochem Metrics 201 wet/dry deposition collector. Wet deposition samples are collected weekly and dry deposition biweekly, as part of the NADP network. Wet-only samples are collected on the event basis for the MAP3S network. Analyses are performed at the Illinois State Water Survey, at Pacific NW Laboratories, and at Oak Ridge National Laboratory.	S. E. Lindberg, Oak Ridge National Laboratory, Environmental Sciences Division, Oak Ridge, Tenn. 37830
University of California at Berkeley Study	California Air Resources Board, Agricultural Experiment Station of the University of California at Berkeley	pH, conductivity, SO_4, NO_3, NH_4, Cl, Na, K, Ca, Mg, Fe, Mn, Zn, Cl, Fe	This site is located at Berkeley, Calif., approximately 20 km east of the San Francisco Bay.	Initial monitoring at Berkeley began in December 1974. This site was also a member of the California Air Resources Board (CARB) network, established in November 1978 and completed in May 1979. This site has existed as an independent site the past two rainy seasons.	Samples are collected on an event basis with an Aerochem Metrics 201 wet/dry collector. Analyses are performed at the University of California at Berkeley laboratory.	John G. McColl, Department of Plant & Soil Biology, University of California, Berkeley, Calif. 94720
Within-Event Sequential Precipitation Chemistry Study	Department of Energy (DOE), Environmental Protection Agency (EPA)	pH, conductivity, SO_4, NO_3, NO_2, NH_4, Cl, Na	One site is located at Brookhaven National Laboratory in Upton, N.Y.	Monitoring began in June 1976. An additional station is planned.	Automatic sequential precipitation samplers developed by Brookhaven National Laboratory are used to collect hourly samples during precipitation events. Analyses are performed by the Analytical Chemistry Laboratory of Brookhaven National Laboratory.	Gilbert S. Raynor, Atmospheric Sciences Division, Department of Energy and Environment, Brookhaven National Laboratory, Upton, N.Y. 11973
Global Precipitation Chemistry Project (GPCP)	National Oceanic and Atmospheric Administration (NOAA), Environmental Protection Agency (EPA), Department of Energy (DOE)	pH, SO_4, NO_3, NH_4, Cl, Na, K, Ca, Mg and SiO_2. Also, PO_4, acidity and weak organic acids in selected samples	Currently one North American station, located in central Alaska, is in operation. In addition, the network includes four other sites (southern Indian Ocean, Bermuda, northern Australia and southern Venezuela), with a sixth site in Argentina presently readying for collection. Future plans call for expansion to 11 stations	The network began operations in April 1979	Four different types of collectors are used in the GPCP, depending on site conditions. Aerochem Metrics 201 wet/dry, HASL wet/dry, Hubbard Brook bulk and a GPCP-type collector designed especially for this project. Samples are collected on the event basis and special measures are used to minimize dry deposition in bulk collections. Field pH is measured at each station. Laboratory pH and all other analyses are performed at the University of Virginia.	James N. Galloway or William C. Keene, Department of Environmental Sciences, University of Virginia, Charlottesville, Va. 22903

TABLE 4-1 (continued)

RECENTLY COMPLETED:

Project	Organization	Parameters	Network	Operation Period	Collection Method	Contact
Northeastern Region Snow Chemistry Reconnaissance Study	Water Resource Division (WRD), U.S. Geological Survey (USGS)	pH, conductivity, SO_4, NO_3, NO_2, NH_4, F, K, Ca, Mg, As, Ba, Be, Cd, Co, Cu, Fe, Hg, Li, Mn, Mo, Ni, Pb, Se, Si, V, Zn, TIC. The suspended material from 20 sites will be analyzed for semiquantitative determinations of 80 elements and 10 major inorganic constituents.	The network consisted of 180 sites extending from Maine to Minnesota and south to eastern West Virginia and western Maryland	The network operated from approximately December 1980 through March 1981	Collectors consisted of 18 inch diameter, 6 foot high cardboard tubes (sonotubes) with polyethylene bags. Three-month bulk collections were conducted. All analyses were done by the National Water Quality Laboratory in Denver, Colo.	Norman E. Peters WRD, USGS P.O. Box 744 Albany, N.Y. 12201
Oxidation Scavenging Characteristics of April Rain (OSCAR) High-Density Precipitation Chemistry Experiment	This project was undertaken as part of the MAP3S/RAINE study, which is supported by the Environmental Protection Agency (EPA) and the Department of Energy (DOE).	pH, conductivity, SO_4, SO_3, NO_3, NO_2, NH_4, Cl, PO_4, Na, K, Ca, Mg, Al, Pb	The high-density network consisted of 47 sites within a 100 km² area surrounding Ft. Wayne, Ind.	The project operated for four precipitation events during April 1981.	Each site was equipped with a nine-stage sequential precipitation collector. The first eight stages each collected 0.7 mm of precipitation and the final stage collected the remaining precipitation of the event, up to 11 mm. All analyses (except field pH) were conducted at Pacific NW Laboratories in Richland, Wash.	Richard C. Easter Battelle Pacific NW Laboratories P.O. Box 999 Richland, Wash. 99352
Oxidation Scavenging Characteristics of April Rain (OSCAR) Intermediate-Density Network	This project was undertaken as part of the MAP3S/RAINE study, which is supported by the Environmental Protection Agency (EPA) and the Department of Energy (DOE).	pH, conductivity, SO_4, NO_3, NO_2, NH_4, Cl, PO_4, Na, K, Ca, Mg, Al	The intermediate-density network consisted of each of the nine MAP3S sites adding from one to five satellite sites, plus 11 stations not connected with the MAP3S program, for a total of 38 sites throughout the northeast. This density provided approximately 100-150 km spacing between stations.	The project operated during four precipitation events in April 1981.	The intermediate-density network sampled precipitation sequentially using a funnel and jar collection system. All analyses (except field pH) were conducted at Pacific NW Laboratories in Richland, Wash.	Gilbert S. Raynor Department of Energy & Environment Brookhaven National Laboratory Upton, N.Y. 11973
Acid Precipitation in Hartford, Conn. Area Study	TRC Environmental Consultants, Inc.	pH	This network consisted of 12 stations within a 48 km radius of Hartford, Conn.	Initial sampling began in August 1980. However, quality assurance analyses indicated problems with pH determination and operation was suspended in September 1981. The network is currently under review.	Samples were collected in a plastic wedge-type rain gage on the event basis. Occasionally sequential sampling was undertaken. pH measurements were determined by the use of narrow range pH paper.	Michael Anderson TRC Environmental Consultants, Inc. 800 Connecticut Ave. E. Hartford, Conn. 06108
EPRI Eastern Regional Chemistry Network	Electric Power Research Institute (EPRI)	pH, acidity, SO_4, NO_3, NH_4, Cl, PO_4, Na, K, Ca, Mg, DOC, Al, total acidity, and strong acidity	The network originally consisted of nine sites spread throughout the northeastern United States.	Sampling was initiated in August 1978 and completed in June 1980	Each site was equipped with two Aerochem Metrics 201 wet/dry collectors. Wet-only samples were collected daily and combined over a week. Samples were analyzed by Rockwell International, Inc.	Ralph Perhac Energy Analysis & Environment Division Electric Power Research Institute 3412 Hillview Ave. Palo Alto, Calif. 94304

TABLE 4-1 (continued)

Program	Organization	Parameters	Network Description	Operation	Methods	Contact
California Air Resources Board, (CARB) Network*	California Air Resources Board	The 1978–79 effort consisted of the monitoring of pH, conductivity, SO_4, Cl, Na, K, Ca, Mg, Cu, Fe, Ni, Zn, and occasionally NH_4 and NO_3. The 1981–82 effort consisted of pH and conductivity analyses.	The UC/CARB network consisted of up to eight sites mainly in the central California area for the 1978–79 effort. Six sites, five in the vicinity of Los Angeles and one near San Diego, existed for the 1981–82 rainy season.	The network has operated during the 1978–79 and 1981–82 rainy seasons. Future expansion is likely.	Each site employed Aerochem Metrics 201 wet/dry precipitation collectors. For the 1978–79 effort, samples were collected on an event basis and shipped to the University of California laboratories at Berkeley or Tahoe for analyses. For the 1981–82 effort, samples were collected weekly and were analyzed by CARB.	Doug Lawson, Air Resources Board, 1102 Q St., P.O. Box 2815, Sacramento, Calif. 95812
Florida Atmospheric Deposition Study	Environmental Protection Agency (EPA)	pH, conductivity, SO_4, NO_3, NO_2, TKN, NH_4, Cl, PO_4, total P, F, Na, K, Ca, and Mg, Cd, Cu, Pb, SiO_2, and Zn were measured quarterly.	A network of up to 24 sites was operated throughout Florida from 1977 to 1979. A reduced network of seven wet/dry collectors existed during 1980.	Monitoring existed from mid-1976 to mid-1981.	Aerochem Metrics 201 wet/dry collectors were utilized, with event wet deposition collection at Gainesville and biweekly or weekly wet deposition collection at other sites. Dry deposition was collected biweekly at all sites. Analyses were performed at the University of Florida laboratory.	Charles D. Hendry, Environmental Science and Engineering, Inc., P.O. Box ESE, Gainesville, Fla. 32602
Minnesota-North Dakota Precipitation Monitoring Network	Department of Energy (DOE), University of Minnesota Computer Center	pH, conductivity, alkalinity, SO_4, NO_3, NH_4, Cl, total P, Na, K, Ca, Mg, Al, Cd, Cr, Cu, Fe, Mn, Ni, Pb, Zn	Three sites existed along a transect from southeastern North Dakota to northeastern Minnesota.	Sampling took place from April 1978 to June 1979.	Aerochem Metrics 201 wet/dry precipitation collectors were used to sample wet precipitation on the event basis and dry fallout samples biweekly or monthly. Analyses were performed at the University of Minnesota.	E. Gorham, Department of Ecological and Behavioral Biology, 108 Zoology Bldg, 318 Church St. SE, University of Minnesota, Minneapolis, Minn. 55455
Pennsylvania Cooperative Fisheries Research Unit Study	U.S. Fish and Wildlife Service, Pennsylvania Fish Commission	pH, alkalinity, acidity, SO_4, NO_3, PO_4.	The monitoring effort began with three sites in north central Pennsylvania (approximately 41°N and 78°W).	The first precipitation collectors were installed in October 1976. The network ceased operations in August 1980.	The network used Taylor two liter bulk rain collectors, with samples collected about every 10 days.	Dean Arnold, 208 Erwin W. Mueller Lab, The Pennsylvania State University, University Park, Pa. 16802
Elk Mountain, Wyoming Site	Office of Water Research and Technology, Department of Interior; National Science Foundation	pH, SO_4, NO_3, NO_2, Cl, F, PO_4, Na, K, Ca, Mg, plus multi-element scans.	One site was located at Elk Mountain (elevation 3,533 m), approximately 160 km northwest of Laramie.	Snow samples were collected on the event basis at Elk Mountain independently by the two researchers during winter 1980.	Snow pack and snowfall samples were collected on the event basis by scoops and coring equipment and were analyzed at the University of Rhode Island or the University of Wyoming.	Carol Baird, 8820 Cottonwood, Lenexa, Kans. 66215; Richard J. McCaffrey, 60 Crestwood Dr., Narragansett, R.I. 02882

*This network was reactivated during the 1981–82 rainy season with six sites, five near Los Angeles and one near San Diego. pH and conductivity analyses were performed by the California Air Resources Board on samples collected weekly. Future expansion is likely. (Network information updated and footnote added in proof. As revised, this network entry should now be listed preceding the Tahoe Monitoring Program on p. 605.)

TABLE 4-2.   CANADIAN ACID RAIN MONITORING STUDIES—NATIONAL, REGIONAL, PROVINCIAL, LOCAL, AND RECENTLY COMPLETED[7]

Study/Network	Funding organization	Parameters monitored	Extent and location	Period of operation	Sampling and analysis	Contact
NATIONAL:						
Canadian Network for Sampling Precipitation (CANSAP)	Atmospheric Environment Service, Environment Canada	pH, conductivity, alkalinity, acidity, SO_4, NO_3, NH_4, Cl, Na, K, Ca, Mg	The network consists of 59 stations distributed across Canada, including Canada's nine WMO stations.	The network was established in 1977.	Sampling stations employ automatic, wet-only Sangamo Type A precipitation collectors. Samples are collected on a daily basis, combined for one month periods and stored in the dark at 2°C until the sample is analyzed at the Inland Waters Directorate (IWD) Water Quality Lab at the Canadian Centre for Inland Waters in Burlington.	Malcolm Still Atmospheric Environment Service 4905 Dufferin St. Downsview, Ontario Canada M3H 5T4
REGIONAL:						
Canadian Centre for Inland Waters (CCIW) Precipitation Network	Canadian Centre for Inland Waters	pH, conductivity, alkalinity, SO_4, NO_3, NH_4, Cl, P, Na, K, Ca, Mg, Cu, Fe, Pb, Ni, Zn, SiO_2	The network consists of 15 sites around the Canadian shores of the Great Lakes.	The initial eight stations began monitoring in 1969.	Sangamo wet/dry collectors are used to collect monthly samples. Analyses are performed at the CCIW labs.	C. H. Chan Canadian Centre for Inland Waters Water Quality Branch 867 Lakeshore Rd. Burlington, Ontario Canada L7R 4A6
Canadian Air & Precipitation Monitoring Network (APN)	Atmospheric Environment Service, Environment Canada	pH, conductivity, acidity, H, SO_4, NO_3, NH_4, Cl, P, K, Ca, Mg	The network includes six sites, each located east of the Ontario-Manitoba border.	The network began with three sites during November 1978.	Samples are collected daily using a wet-only precipitation sampler. Every two weeks, samples are shipped to the Canadian Centre for Inland Waters laboratory in Burlington, Ontario, for analyses.	L. A. Barrie Atmospheric Environment Service 4905 Dufferin St. Downsview, Ontario Canada M3H 5T4
Environmental Protection Service (EPS) Atlantic Precipitation Monitoring Program	Environmental Protection Service, Environment Canada	pH, SO_4, NO_3, NH_4, Cl, Na, Ca, Mg	The network currently consists of six sites—three in Nova Scotia, two in Newfoundland and one on Prince Edward Island.	The first site was established in December 1978.	Samples are collected with a Sangamo Type A precipitation collector. The three Nova Scotia sites collect precipitation on the event basis, whereas the other three sites collect weekly. Analyses are performed at the Bedford Institute of Oceanography in Dartmouth, Nova Scotia, and at the Newfoundland Forest Research Centre in St. John's, Newfoundland.	J. R. Machell Environmental Protection Service Environment Canada Queens Square 45 Alderny Dr. Dartmouth, Nova Scotia Canada B2Y 2N6

TABLE 4-2 (continued)

PROVINCIAL:

Network	Agency	Parameters	Description	Status	Methods	Contact
Quebec Network for the Collection of Precipitation	Quebec Ministry of the Environment	pH, conductivity, alkalinity, acidity, SO_4, NO_3, NH_4, Cl, F, Na, K, Ca, Mg	The network consisted of 40 sites as of 1 April 1982 and five sites will be added by summer 1982.	The first site began operation during August 1980.	Samples are collected using samplers similar to the Sangamo wet/dry collectors. Samples are collected weekly with analyses performed at the Ministry of Environment laboratories in Saint Foy.	Levis Talbot, Ministère de l'Environnement, Qualité des eaux, 2360, chemin Ste. Foy, Ste-Foy, Quebec, Canada G1V 4H2
Acidic Precipitation in Ontario Study (monthly network)	Air Resources Branch, Ontario Ministry of Environment	pH, conductivity, acidity, SO_4, NO_3, NH_4, TKN, P, Na, K, Ca, Mg, Al, Cd, Cu, Fe, Mn, Ni, Rb, Zn	This network consists of 34 sites throughout Ontario, with future expansion expected.	The network has operated since September 1980 and at least five years of data acquisition are expected.	All sites are equipped with Sangamo Type A wet/dry collectors. Samples are collected on a monthly basis and are analyzed at the Ontario Ministry of the Environment Laboratory Service Branch in Toronto.	Walter H. Chan, Air Resources Branch, Ontario Ministry of the Environment, 880 Bay St., Toronto, Ontario, Canada M5S 1Z8
Acidic Precipitation in Ontario Study (event network)	Air Resources Branch, Ontario Ministry of Environment	pH, conductivity, acidity, SO_4, NO_3, NH_4, Na, K, Ca, Mg, gaseous and particulate N and S	Sixteen sites make up this network: four each in the Kingston, London, Dorset, and Atikokan areas.	This network has operated since January 1981.	Sites are equipped with Aerochem Metrics 201 wet/dry samplers. Samples are collected on a 24 h modified event basis and are analyzed at the Ministry's Laboratory Service Branch in Toronto.	Walter H. Chan, Air Resources Branch, Ontario Ministry of the Environment, 880 Bay St., Toronto, Ontario, Canada M5S 1Z8
Ontario Hydro Atmospheric Deposition Monitoring Network	Chemical Research Department, Ontario Hydro Research Division	pH, SO_4, NO_3, NH_4, Cl, Na, K, Ca, Mg	The network currently includes six stations located throughout Ontario.	This network was established in 1975.	Sites are equipped with wet-only Sangamo collectors. Precipitation is sampled on an event basis and analyzed at the Ontario Hydro Laboratory.	O. T. Melo, Chemical Research Department, Ontario Hydro Research Division, 800 Kipling Ave., Toronto, Ontario, Canada M8Z 5S4
Precipitation Quality Monitoring Program	Department of the Environment, Province of Alberta	pH, conductivity, SO_4, NO_3, NH_4, Cl, total P, Na, K, Ca, Mg	The network consisted of six sites throughout the province as of mid-1981 and will be expanded to 10 sites in 1982.	Sampling was initiated in April 1978.	Bulk samples are collected monthly using Sangamo Type A precipitation collectors. Analyses are performed by the Alberta Environment Centre at Vegreville, Alberta.	J. E. Torneby or R. P. Angle, Air Quality Control Branch, Alberta Environment, 9820-106 St., Edmonton, Alberta, Canada T5K 2J6
Nova Scotia Department of the Environment Precipitation Network	Nova Scotia Department of the Environment	pH, conductivity, alkalinity, acidity, SO_4, NO_3, NH_4, total N, Cl, total and dissolved P, Na, K, Ca, Mg, Al, As, Cd, Co, Cr, Cu, Fe, Mn, Ni, Pb, Se, Zn, TOC	Currently this network includes five sites throughout Nova Scotia. A maximum of nine sites operated between September 1977 and December 1979.	The network began operation in September 1977, and should continue at least until 1984.	Each site is equipped with a Sangamo wet/dry collector. Weekly samples are collected and analyzed at the Environmental Chemistry Laboratory of the Department of Health in Halifax.	J. Underwood, Nova Scotia Department of the Environment, P.O. Box 2107, Halifax, Nova Scotia, Canada B3J 3B7

TABLE 4-2 (continued)

Network	Agency	Parameters	Description	Collection	Status	Contact
Environment New Brunswick Precipitation Monitoring Network	Environment New Brunswick, Province of New Brunswick	pH, conductivity, alkalinity, SO_4, NO_3, NH_4, Cl, Na, K, Ca, Mg	The network currently consists of three sites, with two additional stations to be added by 30 May 1982. At this time one of the original three sites will cease operations.	Wet precipitation samples are collected daily with Sangamo Type A collectors and combined to form a monthly composite sample. Analyses are performed by Laboratory Services, Environment New Brunswick at Fredericton, New Brunswick.	The initial stations were established in November 1980. The network will be reviewed at the end of 1986.	Jane Spavold, Environmental Service Branch, Environment New Brunswick, P.O. Box 6000, Fredericton, New Brunswick, Canada E3B 5H1

LOCAL:

Network	Agency	Parameters	Description	Collection	Status	Contact
Long Range Transport—Snow Total Deposition Study	Noranda Mines Limited	pH, SO_4, SO_3, NO_3, Cl, Na, K, Ca, Mg, selected heavy metals	Samples are collected at 28 sites, all in northwest Quebec.	Snow core samples are collected once a year. Analyses are performed by Noranda Mines Limited.	Initial sampling began in 1977.	F. Frantisak, Director of Environmental Services, Noranda Mines Limited, P.O. Box 45, Toronto, Ontario, Canada M5L 1B6
Event Rain Sampling and Chemical Analyses in the Oil Sands Area of Northern Alberta Study	Research Management Division, Alberta Environment	pH, conductivity, SO_4, NO_3, Cl, F, Na, K, Ca, Mg, Al, Cd, Cu, Fe, Mn, Ni, Pb, V, Zn	The network consists of 13 sites in northeastern Alberta, near Ft. McMurray.	Samples are collected on the event basis, using plastic bags fitted in a large barrel. Analyses are performed at the Alberta Environment provincial laboratory at Vegreville, Alberta.	The network began in May 1981. Expansion to the rest of the province is proposed for 1982.	Air System Manager, Research Management Division, Alberta Environment, 9820–106 St., Edmonton, Alberta, Canada T5K 2J6
Acid Precipitation in Ontario Study, Limnology Unit Network	Ontario Ministry of the Environment	pH, conductivity, alkalinity, SO_4, NO_3, NH_4, TKN, Cl, total P, Na, K, Ca, Mg, Al, Cu, Fe, Mn, Ni, Pb, Si, Zn, DOC, DIC	The network has included up to 19 stations located around lakes in Ontario. Currently five sites exist within a 50 km radius of Dorset, approximately 225 km north of Toronto.	Bulk collectors are present at all five sites. One site has two Earth Science wet deposition collectors and two bulk collectors. Samples are collected when there is a large enough volume for analysis (on the average of seven to 10 days). Perishable parameters are analyzed within 24 h of collection on site, while the remaining parameters are analyzed at the Ontario Ministry of the Environment laboratories in Toronto.	The network was established in June 1976. The five current stations probably will be kept in operation for at least five more years.	P. J. Dillon, Limnology and Taxonomy Section, Ontario Ministry of the Environment, Box 213, Rexdale, Ontario, Canada M9W 5L1
Northwest British Columbia Precipitation Monitoring Network	Atmospheric Environment Service, Ministry of Environment	pH, strong and total acidity, SO_4, NO_3, Cl, F, PO_4, Na, K, Ca, Mg, Al	The network consists of five sites in northwest British Columbia.	Samples are collected after every event with a modified Hubbard Brook type collector. Analyses are performed by the British Columbia Ministry of Environment.	The network was initiated in September 1980.	M. S. Kotturi, Air Studies Branch, Ministry of Environment, Parliament Buildings, Victoria, British Columbia, Canada V8N 1X4
British Columbia Coastal Site Precipitation Monitoring Network	Atmospheric Environmental Service, Ministry of Environment	pH, strong and total acidity, SO_4, NO_3, Cl, F, PO_4, Na, K, Ca, Mg, Al	The network consists of three coastal sites in British Columbia.	Samples are collected after every event with a modified Hubbard Brook type collector. Analyses are performed by the British Columbia Ministry of Environment.	The network was initiated in September 1980.	M. S. Kotturi, Air Studies Branch, Ministry of Environment, Parliament Buildings, Victoria, British Columbia, Canada V8N 1X4

TABLE 4-2 (continued)

Program	Agency	Parameters measured	Network description	Sampling method	Status	Contact
Newfoundland Provincial Precipitation Monitoring Network	Department of Environment, Government of Newfoundland and Labrador	pH, conductivity, acidity, SO_4, NO_3, NH_4, Cl, Na, K, Ca, Mg	The network consists of three sites in eastern Newfoundland.	An automatic wet-only precipitation collector is used for weekly sampling. All chemical analyses are performed at the Canadian Forestry Service laboratory in St. John's, Newfoundland	The network started with two sites in September 1980 and is projected to continue for 8 to 10 years. The network is proposed to expand to six sites by 1983.	Les Hulett Department of Environment Government of Newfoundland and Labrador 100 Elizabeth Ave St. John's, Newfoundland Canada A1C 1P7
Long Range Transport Study (LORA)	Noranda Mines Limited	pH, SO_4, SO_2, NO_3, Cl, Na, K, Ca, Mg and selected heavy metals in precipitation. SO_4, SO_2, NO_3, NO_2, and NH_3, in ambient air	At its inception, the network consisted of seven sites in northwest Quebec. In 1979 the network was cut back to its current size of three sites.	Wet-only samples are collected by event and also for eight day composite samples. Twenty-four hour ambient air samples also are collected.	Initial sampling began in 1977	F. Frantisak Director of Environmental Services Noranda Mines Limited P.O. Box 45 Toronto, Ontario Canada M5L 1B6
Manitoba Network for Precipitation Collection (MNPC)	Environmental Management Division, Province of Manitoba	pH, SO_4, NO_3, conductivity, acidity, Ca, NH_4, Mg, Na, Cl and K (in order of priority)	The network consists of two sites in northeast Manitoba	The network collects wet samples daily and dry samples monthly, utilizing a Sangamo Type A sampler. Wet samples are sent to a central laboratory weekly for analysis	The network was established in November 1980	Dave Bezak Environmental Management Division Box 7, Building 2 139 Tuxedo Avenue Winnipeg, Manitoba Canada R3C OV8

RECENTLY COMPLETED:

Program	Agency	Parameters measured	Network description	Sampling method	Status	Contact
Ontario Ministry of the Environment, Air Resources Branch (ARB) Precipitation Network	Ontario Ministry of the Environment	pH, acidity, SO_4, NO_3, NH_4, Cl, F, Na, K, Ca, Mg, Al, Cd, Cr, Cu, Fe, Ni, Pb, Si, Zn	Located in the Sudbury area, originally 10 sites operated, with expansion to 21 sites during mid-1979	Wet deposition was collected with Sangamo Type A collectors. Bulk deposition also was collected at four stations	Sampling began in December 1977. The network was terminated in May 1980	Walter H. Chan Air Resources Branch Ontario Ministry of the Environment 880 Bay St Toronto, Ontario Canada M5S 1Z8

TABLE 4–3.   MEXICAN ACID RAIN MONITORING STUDIES--NATIONAL[7]

Study/Network	Funding organization	Parameters monitored	Extent and location	Period of operation	Sampling and analysis	Contact
Acid Rain in Mexico City Study	Department of Environmental Pollution, University of Mexico; Mexican Meteorological Service of the Ministry of Agriculture and Water Resources	pH, SO_4, NO_3, and NH_4, with conductivity to be added	As of May 1981 (the beginning of the rainy season), the network expanded to 25 sites nationally, including sites in southern Mexico and sites near the U.S.–Mexico border.	Sampling began during May 1980, with 12 precipitation collectors in Mexico City.	Samples are collected on an event basis in polyethylene bottles. Analyses are performed at the National University of Mexico in Mexico City on both event and weekly composite samples.	Humberto Bravo A. Depto. Contaminacion Ambiental Centro de Ciencias de la Atmosfera Ciudad Universitaria Mexico Mexico 20, D.F.

Multi-State Atmospheric Power Production Pollution Study/Research
in Acidity from Industrial Emissions (MAP3S/RAINE)--
    Established to create a data base to be used in developing models to
predict the fate of energy production related emissions, the MAP3S/RAINE
network, with the addition of Oak Ridge National Laboratory in 1981, now
consists of nine sites.[7,13,38,39] Since the establishment of the initial
four sites in 1974, the MAP3S/RAINE program has been collecting wet deposition
samples on an event basis. An "event" in this context refers to any 24-hour
period during which precipitation has occurred.[39] The network is geared
toward the northeastern quadrant of the United States.[7,39]

Canadian Network for Sampling Precipitation (CANSAP)--
    Established in May 1977, CANSAP consists of 56 stations distributed
across Canada, including Canada's nine WMO stations.[7,13] Sponsored by the
Atmospheric Environment Service and Environment Canada, CANSAP collects wet
deposition samples daily and combines samples for a 1-month period before
analysis.[7] This network will begin event sampling in 1983.

Limitations of the Present Networks--
    Despite the relatively recent flurry of monitoring activity, the
Interagency Task Force on Acid Precipitation concludes, "The chemical
composition of atmospheric deposition in this country has not been
measured...long enough to permit adequate time trend analyses...(and
has)...been too limited in geographic extent to produce a nationwide
picture."[37] The Interagency Task Force goes on to identify the following
limitations of present networks:

   • "Many use different analytical laboratories and different methods of
     analysis, so their results are not always comparable. Only a few
     sample sites have been selected by using rigorously defined siting
     criteria;

   • Additional quality assurance is needed for the field and laboratory
     operations of all networks. Additional training of personnel would
     improve sample collection procedures;

   • Most sites are in rural areas of the northeastern or north-central
     states. In the western United States, where future energy
     development could take place, and in urban areas, where materials
     damage is most common, there are few collection sites;

   • Monitoring techniques and strategies used by scientists of the
     United States and other countries may be inconsistent;

   • Methods for sampling dry deposition are inadequate; and

   • Few sites are equipped to sample gaseous pollutants and aerosols, or
     to provide adequate meteorological data."[37]

    In spite of the above limitations and other past problems resolving
differences in data collection, one study[40] shows that good agreement can be

attained when data from separate networks are compared. In this study, data from the no longer operational EPRI network (EPRI Eastern Regional Chemistry Network) were compared to data from MAP3S (now MAP3S/RAINE). The data showed good agreement for H^+, NO_3^-, $SO_4^=$, and NH_4^+, although differences were noted for Cl^- and Na^+.[40]

RESULTS OF MONITORING PROGRAMS

This section discusses the data available from the previously mentioned monitoring networks and what they indicate in terms of geographic distribution (both around the world and within North America), variations in acidity measurements, and short- and long-term trends. Whereas acid rain has been documented in all parts of the world, emphasis is placed upon data for the North American continent and, in particular, the northeastern United States. It is shown that acidity measurements can vary within a given region as well as within a specific storm and that short-term or seasonal trends are more apparent than long-term trends.

Geographic Distribution of Acid Deposition

The occurrence of acid rain is extensive enough so as to be referred to as a worldwide phenomenon. A map showing the distribution of rainfall pH around the world is shown in Figure 4-1.[13] Referring to all acidity data indicated on this map, Scandanavia, the northeastern United States, and southern Canada are receiving the most highly acidic rain and, accordingly, have received the most publicity and documentation.

The pH of precipitation is being measured at a number of remote sites as part of monitoring programs being carried out by the National Oceanic and Atmospheric Administration and the World Meteorological Organization. These measurements will make it possible to investigate the magnitude and nature of worldwide background pH levels as well as to evaluate and improve modeling results. Once the background pH levels have been established, the data will provide a basis for validating modeling results and monitoring the effects of regulatory actions.

Recent results show considerable variability from site to site and from year to year, and a great deal of variation about the mean at each site, as evidenced by the ranges presented in Table 4-4. This data, when averaged over all of the sites, yields a mean pH of 5.26. The average range in pH for the various sets of data covers 2.49 pH units. The greatest range, from 3.20 to 7.70 was observed at Godhaven, Greenland during the 1975 to 1980 period.

The difficulty in trying to determine a background pH is demonstrated in a study of the local variation found on the island of Hawaii reported by Miller et al.[24] They found a significant increase in acidity between a sea level site at the east end of the island and a site near the top of the Mauna Loa volcano. These differences remain unexplained, but volcanic outgassing is among the suggested causes.

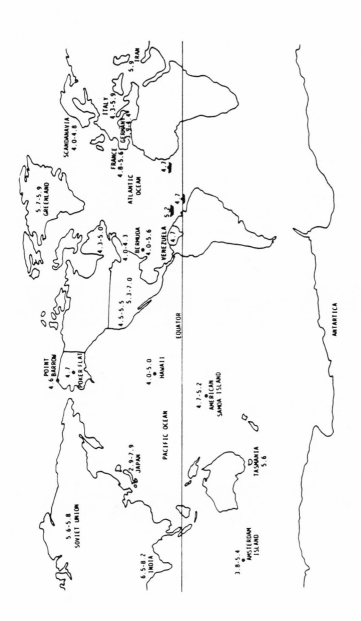

Figure 4-1.   Worldwide distribution of rainfall pH.[13]

TABLE 4-4.   AVERAGE VALUES OF pH FROM NOAA/WMO SITES[a]

Location	Average pH	Range	Years	No. of values
Bishop, California	6.42	4.31-8.30	73-80	42
Alamosa, Colorado	6.77	4.99-8.21	73-80	68
Mauna Loa, Hawaii	5.05	3.12-6.69	73-80	53
Salem, Illinois	4.40	3.98-6.40	73-80	72
Caribou, Maine	4.90	3.93-7.45	73-80	74
American Samoa	5.45	4.51-7.44	73-80	72
Bulgaria	5.48	5.27-5.73	79-80	13
Denmark	4.59	3.50-7.10	76-79	18
Ireland	5.38	4.20-6.80	73-80	96
Finland	4.70	4.00-6.50	73-80	93
France	4.51	3.64-6.52	77-79	35
Ft. Simpson, NWT, Canada	6.21	3.80-7.14	73-78	18
Mt. Forest, Canada	4.72	3.91-6.52	73-80	76
Sable Island, Canada	4.89	4.00-5.98	75-80	46
Godhaven, Greenland	5.44	3.20-7.70	75-80	53

[a]Personal communication between GCA Corporation and E. Gardner Evans, U.S. EPA. September 7, 1982.

The following discussion of acid rain distribution is confined to North America with particular emphasis on the northeastern portion of the United States. As noted previously, acidic rain has been documented in New England, Florida, California, Colorado, Minnesota, and southern Canada. The areal extent of precipitation acidity in North America is illustrated by pH contours for the United States and Canada in Figure 4-2.[41] These data represent measurements for the 1974 to 1975 time period. A similar map is provided in Figure 4-3 for the 1976 to 1979 time period.[42] The significance of the geographic distribution of acid rain in the Northeast has been attributed primarily to fossil fuel combustion and the attendant emissions of sulfur and nitrogen oxides. As to the severity of the phenomenon in the New York-New England area versus the remainder of the country, theories have been advanced regarding long-range transport of emissions from coal-fired boilers in the Ohio River Valley as well as the importance of local oil-fired units within the affected area.

Theories concerning long-range transport of emissions into the affected region are difficult to refute based upon much of the available evidence. For example, it has been determined that air mass trajectories associated with

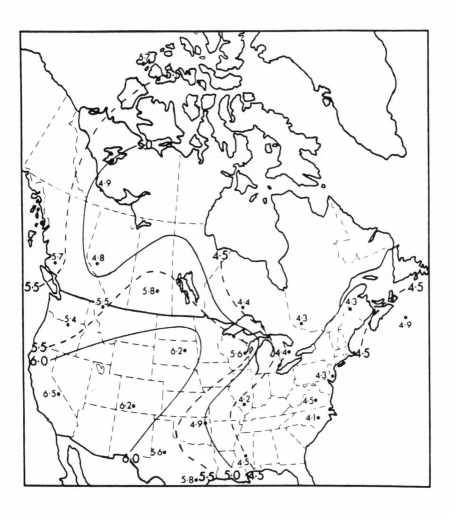

Figure 4-2.   Precipitation amount weighted mean pH at North American WMO
              stations for 1974-1975.[41]

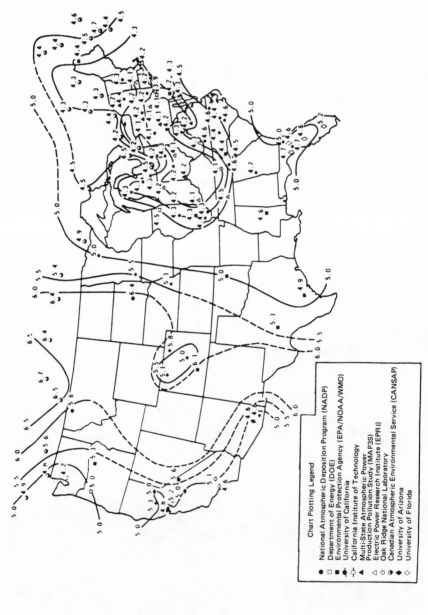

Figure 4-3.   Weighted mean pH of precipitation in United States, 1976-1979.42

Chart Plotting Legend

● □ ■ ◆ ◊ ◁   National Atmospheric Deposition Program (NADP)
Department of Energy (DOE)
Environmental Protection Agency (EPA/NOAA/WMO)
University of California
California Institute of Technology
◁ ⊙ ◉ ◆ ◊   Multi-State Atmospheric Power
Production Pollution Study (MAP3S)
Electric Power Research Institute (EPRI)
Oak Ridge National Laboratory
Canadian Atmospheric Environmental Service (CANSAP)
University of Arizona
University of Florida

major sulfate episodes in the Northeast pass over the Ohio River area.[43] A recent study[44] evaluated the long-range transport potential associated with the largest power generating facilities located along the Ohio River. Considering such factors as magnitude of SO_x emissions, stack data, regional climatology, and assessment of long-range transport potential in terms of plume penetration of the top of the mixing layer, this study found that the potential for long-range transport has increased substantially over the past decade (see Figure 4-4). The importance of these sources in the Ohio River Valley has been addressed in a recent summary of the major findings and implications of EPRI's Sulfate Regional Experiment (SURE).[45] According to EPRI, a major result of this program "is the demonstration of a clear geographic association between sulfate concentrations and major source areas of SO_2. Both the day-by-day patterns of sulfate concentration and the patterns during elevated-sulfate episodes show this association unmistakably. These patterns also indicate, but do not define exactly, a zone of influence for major SO_2 source areas. This zone normally extends 100 to 300 km (62 to 186 miles) downwind but may on rare occasions extent beyond 500 km (311 miles)." Graphic representation of some of the SURE data is shown in Figure 4-5, wherein SO_4^- concentrations exceeded 10 percent of the time are indicated in conjunction with major SO_2 source areas. "The pattern of elevated levels clearly surrounds major SO_2 source areas in the Ohio River basin."[45]

Additional studies support the contention that transport of acid rain precursors into a given region is largely responsible for acidic precipitation in that region. Continuous daily sampling and analysis of aerosols over an 18-month period at Whiteface Mountain, New York, and comparison of daily sulfate and elemental concentrations with surface air trajectories showed that regions to the southwest of Whiteface Mountain contributed most to the sulfate and metal concentrations in air masses reaching the site.[46] These data are presented in Figure 4-6. A recent study conducted by the Harvard School of Public Health and the University of Michigan indicated that the Ohio River Valley/Midwest Region is the major source of southern New England's transported sulfate pollution with air masses originating along the Eastern Seaboard also contributing to high sulfate levels in the region.[47] This study--funded by Wisconsin Power and Light, EPRI, the National Institute of Environmental Health Sciences, and EPA--attempted to characterize regional contributions to ambient air samples collected at a downwind receptor by analyzing particle elemental composition and wind trajectory data. Analysis of the elemental data and back-trajectory wind data indicated that for high sulfur aerosol days at the sampling site, the Ohio Valley/Midwest and Eastern Seaboard regions were the major contributors. "During the warm season of the year, trajectories from these two sectors impact southern New England with approximate equal frequency, but the sulfur concentrations on Ohio Valley/Midwest sector days average roughly 40 percent higher than during days experiencing transport from the Eastern Seaboard sector. During the cold season, the mean sulfur concentrations do not differ between the two sector groups, but the Ohio Valley/Midwest trajectories are more prevalent." The researchers also reported several inadequacies with respect to the use of elemental ratios for determining source regions.

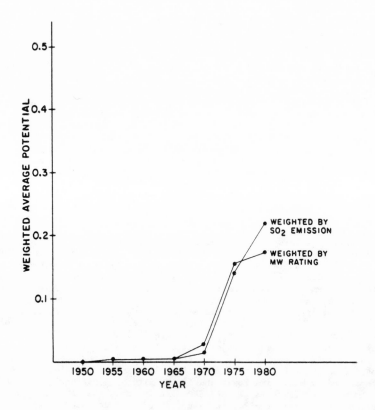

Figure 4-4.   Trend in long-range transport potential
for the study plants.[44]

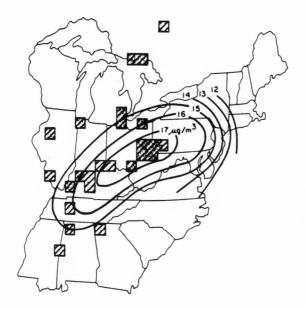

Figure 4-5.   Elevated sulfate concentrations and major SO_2 source areas.
The solid lines demarcate areas in which the 24-hour average
sulfate concentration (given in $\mu g/m^3$) exceeded the indicated
value 10% of the time during SURE.   The shaded boxes indicate
areas in which SO_2 emissions for summer 1977 exceeded
1000 Mt/d.[45]

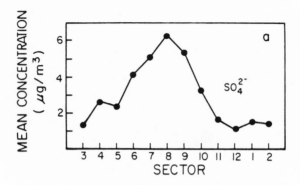

Figure 4-6a. Mean concentration of sulfate
as a function of sector.[46]

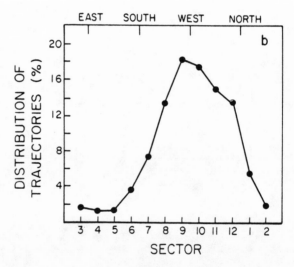

Figure 4-6b. Distribution of air trajectories
as a function of sector.[46]

It has also been proposed that local sources in the Northeast--especially oil-fired combustion units--may play a major role in the formation of acid rain within the region.[13] This area of the country (as well as Florida and California, where acid rain has also occurred) is heavily dependent on residual and other fuel oils as opposed to coal for the generation of power and for heating purposes. Since emissions of primary sulfates per unit of sulfur in the fuel are generally higher for oil than coal,[48] these local sources may be important contributors to the acid rain phenomenon in the Northeast.

Research conducted at the University of Rhode Island has also suggested that local sources in the Northeast may be more responsible for acid rain in the region than midwestern sources.[49] This research has been based upon analysis of aerosols with respect to trace elements (particularly vanadium and manganese) and has also contended that tracing origins of sulfate by air mass trajectories may not be as reliable a method as trace element analysis.

Clearly, there are conflicting views as to the major causes of northeastern acid rain and more research is required before any mitigative strategies are adopted.

Acid precipitation has also been measured in other parts of the United States including Florida, Colorado, and California. Recent monitoring performed by the California Institute of Technology has indicated that acid fog detected in that state may be prevalent enough to corrode metal, damage vegetation, and pose a threat to human health.[50] Values of pH ranging from as low as 1.7 to 4.0 have been detected at various locations throughout the state. The low pH value of 1.7 was measured at a site at Corona Del Mar on December 6, 1982, and was predominantly influenced by nitrogen oxides (a 2.5:1 ratio of nitrogen oxides to sulfur dioxide was detected in the samples). Historical measurements of acid precipitation in Florida, Colorado, and California are discussed under the subsection entitled Long-Term Trends.

Variability of Acidity Within and Among Storms

Detailed observations of precipitation pH show that there are frequently very large variations in acidity not only from storm to storm at individual sites but also spatially and temporally within the same precipitation event. Differences found within an individual storm might conceivably result from spatial and temporal differences in the cloud structure (e.g., vertical motions, droplet sizes, vapor pressures) and the associated variations in rainout efficiency, plus differences in the efficiency with which acidic substances are washed out from below the cloud. On the other hand, these differences in pH might also be caused by localized source differences of either acidic substances and precursors or of neutralizing material. This subsection reports some of the variations that have been observed to indicate the probable complexity of the mechanisms involved.

Deposition as a Function of Precipitation Amount--
Pack[51] observed that most of the formulations for wet deposition assume, and much of the data indicate, that removal rates are proportional to precipitation rates. He also states that the concentration of various ions

(e.g., H^+ and $SO_4^=$) is often highest in light precipitation, as shown in Figure 4-7.[52] Pack concludes with the statement that "speaking loosely, it appears that the higher ion concentrations in light rain tend to balance the lower values in heavier precipitation so that the total material deposited on the ground is much less variable than would otherwise be the case."

Spatial Variability Within a Monitoring Network--
    In Figure 4-8 Semonin[53] shows a precipitation weighted mean pH pattern based on measurements at 81 sites within an area of 1,800 square kilometers in the St. Louis area. The data were collected during 22 precipitation events as part of the Metropolitan Meteorological Experiment (MEXTROMEX). The areal mean of the data is pH 4.9 with a range of values from 4.3 to 6.8. Semonin suggests that these results may reflect a rapid response of precipitation formation processes to scavenging of either water-soluble alkaline or acid aerosol from unevenly distributed local sources. Semonin also presents network measurements for two of the individual storm events, one with a weighted mean of pH 4.8 and a range of values from 3.4 to 8.2, and the other with a mean of pH 6.4 and a range from 5.2 to 7.9. Even knowing the locations and general character of industrial effluents, however, it was impossible for him to determine uniquely the causes of acid or alkaline rainfall.

Temporal Variability Within a Monitoring Network--
    Analyses of the acidity of precipitation measured at eight of the MAP3S/RAINE monitoring sites[39,54] have demonstrated significant temporal variability. Table 4-5 demonstrates the extreme variability in H^+ concentrations observed over a 3-year period.[39] Further analysis[54] of these data indicates a seasonal pattern of wet deposition of $SO_4^=$ and to a lesser extent H^+. These are demonstrated in Figures 4-9 and 4-10 which are plots of cumulative ionic concentrations as a function of cumulative precipitation. The periodic oscillations shown are attributable to the summer sulfate concentration maximum.[54] The same relationship for NO_3^-, however, does not demonstrate a strong cyclic variability, as shown in Figure 4-11.[54] The significance of this seasonal variability is discussed in greater detail later in this section.

    Several years of hourly sequential precipitation observations from central Long Island also demonstrate wide variability in acidity, as shown in Table 4-6. Variations in acidity were examined by season and synoptic type,[55,56] also shown in Table 4-6 and Figure 4-12. The maximum H^+ concentration observed for "all cases" is approximately three normal standard deviations from the mean.

    All of these data indicate that acid rain is likely to be episode-specific. Clearly, more investigation of the statistics of episodes is warranted.[3,55,56]

Temporal Variation Within a Storm--
    The temporal variation of pH in three rain storms at Gainesville during 1976 as reported by Hendry[57] is shown in Figure 4-13. All plotted values except the final one for each storm represent a 5-minute average. In each storm, the least acidic value was observed at the start of the storm. Figure 4-14 shows a similar plot of pH measurements made during two rainfall

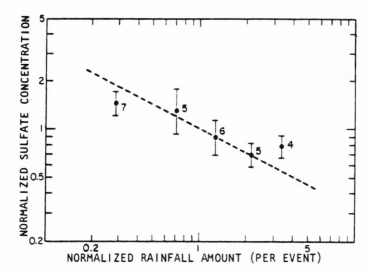

Figure 4-7.   Variation of $SO_4^=$ concentration with precipitation amount, MAP3S station data.[52]

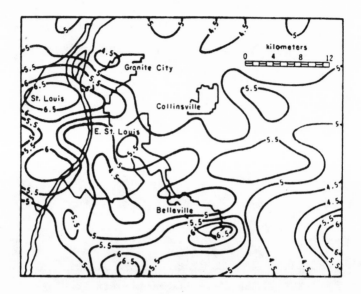

Figure 4-8.   Precipitation weighted mean pH pattern for the St. Louis
               area. (Based on measurements at 81 sites during 22
               precipitation events).[53]

TABLE 4-5. CONCENTRATION OF FREE HYDROGEN IONS MEASURED BY
MAP 3S /RAINE NETWORK[39]

| Site | Concentration, μml^{-1} | | | | Period, years |
	Min.	Max.	Mean	Standard deviation	
Whiteface, NY	8.9	199.5	59.1	37.1	1977, 1978, 1979
Ithaca, NY	8.5	398.1	93.7	60.6	1977, 1978, 1979
Penn State, PA	1.3	354.8	95.6	67.6	1977, 1978, 1979
Charlottesville, VA	7.6	851.1	91.4	91.7	1977, 1978, 1979
Urbana, IL	0.2	158.5	55.5	36.7	1978, 1979
Brookhaven, NY	0.4	229.1	56.0	50.8	1979
Lewes, DE	10.0	323.6	62.5	62.2	1979
Oxford, OH	7.4	263.0	76.4	50.4	1979

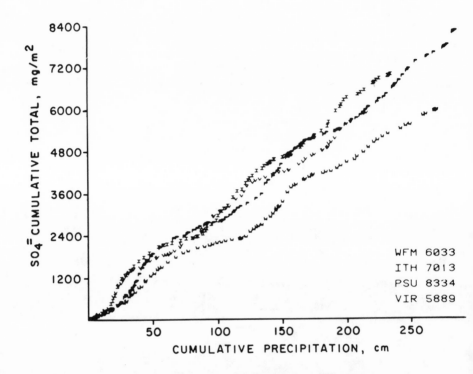

Figure 4-9.   Cumulative wet deposition of sulfate as a
function of cumulative precipitation
observed at four MAP3S/RAINE monitoring
sites.[54]

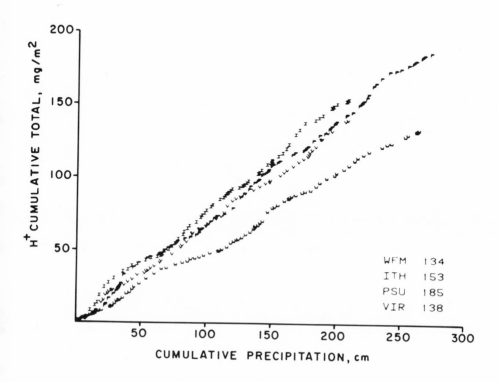

Figure 4-10. Cumulative wet deposition of H^+ as a function
of cumulative precipitation observed at four
MAP3S/RAINE monitoring sites.[54]

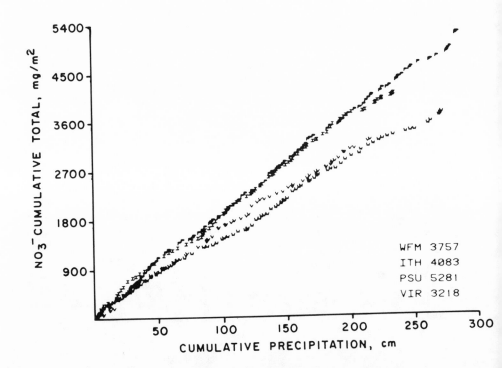

Figure 4-11. Cumulative wet deposition of NO_3^- as a function
of cumulative precipitation observed at four
MAP3S/RAINE monitoring sites.[54]

TABLE 4-6.   VARIATION IN HYDROGEN ION CONCENTRATION (μg of H^+/litre) IN PRECIPITATION[56]

Classification	Wt. mean	Mean	Standard deviation	Min.	Max.	n
All cases	52.4	45.1	66.7	0.1	616.1	1765
Season						
Winter	19.8	24.9	26.7	0.5	182.0	507
Spring	56.0	56.5	69.8	0.2	537.0	439
Summer	96.2	75.4	98.5	0.2	616.6	317
Fall	40.9	36.4	58.0	0.1	489.8	502
Synoptic Type						
Low	33.4	32.5	63.4	0.1	616.6	178
Warm Front	33.4	37.9	49.5	0.2	478.6	865
Occluded Front	28.1	32.9	37.7	0.2	141.3	126
Stationary Front	56.2	57.9	85.2	0.1	436.5	202
Cold Front	92.7	61.4	85.9	0.3	549.5	314
Squall Line	107.0	81.4	98.5	0.3	562.3	66
Hurricane	2.5	2.5	1.2	1.1	4.4	10

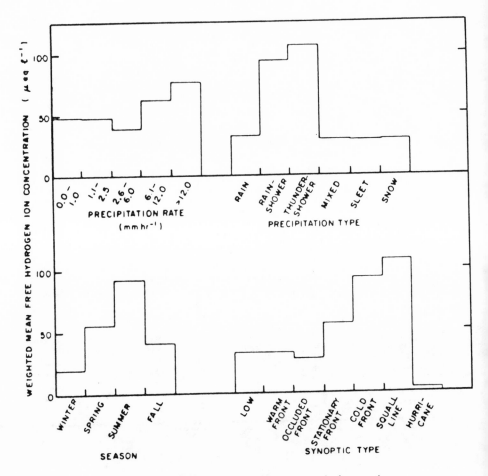

Figure 4-12.   Variation in weighted mean hydrogen ion
concentration with season, synoptic
type, precipitation type and precipitation
rate.[56]

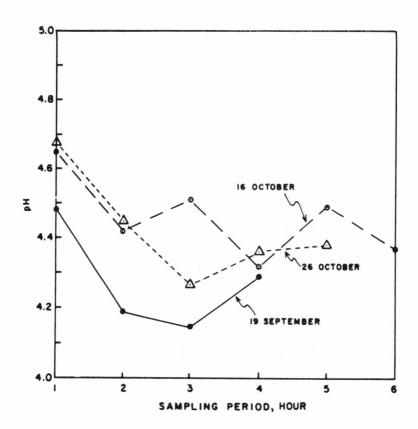

Figure 4-13.   Variation of pH during three storms
in Gainesville, Florida.[57]

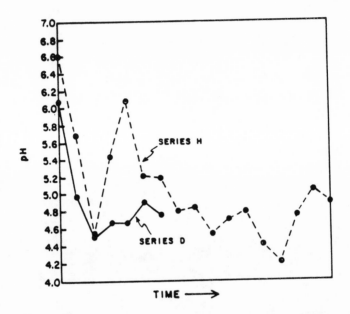

Figure 4-14. Variation of pH during two storms
in Tucson, Arizona.[57]

events in Tuscon, Arizona in the summer of 1977. The observations made in Series D covered a 13-minute period during which 4.5 mm of rain fell; Series H covered a 33-minute period during which 10.7 mm of precipitation fell. In both of these examples, the least acidic values also occurred at the beginning of the storm.[57]

In contrast, Raynor[58] has reported measurements from two storms at the Brookhaven National Laboratory, one of rain and one of snow, in which the precipitation became less acidic during the progression of the storm. In other storms, he reported that the cleansing effect of precipitation was not evident, either because the rates of rainfall were too low or the air was too clean at the beginning of precipitation.

Long-Term Trends

Because of the lack of long-term monitoring data, acidity trends in the United States have been poorly defined and necessarily based on calculated pH. Cogbill and Likens[2] pieced together precipitation data from the 1950's and 1960's and calculated the pH by assuming a stoichiometric relationship between the major chemical ions in rainwater. By comparing predicted pH values with actual measurements taken in the early 1970's, they estimated an error of 0.1 pH units. Maps illustrating their work appear in Figures 4-15 and 4-16. In the absence of more reliable data, their study has often been cited in estimating long-term trends. It shows both an increase in the area affected and lower pHs for precipitation appearing in New England and New York. However the validity of their conclusions has been questioned for the following reasons:

- Sampling methods before 1972 did not associate acid precipitation with an event and collected total wet plus dry deposition.[59]

- Precipitation samples were not stored correctly from the earlier time period[59] and it has been noted that measurements taken in the field often differ from laboratory measurements of the same sample.[40]

- Calculated values have been assigned a margin of error of 0.5 pH units by one critic.[60]

- The sampling sites for the different time periods were not the same.

Because pH has been found to vary between locations and storms, some critics have reanalyzed the data, examining trends at individual sites.[3,6,59] The initial comparisons between 1955-56 and 1965-66 published by Cogbill and Likens[2] had 10 common sites. Four of those showed increases in pH, two showed decreases, and the other four remained the same. Only two of the same sites were measured in the 1955-56/1972-73 comparison, one showing increasing pH, and the other showing a decrease. Between 1965-66 and 1972-73, eight stations were common, with pH increases at three, decreases at two, and no changes at three. It has been stated that if only the common stations were compared, no trend over time could be deduced.[3,6,59]

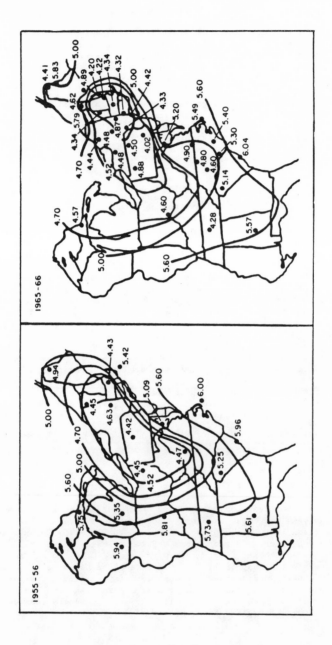

Figure 4-15. The weighted annual average pH of precipitation in the eastern United States in 1955-1956 and 1965-1966. (Modified from Likens et al.).2

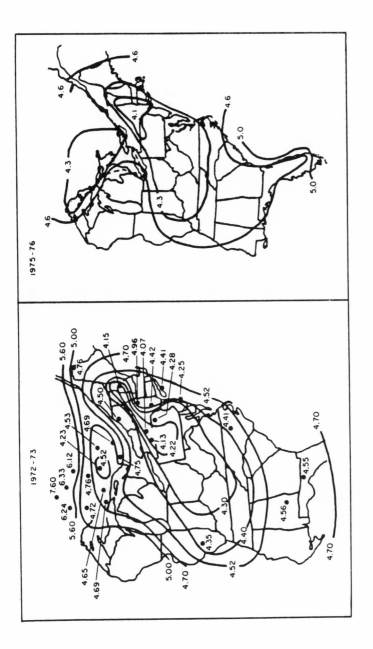

Figure 4-16. The weighted annual average pH of precipitation in eastern North America in 1972-1973 and 1975-1976. (Modified from Likens et al.).[1,2]

In August of 1980, the Utility Air Regulatory Group (UARG) requested
Environmental Research and Technology, Inc. (ERT) to further examine the
quality and analysis of historical data regarding precipitation chemistry.[61]
The data which were collected in the eastern United States were examined for
the consistency of sampling and chemical analysis methods used. Attempts were
made to quantify uncertainties, biases or equivalence associated with (a)
sampling, analytical, and calculational methods to deduce precipitation
acidity, (b) use of data from different times and conditions, (c) failure to
collect brief or light rainfall, (d) failure to collect initial precipitation
in an event, (e) failure to analyze for magnesium in certain samples, and (f)
failure of previous investigations to consider all available data. The
results of these assessments were examined in conjunction with interpretation
of spatial and temporal changes showing apparent trends in increased
precipitation acidity over the eastern United States, taking into account
natural variability in pH, climatological influences, and the role of cation
contributions associated with dust scavenging. ERT has stated that when the
data from the few midwestern monitoring sites are interpreted on the basis of
a 0.5 pH measurement uncertainty, no evidence of westward expansion of acidity
can be established.[60] ERT has also pointed out that the apparent increase
of acidity in the Southeast shown by published isopleth maps (Figures 4-15 and
4-16) may well have resulted from the use of an incomplete data base.[3]
Cogbill and Likens themselves pointed out that the decrease in pH in New York
and New England evident in the 1965-66 data was primarily caused by increased
resolution from additional monitoring sites.[2] The supposition of a trend
toward increasing acidity has also been disputed on the grounds that the nine
sites monitored by the United States Geological Survey from 1965 to 1978 in
New York State where acid precipitation does occur have shown no significant
trend over the time period. Time series analyses of these sites show rather
large variations over the entire sampling period as seen in Figure 4-17.[2]
Even the monthly data from Hubbard Brook showed no strong evidence of a trend
toward increasing acidity.[5,6] One must keep in mind, however, that because
the pH currently observed at Hubbard Brook is near 4.0, a relatively large
increase in H^+ concentration would be required to significantly lower the
average pH any further.[62]

It has also been suggested that the "apparent" trend toward more acidic
rain may be caused by factors other than the increase of strong acids in
precipitation. Stensland[4] suggests that rather than an addition of anions
(such as $SO_4^=$ and NO_3^-), there may have been a decrease in cations
(such as Ca^{++} and Mg^{++}) from scavenged soil dust. A drought occurred in
the mid-1950s followed by a less severe drought in the mid-1960s with a wet
period occurring during the later measurements.

In response to these criticisms, Likens and Butler[62] reevaluated the
1955-56 map produced by Cogbill and Likens[2] and stated, "Based on a careful
reevaluation of all the available data we find no compelling reason to
correct the original map (except not to specify values greater than pH 5.6
because of the relatively large errors involved). In fact the pattern shown
in the 1955-56 map is quite similar to the best estimate of Stensland[63]
after he applied various assumptions and empirical corrections to
Junge's[64-66] data." Likens and Butler[62] go on to say that "the trend of ,
increasing acidity of precipitation in the northeastern U.S. from 1955-56

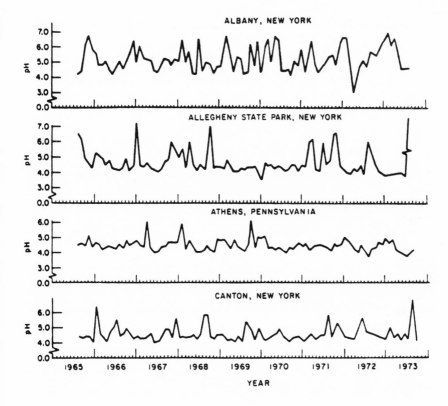

Figure 4-17. History of acidic precipitation at various sites in and adjacent to the State of New York.[2]

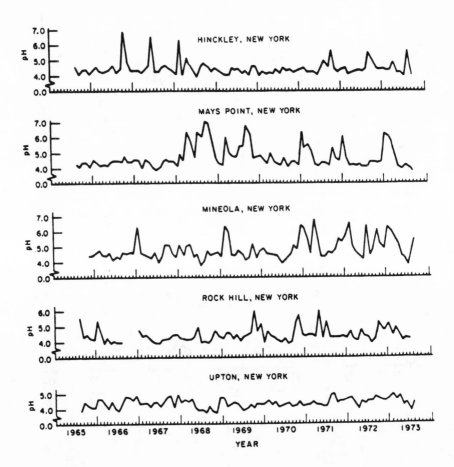

Figure 4-17 (continued).

to 1965-66 was substantiated from an error analysis of these data" (performed by Liljestrand and Morgan[67]).

As previously mentioned, one of the criticisms of the conclusions drawn by Cogbill and Likens[2] was that the sampling sites for the different time periods were not the same. Likens and Butler[62] insist that this observation, taken into account when reexamining the Cogbill and Likens[2] data, actually supports, rather than disputes those conclusions; "Thus, we find it remarkable that the annual patterns are so internally consistent...(which) suggests to us that there is only a small likelihood that these general patterns were generated by chance."[62]

The eastern United States is not the only area of the country where acid precipitation has been measured and trends proposed. Liljestrand and Morgan[21] took measurements in the Pasadena, California area in 1978 and reported a volume-weighted, mean pH of 4.06, representing a significant drop from calculated pH levels for before 1970, which were generally above 5.6. It was noted, however, that the 1978 measurements were taken during anomalous weather conditions; data were collected while California was in a drought and two tropical storms accounted for 20 percent of the rain. Yet, for the 1974-75 wet season, McColl and Bush[68] reported a mean pH of 5.0 in the Berkeley, California area. (At both Berkeley and Pasadena, nitric acid was found to be the major component of the acidity.) Lewis and Grant[20] documented acidic rain in the Como Creek watershed near the Continental Divide in Colorado. Within widely scattered data they found a significant downward trend in pH for the 3 years of data collection, with the regression pH dropping from 5.43 to 4.63, but noted that such a trend should not be extrapolated. No previous study documented pH for that area.

Measurements in Florida showed that the northern three-quarters of the state receives precipitation with an annual average pH below 4.7 as seen in Figure 4-18.[26] The contours tend to parallel the coast presumably because of the neutralizing effect of the maritime air. No long-term pH data had been collected in Florida, but calculated values for five locations indicated that the pH was greater than 5.6 in the mid-1950s. Researchers at the University of Florida compared their 1978-79 data (shown in Figure 4-18) with 1955-56 data for several localities (Pensacola-Jay, Talahassee, Jacksonville, Tampa-Bradenton, and West Palm Beach-Stuart) and found that rainfall has become much more acidic in the past 25 years with nitrate concentrations being 4.5 times higher in 1978-79 compared to 1955-56.[26]

As indicated in Figure 4-18, the northern part of Florida experiences more acidic rain than the southern areas. As a possible explanation for this phenomenon, researchers at Florida State University's Department of Oceanography in Tallahassee have reported that their sampling indicates that rains there are more acidic when emanating from the north.[27] In studying 14 precipitation events between November 1978 and January 1979, they found that air masses from the north produced rain with an average pH of 4.4 and a low of 3.7, whereas southern air from the Gulf of Mexico produced rainfall with an average pH of 5.3 and a low of 4.6. These data conflict somewhat with subsequent data described under the Seasonal Trends section wherein it is reported that acid rain occurs more frequently in summer than in winter and

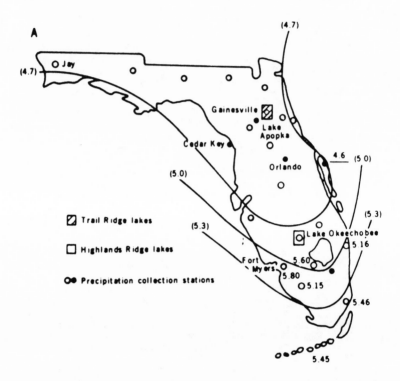

Figure 4-18.   Isopleths of measured pH in
Florida precipitation
(1978-1979).[26]

that summer winds are mostly from the south. Clearly, more monitoring is required to fully assess the situation, although it is noted that most of Florida's precipitation is a result of convective activity rather than intrusion of air masses from either the south or north.

A statistical overview of 3 years' of observations from the MAP 3S/RAINE network revealed very little long-term trend to the data.[39] However, several additional years of data must be collected to determine whether or not pronounced excursions emerge, as experience elsewhere might suggest.

Although the supporting data are fragmentary, measurements taken at common sites from 1955 to 1980 suggest increasing precipitation acidity in Washington, D.C.; Nantucket, Massachusetts; and Tampa, Florida.[62] However the trend for similar long-term data for Albany, New York; Caribou, Maine; and Sault St. Marie, Michigan is statistically unclear.[62]

North American trends have also been proposed by looking at the pH records stored in glaciers and continental ice sheets. Present-day pH values tend to average about 5, but Greenland ice from 180 years ago showed pH values ranging from 6 to 7.6.[1] Also, several other researchers[69-72] have determined that the pH of precipitation preserved in glaciers on continental ice sheets is generally greater than 5.0.[62] Recent data from Hammer[72] and Delmas et al.[73] show that precipitation falling in remote areas of Greenland and Antarctica has a pH of about 5.5.

Short-Term or Seasonal Trends

Several information sources indicate that seasonal trends exist with respect to acid precipitation data. Likens and Bormann,[14] after studying data from the Northeast, noted that in general, summer rains are more acidic than winter precipitation. This trend seems to be supported by several other studies. For example, precipitation in Florida is more acidic in summer (when winds are typically out of the south) than in winter by 0.2 to 0.3 pH units as indicated in Figure 4-19.[26] It was supposed that convective showers of summer are more efficient at scavenging sulfates and nitrates from the atmosphere than are winter frontal storms. It was noted that 65 percent of the precipitation fell during the summer months and that sulfates showed similar temporal trends as acidity, whereas nitrates did not show such seasonal variations.

Other studies conducted in the Northeast also indicate seasonal peaks in rainfall acidity during the summer months. Wolff et al.[15] monitored 72 precipitation events between 1975 and 1977 within the New York metropolitan area and found the mean pH of all events to be 4.28; the lowest values occurring during July through September and the maximum values from October through December. They found the lowest pH values occurred in precipitation from showers and thunderstorms associated with cold fronts and air masses from the west and southwest. Data from various monitoring sites in the Northeast showing the summer peaks in rainfall acidity are provided in Figure 4-20.[74] Monitoring performed at Whiteface Mountain from July 1978 to December 1979

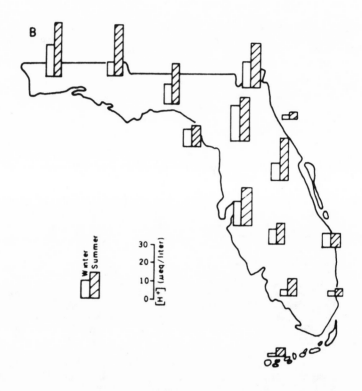

Figure 4-19.   Volume weighted [H⁺] in winter
(November-April) and summer
(May-October) in Florida
precipitation (1978-1979).[26]

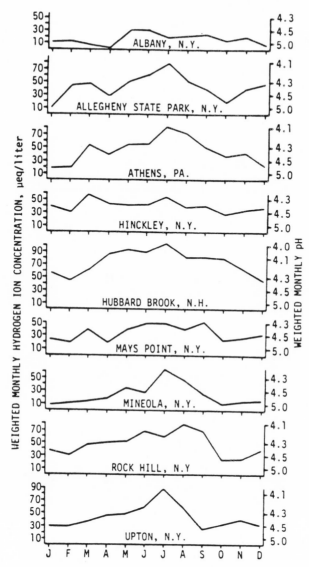

Figure 4-20. Weighted hydrogen ion concentration and pH of precipitation
curves showing seasonal peak in rainfall acidity during
summer months in the northeastern United States. The
curves are based on 8 or more years of data for each
location.[74]

also indicated a seasonal trend with respect to sulfate measurements. During 1979, daily sulfate concentrations in excess of 10 $\mu g/m^3$ occurred primarily in April-August and occasionally in September and October as shown in Figure 4-21.[46] The frequency distribution associated with sulfate concentrations in excess of 4 $\mu g/m^3$ (the annual average concentration) was as follows:

- January   1
- February   3
- March   8
- April   7
- May   12
- June   17
- July   21
- August   10
- September   9
- October   7
- November   5
- December   1

Daily concentration data for other elements measured in the study (Mg, Al, K, Ca, Fe, Zn, and Pb) showed trends that were very similar to the sulfate data.

SUMMARY

Although there is little debate over whether or not acidic precipitation is falling on various portions of the globe, there is some uncertainty as to whether the situation is becoming more or less severe. This section has addressed the extent of current and past acid rain monitoring networks both in the United States and around the world. The types of sampling systems currently used include: bulk collection (wet and dry deposition collected together), wet samplers, and wet/dry collectors (wet and dry samples collected separately). Wet deposition monitoring is deemed to be much more reliable than dry collection systems. The effects associated with such meteorological phenomena as fog, dew, and frost remain essentially unstudied at the present time.

In North America there are now over 70 monitoring networks, major ones being the National Atmospheric Deposition Program (including 97 sampling locations in the continental United States, Alaska, Hawaii, and American Samoa); the NOAA/WMO Precipitation Chemistry Network (including 130 sites

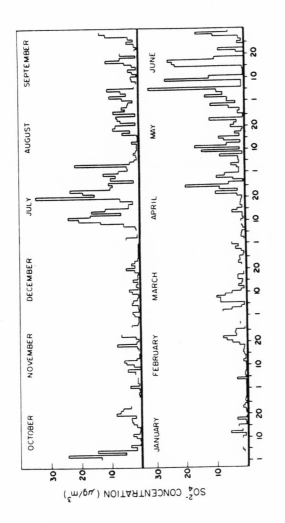

Figure 4-21. Daily sulfate concentrations for 1979.46

worldwide, 10 of which are located in the continental United States); the
MAP3S/RAINE network (which includes 9 sites in the northeastern United
States); and the Canadian Network for Sampling Precipitation (which includes
56 stations across Canada). Although there are some limitations with respect
to the current acid rain monitoring data base (differences—in some
cases—between networks with respect to monitoring techniques, quality
assurance, analytical procedures, and dry deposition sampling methods and the
need for additional sampling locations in the western United States), it has
been shown that good agreement can be obtained when data from many networks
are compared. Given the number of sites now in place or soon to be
operational, improvements being made in equipment, and the greater consistency
of quality assurance techniques for sampling and analysis, the future
availability of wet deposition data looks promising. However, the potential
of existing instrumentation and equipment for monitoring and analyzing dry
deposition exhibits much less promise and sampling and analysis techniques for
other meteorological phenomena such as dew, frost, and fog must be developed
or greatly improved.

The vast amount of monitoring data that has been recorded over the last
10 to 20 years indicates that acid rain is a worldwide phenomenon and that the
most severely impacted areas of the world are northern Europe (Scandanavia)
and the northeastern United States and southern Canada. There is evidence to
support the theory that acid rain in the Northeast is (at least partly) caused
by long-range transport of NO_x and SO_x precursors from the Midwest. At
the same time, local sources of SO_x in the Northeast may play an important
role in the formation of acid rain because there are a large number of fuel
oil burning facilities which emit primary sulfates.

Detailed observations of rainfall acidity show variations in acidity not
only from storm to storm at a particular location but also within the same
precipitation event. Due to the complexity of the mechanisms involved, it
appears that precipitation acidity varies with type of storm, precipitation
rate, spatial and temporal differences in cloud structure, and the time during
the storm when measurements are taken.

Much of the recorded data have been scrutinized to determine whether or
not short- or long-term trends are readily apparent. Because of the lack of
long-term monitoring data, acidity trends in the United States have
necessarily been based on comparisons of recent monitoring data with
calculated pH values for the 1950-1960 period. These comparisons indicate an
apparent increase in acidic precipitation in the Northeast and in Florida and
California. However, arguments have been presented that challenge the
validity of calculated pH data, which even though refuted by the original
investigators, tend to cast some doubt on the issue. Additionally, data
released earlier this year on pH monitoring of lakes over the last 7 years in
New York State's Adirondack Mountains revealed some small declines in lake
acidity.[75] This lake monitoring program, conducted by the New York
Department of Environmental Conservation, detected slight fluctuations in pH

(⩽0.2 pH) over the 1975-79 and 1980-81 time periods. Reductions in acidity levels in some of the lakes--the majority of which are in the "endangered" (pH of 5.0 to 6.0) category--were not significant enough to remove any of them from the endangered category. Seasonal trends indicating higher precipitation acidity during summer months are more apparent and easier to justify because of the substantial data base developed within the past 10 years. In some cases, the more acidic rain during the summer months is attributed to localized emissions and wind patterns while in others it is suggested that the nature of summer storms in terms of volume of precipitation and scavenging efficiency promote the higher acidity levels recorded. The accumulation of data from existing monitoring networks around the country will hopefully resolve any questions regarding long-term trends such that appropriate mitigative strategies directed at the source of the problem can be developed and implemented.

REFERENCES

1. Likens, G. E., R. F. Wright, J. N. Galloway, and T. J. Butler. Acid Rain. Sci. Amer., 241(4):43-51, 1979.

2. Cogbill, C. V. and G. E. Likens. Acid Precipitation in the Northeastern United States. Water Resources Research, 10(6), 1974.

3. Environmental Research and Technology. Comments on External Review Draft No. 1 of the Air Quality Criteria for Particulate Matter and Sulfur Oxides. 1980.

4. Stensland, G. J. Precipitation Chemistry Trends in the Northeastern United States. In: Polluted Rain, T. Toubara, et al., eds. Pergamon Press, New York, New York, 1980, p. 87.

5. Acid Rain Coordination Committee. The Federal Acid Rain Assessment Plan. Executive Office of the President, Council on Environmental Quality.

6. Perhac, R. M. Testimony for the Electric Power Research Institute before the Subcommittee on Environmental Pollution of the Senate Committee on Environment and Public Works.

7. Wisniewski, J. and J. D. Kinsman. An Overview of Acid Rain Monitoring Activities in North America. Bulletin of the American Meteorological Society, 63(6):598-618, June 1982.

8. Cowling, E. B. Acid Precipitation in Historical Perspective. Env. Sci. and Tech., 16(2):110A-123A, 1982.

9. Smith, R. A. Air and Rain: The Beginnings of a Chemical Climatology. Longmans, Green. London, 1872.

10. Emanuelson, A., E. Erikson, and E. Egner. Tellus, 6:261-267, 1954.

11. Barnes, R. A. The Long Range Transport of Air Pollution--A Review of the European Experience. J. Air Pollution Control Assoc., 29(12):1219-1235, 1979.

12. Oden, S. The Adicity Problem--An Outline of Concepts. In: Proceedings of the First International Symposium on Acid Precipitation and the Forest Ecosystem. USDA Forest Service and Ohio State University. Columbus, Ohio. 1975.

13. Szabo, M. F., M. P. Esposito, and P. W. Spaite. Acid Rain: Commentary on Controversial Issues and Observations on the Role of Fuel Burning. DOE/MC/19170-1168. March 1982.

14. Likens, G. E. and F. H. Bormann. Acid Rain: A Serious Regional Environmental Problem. Science, 184:1176-1179. June 14, 1974.

15. Wolff, G. T., P. J. Lioy, H. Golub, and J. S. Hawkins. Acid Precipitation in the New York Metropolitan Area: Its Relationship to Meteorological Factors. Env. Sci. and Tech., 13(2), 1979.

16. Dana, M. T. SO_2 Versus Sulfate Wet Deposition in the Eastern United States. J. of Geophys. Res., 85(NOC8):4475-4480, August 1980.

17. Wilson, R., V. Mohnen and J. Kadlecek. Wet Deposition in the Northeastern United States. DOE/EV/02986-1. State University of New York, Albany. 1980. 143 pp.

18. Raynor, G. S. and J. V. Hayes. Acidity and Conductivity of Precipitation on Central Long Island, New York in Relation to Meteorological Variables. Water, Air and Soil Pollution, 15(2):229-245, February 1981.

19. Schofield, C. L. Acid Precipitation: Effects on Fish. Ambio., 5(5-6):228-230, 1976.

20. Lewis, W. M. and M. C. Grant. Acid Precipitation in the Western United States. Science, 207, 1980.

21. Liljestrand, H. M. and J. J. Morgan. Chemical Composition of Acid Precipitation in Pasadena, California. Env. Sci. and Tech., 12(12), 1978.

22. McCall, J. G. and M. K. Firestone. Acid Precipitation in California and Some Ecological Effects. In: Effects of Air Pollutants on Mediterranean and Temperate Forest Ecosystems. PB81-133720. Pacific Southwest Forest Experiment Station, December 1980.

23. Leonard, R. L., C. R. Goldman, and G. E. Likens. Some Measurements of the pH and Chemistry of Precipitation at Davis and Lake Tahoe, California. Water, Air and Soil Pollution, 15(2):153-167, February 1981.

24. Miller, J. M. and A. M. Yoshimaga. The pH of Hawaiian Precipitation: A Preliminary Report. Geophys. Res. Lett., 8(7):779-782, July 1981.

25. Pack, D. H., G. J. Ferber, J. C. Heffter, K. Telegadas, J. K. Angell, W. H. Hockes, and L. Machta. Meteorology of Long Range Transport. Atmos. Environ., 12:425-444, 1978.

26. Brezonik, P. L., E. S. Edgerton, and C. D. Hendry. Acid Precipitation and Sulfate Deposition in Florida. Science, 208, 1980.

27. Tonaka, S., M. Daizi, and J. W. Winchester. Sulfur and Associated Elements and Acidity in Continental and Marine Rain from North Florida. J. of Geophys. Res., 85(C8):4519-4526, August 1980.

28. Moadsen, B. C. Acid Rain at Kennedy Space Center, Florida: Recent Observations. Atmos. Environ., 15(5):853-862, 1981.

29. Hendry, C. D. and P. L. Brezonik. Chemistry of Precipitation at Gainesville, Florida. Env. Sci. and Tech., 14(7):843-849, July 1980.

30. Neimann, B. L. J. Root, N. VanZwalenburg, and A. L. Mahan. An Integrated Monitoring Network for Acid Deposition: A Proposal Strategy. Interim Report, R-023-EPA-79, 236 pp.

31. Galloway, J. N. and G. E. Likens. Calibration of Collection Procedures for the Determination of Precipitation Chemistry. Water, Air and Soil Pollution, 6:241-258, 1976.

32. Galloway, J. N. and G. E. Likens. The Collection of Precipitation for Chemical Analysis. Tellus, 30:71-82, 1978.

33. Last, F. T., G. E. Likens, B. Ulrich, and L. Walloe. Acid Precipitation--Progress and Problems. In: Proceedings, International Conference on the Ecological Impact of Acid Precipitation. Sandefjord, Norway, pp. 10-12. March 1980.

34. Fowler, D. Removal of Sulfur and Nitrogen Compounds from the Atmosphere in Rain and by Dry Deposition. In: Proceedings, International Conference on the Ecological Impact of Acid Precipitation. Sandefjord, Norway, pp. 22-31. March 1980.

35. dePena, R. G., J. A. dePena, and V. C. Bowersox. Precipitation Collectors Intercomparison Study. Department of Meteorology, Pennsylvania State University. 1980.

36. Galloway, J. N., et al. A National Program for Assessing the Problem of Atmospheric Deposition (Acid Rain). Report to the National Council on Environmental Quality. 1978.

37. Interagency Task Force on Acid Precipitation. National Acid Precipitation Assessment Plan. Washington, DC, 1982.

38. Office of Research and Development. Research Summary, Acid Rain. EPA-600/8-79-028, 1978.

39. The MAP3S/RAINE Research Community. The MAP3S/RAINE Precipitation Chemistry Network: Statistical Overview for the Period 1976-1980. Atmos. Environ., 16(7):1603-1631, 1982.

40. Pack, D. J. Precipitation Chemistry Patterns: A Two Network Data Set. Science, 208, 1980.

41. Ecological Effects of Acid Precipitation. In: Workshop Proceedings. Prepared for Electric Power Research Institute, 1979.

42. Henderson, R. E., et al. An Overview of the Atmospheric Processes and Modeling Aspects of Acid Rain. Prepared by MITRE Corporation for U.S. Department of Energy. Contract No. 80ET13800-T014. Final Report, 1981.

43. U.S. EPA, Washington, DC. Ohio River Basin Energy Study: Main Report.
    EPA-600/7-81-008. January 1981.

44. Koerber, W. M. Trends in SO_2 Emissions and Associated Release Height
    for Ohio River Valley Power Plants. In: Proceedings of the 75th Annual
    Meeting of the Air Pollution Control Association, New Orleans, LA. June
    20-25, 1982.

45. Electric Power Research Institute (EPRI). R&D Status Report--Energy
    Analysis and Environment Division. EPRI Journal, 7(6), July/August 1982.

46. Husain, L., et al. Sources of Aerosol Sulfate and Trace Elements at
    Whiteface Mountain, New York. In: Proceedings of the 75th Annual
    Meeting of the Air Pollution Control Association, New Orleans, LA, June
    20-25, 1982.

47. Inside EPA Weekly Report. Vol. 3, No. 49. December 10, 1982.

48. Homolya, J. B. and S. Lambert. Characterization of Sulfate Emissions
    from Non-Utility Boilers Firing Low-S Residual Oils in New York City. J.
    Air Pollution. Control Assoc., 31(2), February 1981.

49. Inside EPA Weekly Report. Vol. 3, No. 44. November 5, 1982.

50. Inside EPA Weekly Report. Vol. 3, No. 46, November 19, 1982; and Vol. 3,
    No. 50, December 17, 1982.

51. Pack, D. H. Acid Precipitation--The Physical Systems. In: Proceedings,
    Advisory Workshop to Identify Research Needs on the Formation of Acid
    Precipitation, Alta, Utah. Electric Power Research Institute, Palo Alto,
    California, 1978.

52. Report to the MAP3S Precipitation Chemistry Meeting. Argonne National
    Laboratory, Ithaca, NY, May 11-12, 1978.

53. Semonin, R. G. The Variability of pH in Convective Storms. In:
    Proceedings of the First International Symposium on Acid Precipitation
    and the Forest Ecosystem. Columbus, Ohio, 1975.

54. Wilson, J. W., V. A. Mohnen, and J. A. Kadlecek. Wet Deposition
    Variability as Observed by MAP3S. Atmos. Environ., 16(7), 1982.

55. Chamberlain, J., et al. The Physics and Chemistry of Acid
    Precipitation. JASON/SRI International Report, JSR-81-25, 1981.

56. Raynor, G. S. and J. V. Hayes. Acidity and Conductivity of Precipitation
    on Central Long Island, New York, in Relation to Meteorological
    Variables. Water, Air and Soil Pollution, 15, 1981.

57. Hendry, C. Chemical Composition of Rainfall at Gainesville, Florida.
    M.S. Thesis, Department of Environmental Engineering Sciences, University
    of Florida, Gainesville, Florida, 1977.

58.   Raynor, G. C. Meteorological and Chemical Relationships from Sequential
      Precipitation Samples. In: Control of Emissions from Stationary
      Combustion Sources: Pollutant Detection and Behavior in the Atmosphere,
      W. Licht, A. J. Engel, and S. M. Slater, eds. Amer. Inst. of Chem. Eng.
      Symp. Series No. 188, Vol.75, AIChE, New York, New York, 1979.
      pp. 269-273.

59.   Comments of Amax Inc. on External Review. Draft No. 1, July 31, 1980.

60.   Environmental Research & Technology, Inc. Comments on External Review
      Draft No. 1 of the Air Quality Criteria for Particulate Matter and Sulfur
      Oxides. 1980.

61.   Hansen, D. A. and G. M. Hidy. Examination of the Basis for Trend
      Interpretation of Historical Rain Chemistry in the Eastern United States,
      Draft, November 1980.

62.   Likens, G. E. and T. J. Butler. Recent Acidification of Precipitation in
      North America. Atmos. Environ., 15(7):1103-1109, 1981.

63.   Stensland, G. J. Calculating Precipitation pH, With Application to the
      Junge Data. In: Semonin, L. M., et al. Study of Atmospheric Pollution
      Scavenging. 17th Prog. Report, EY-76-S-02-1199. Illinois State Water
      Survey, Urbana, 1979.

64.   Junge, C. E. The Distribution of Ammonia Nitrate in Rain Water over the
      U.S. Trans. Am. Geophys. Union, 39:241-248, 1958.

65.   Junge, C. E. and P. E. Gustafson. Precipitation Sampling for Chemical
      Analysis. Bulletin of the American Meteorological Society, 37:244-245,
      1956.

66.   Junge, C. E. and R. T. Werby. The Concentration of Chloride, Sodium,
      Potassium, Calcium, and Sulfate in Rainwater Over the U.S. J. of
      Meteorology, 15:417-425, 1958.

67.   Liljestrand, H. M. and J. J. Morgan. Error Analysis Applied to Indirect
      Methods for Precipitation Acidity. Tellus, 31:421-431, 1979.

68.   McColl, J. G. and D. S. Bush. Precipitation and Throughfall Chemistry in
      the San Francisco Bay Area. J. of Environ. Qual., 7:352-357, 1978.

69.   Manteev, A. A. Chemical Hydrology of Regions of East Antarctica. J. of
      Geophys. Res., 75:3686-3690, 1976.

70.   Langway, C. C., H. Oeschger, B. Adler, and B. Renaud. Sampling Polar Ice
      for Radiocarbon Dating. Nature, 206:500-501, 1965.

71.   Rainwater, F. H. and H. P. Guy. Some Observations on the Hydrochemistry
      and Sedimentation of the Chamberlin Glacier Area, Alaska. USGS Paper
      414-C:1-14, 1961.

72. Hammer, C. U. Past Volcanism Revealed by Greenland Ice Sheet Impurities. Nature, 270:482-486, 1977.

73. Delmas, R. J., A. Aristarain, and M. Legrand. Acidity of Antarctic Snow: A Natural Reference Level for Acid Rains. In: Ecological Impact of Acid Precipitation. SNSF Project, Oslo, 1980. pp. 104-105.

74. Hornbeck, J. W., G. E. Likens, and J. S. Eaton. Seasonal Patterns in Acidity of Precipitation and Their Implications for Forest Stream Ecosystem. Water, Air and Soil Pollution, 7:355-365.

75. Inside EPA Weekly Report. Vol. 3, No. 24. June 18, 1982.

5

Regional Transport and Deposition Modeling

INTRODUCTION

Due to widespread concern regarding the causes and effects of acid precipitation, long-range (regional) atmospheric transport and deposition models are being applied to investigate source/receptor relationships. These models are used to estimate the transboundary fluxes and regional ambient concentration and deposition patterns resulting from the synoptic-scale transport, diffusion, chemical transformation, and removal of pollutants. More specifically, they offer a mathematical means of expressing the possible relationships between sources of sulfur and nitrogen oxide emissions and acid deposition at receptor sites hundreds of kilometers away. Model simulations attempt to predict the geographical region where maximum impacts of emissions from a source area are expected to occur, thus aiding monitoring site selection for large-scale field experiments. Modeling is the only practical method for estimating atmospheric deposition at locations where monitoring is not, or cannot be, carried out. Sensitivity analyses with long-range transport models can help determine the relative importance of physical variables, quantify the range of uncertainty of model predictions, and define priorities for future research.

Although modeling is the accepted technique for predicting short-range concentrations of regulated pollutants, the development and validation of long-range transport models to describe acid deposition are in their early stages. Current acid deposition models, which to date have received little independent verification, cannot be expected to provide reliable estimates of air quality changes associated with realistic emission control scenarios or policy options.[1,2] No such models have yet received official approval for regulatory applications. However, regional sulfate models have been developed to the point where, according to Hilst,[1] the root-mean-square error is around 50 percent. The use of long-range transport models is considered to be the best currently available methodology for investigating the transport, transformation, and deposition of atmospheric pollutants on a regional scale.[2]

Important processes that determine the downwind concentration of a pollutant and which are generally accounted for in the models include:

- release into the atmosphere - determined by source characteristics such as stack parameters and emission rate;

- advective transport - controlled by the wind vector, averaged over appropriate time and space scales;

226

- dilution by dispersion and diffusion - brought about largely by turbulent fluctuations in the mean wind and by wind shear;

- creation, destruction, or modification of the pollutant species by chemical reactions during transport; and

- physical loss due to wet and dry deposition.

There are several modeling techniques that can simulate the long-range transport and chemical processes that lead to acid deposition. The most popular techniques currently in use employ one of two basic coordinate reference systems to track pollutant transport, dilution, and transformation. Lagrangian models use a reference system which moves with a moving air parcel or plume segment. Puffs or plume segments, independently advected and diffused, are superimposed on trajectories calculated from the wind field. For the user, an advantage of Lagrangian trajectory models is their ability to handle, in simplistic ways, changing wind and stability conditions. Eulerian models use a fixed-coordinate system through which air parcels are advected and diffused. Models in which a fixed grid is superimposed on the region of interest, the so-called grid model, are considered particularly appropriate when dealing with very long transport distances. Grid models deal directly with the set of equations selected to describe the physical phenomena taking place.

There are over 20 active long-range transport/acid precipitation modeling efforts in the United States and Canada, the majority of which are using Lagrangian models, at least in part. Research on Eulerian models suitable for long-range transport has increased recently, providing more balance in the overall modeling effort. These 20 model development programs provide a broad mix of techniques including a combination of Lagrangian and Eulerian reference systems, steady-state or time-dependent assumptions, reactive or nonreactive mechanisms, different removal mechanisms, and the use of diffusion coefficients or eddy diffusivities in the treatment of turbulence. The models cover simulation periods ranging from episodes to one year. Table 5-1 lists the principal long-range models being used in the United States and Canada along with the sponsoring organizations, model types, and the principal references.[3]

Only a few results from long-range, acid deposition modeling studies have appeared in the general literature to date. A summary of the results from six of these studies, believed to represent the state-of-the-art, is presented below, along with a brief description of each model. For convenience, the discussion has been separated into two parts. The first three models, here designated as event simulation models, use hourly meteorological data and perform the basic transport, diffusion, transformation, and removal calculations once per hour. The results are particularly well-suited to the calculation of short-term (episode) averages, although in principle the time period can be extended to one year or longer. The second three models, designated as statistical models, use long-term averages of meteorological data to describe mean plume position and spread, and transformation and deposition rates, and are therefore more efficient for long simulation periods.

TABLE 5-1.   SUMMARY OF PRINCIPAL REGIONAL AIR QUALITY SIMULATION MODELS
IN THE UNITED STATES AND CANADA[a]

Name of organization	Model acronym	Type of model	Time period	Principal references
Battelle-Pacific Northwest Labs	PNL	Lagrangian	Monthly to annual	McNaughton (1980)[4]
Brookhaven National Labs	AIRSOX	Lagrangian	Monthly to annual	Kleinman et al. (1980)[5]
Argonne National Labs	ASTRAP	Lagrangian	Monthly to annual	Shannon (1980)[6]
ERT, Inc.	SURAD	Eulerian	Episodes	Lavery et al. (1980)[7]
ERT, Inc.	MESOPUFF	Lagrangian	Episodes	Bass (1980)[3]
Teknekron Research, Inc.	RCDM	Analytical Eulerian	Annual	Fay and Rosenzweig (1980);[8] Niemann et al. (1980)[9]
Teknekron Research, Inc.	REGMOD	Eulerian	Episodes	Prahm and Christensen (1977);[10] Niemann et al. (1980)[9]
Washington University	CAPITA-Monte Carlo	Statistical Lagrangian	Monthly to annual	Patterson et al. (1980)[11]
SRI International	ENAMAP-1	Lagrangian	Monthly to annual	Bhumralkar et al. (1980)[12]
EPA Meteorology Lab	RPAQSM	Eulerian	Episodes	Lamb (1980)[13]
Atmospheric Environ. Service	AES-LRT	Lagrangian	Monthly to annual	Voldner et al. (1980)[14]
Ministry of the Environment	OME-LRT	Statistical Lagrangian	Annual	Venkatram et al. (1982)[15]

(continued)

TABLE 5-1 (continued)

Name of organization	Model acronym	Type of model	Time period	Principal references
NOAA/ARL	ATAD	Lagrangian	Monthly	Heffter (1980)[16]
Colorado State University	RADM	Lagrangian	Monthly	Henmi (1980)[17]
University of Wisconsin	ATM-SOX	Statistical Eulerian	Monthly	Wilkening and Ragland (1980)[18]
MEP, Ltd.	LRT	Lagrangian	Seasonal	Weisman (1980)[19]
Environnement Québec	TGD-EQ	Statistical Lagrangian	Seasonal to annual	Lelievre (1981)[20]
Battelle-Pacific Northwest Labs	STRAM	Segmented plume	Episodes	Hales et al. (1977)[21]
ERT, Inc.	MESOPLUME	Segmented plume	Episodes	Benkley and Bass (1979)[22]
SAI	NGPRM	Eulerian	Episodes	Liu and Durran (1977)[23]
ERT, Inc.	MESOGRID	Eulerian	Episodes	Morris et al. (1979)[24]
Savannah River Lab	SPM	Segmented plume	Episodes	Pendergast (1979)[25]
Lawrence Livermore Lab	ADPIC-MATHEW	Particle-in-cell	Episodes	Lange (1978)[26]
BNL-NCAR-Drexel	LAMPS	Lagrangian	Episodes	Kreitzberg and Leach (1978)[27]

[a]Modified from Bass.[3]

EVENT SIMULATION MODELS

The initial testing of long-range transport models has been carried out principally by predicting concentrations of SO_2 and sulfate over regional-scale distances and comparing the results with ambient concentrations of the two pollutants. These pollutants were selected in part because of the ready availability of SO_2 emission data and ambient measurements of both SO_2 and sulfate, and in part because of their recognized role in the acid deposition phenomenon. The results of several recent event simulation modeling studies are presented below.

The PNL Regional Model

Battelle, Pacific Northwest Laboratories (PNL), has developed a regional transport model for sulfur oxides that determines monthly and annual concentrations of sulfur dioxide (SO_2) and sulfate $(SO_4^=)$, and the total monthly and annual wet deposition of sulfur. The PNL model as described by Powell et al.[28] and later by McNaughton,[4] simulates transport of large point source plumes by following their trajectories with reference to a fixed grid. The wind field used is obtained by averaging National Weather Service (NWS) radiosonde data in a 100- to 1000-meter layer. The average wind vectors are interpolated to generate a representative wind field. The fields are then interpolated every hour between 12-hour observation intervals. Trajectories originate hourly at each point source and calculations of diffusion, transformation, and wet and dry deposition are made using mass conservation equations. The mass of pollutant is added to the appropriate grid cell to determine time-averaged concentration fields.

The transformation of SO_2 to $SO_4^=$ is assumed to be linear. The transformation rate is constant spatially, but can vary with time. Dry deposition rates for SO_2 and $SO_4^=$ are accounted for by deposition velocities, which are assumed to be constant. Wet removal of SO_2 is directly proportional to the hourly precipitation rate, whereas wet removal of $SO_4^=$, based on a formulation by Scott,[29] is proportional to the hourly precipitation rate raised to the 0.625 power. Mixing height is given a sinusoidally varying cycle to represent the buildup of the daytime mixed layer and the nocturnal stable layer.

The PNL regional model was applied to the eastern United States and eastern Canada. In one recent version of the model, the SO_2 transformation rate is increased to 10 percent per hour during precipitation events to account for in-cloud processes, as suggested by Scott and Laulainen.[30] The SO_2 and $SO_4^=$ wet removal rate constants are based on work by Dana et al.[31]

Transport during the 2 months of August and October 1977 was simulated using 1973-1974 large point source sulfur emission data from NEDS[32] and the Federal Power Commission (now the Federal Energy Regulatory Commission).[33] According to the modelers, these large point sources account for approximately 65 percent of the total emissions in the region; remaining emissions are from area sources and small point sources.

Model statistics for two cases are compared to observations in Table 5-2.[34] Case 1 takes into account increased transformation during precipitation events. In both cases, the PNL regional model underpredicts SO_2 and $SO_4^=$ monthly average concentrations. The modelers attribute this underprediction to the fact that only 65 percent of the total emissions are used.

The sulfur wet deposition statistics are compared to data taken at four stations in the U.S. Department of Energy's MAP3S precipitation chemistry network (Dana[35]) in Table 5-3. Without the increase in transformation during rain events, Case 2, the PNL model underpredicts sulfur deposition by as much as a factor of 3. Case 1 results are in much better agreement, perhaps agreeing too closely with data considering that only 65 percent of the total emissions are being transported (although these emissions represent most of the "tall stack" emissions). The observed and Case 2 predicted $SO_4^=$ concentration fields for August 1977 are shown in Figure 5-1.[34]

The PNL model is still in a testing and developmental stage and no conclusions can be reached from the preliminary results. The model is promising and may eventually serve as a useful tool to judge the impacts of proposed industrial development scenarios.

The SRI ENAMAP-1 Regional Model

SRI International developed a trajectory-type regional air pollution model, EURMAP-1 (European Regional Model Air Pollution), for the Federal Environmental Agency of the Federal Republic of Germany.[36] EURMAP-1 calculates long-term average concentrations, and dry and wet deposition of SO_2 and $SO_4^=$. This model was adapted for the region of eastern North America and has been renamed ENAMAP-1 (Eastern North America Model Air Pollution).[12] The basic principle of the model is that "puffs" of SO_2/ $SO_4^=$ are emitted at equal time intervals from all sources. The puffs are assumed to be well mixed in the horizontal and vertical directions. The transport of the puffs is then calculated using the mixed layer wind field.

During transport, pollutant mass is removed from a puff by dry deposition at a user-specified rate. Wet removal of SO_2 and $SO_4^=$ during rain events occurs at a constant rate proportional to the rainfall rate. Transformation of SO_2 to $SO_4^=$ is treated linearly. Sulfur dioxide and sulfate concentrations for each puff are determined over time using mass balance equations. The mass is added to the appropriate grid cell to determine time-averaged grid concentration fields.

The wind field is determined by objective analysis of available upper-air observations at the 850-millibar level (approximately 1500 meters above mean sea level). The resulting wind speeds are decreased by one-fourth, and the wind directions are rotated 15 degrees counterclockwise to account for surface layer friction effects. The wind fields are then interpolated every 3 hours between 12-hour data intervals.

TABLE 5-2. SUMMARY OF PNL MODEL EVALUATION STATISTICS FOR POLLUTANT CONCENTRATIONS[34]

Summary of model evaluation statistics for air concentrations	Ambient $SO_4^=$ concentration				Ambient SO_2 concentration			
	August 1977		October 1977		August 1977		October 1977	
	Case 1	Case 2	Case 1	Case 2	Case 1	Case 2	Case 1	Case 2
Mean observed concentration ($\mu g/m^3$)	10.25	10.25	6.24	6.24	14.97	14.97	21.70	21.70
Mean predicted concentration ($\mu g/m^3$)	8.09	5.73	5.74	4.46	11.56	13.29	11.85	12.92
Correlation of observed to predicted concentration	0.65	0.65	0.39	0.59	0.57	0.56	0.75	0.76
Variance observed data	3.41	3.41	1.82	1.82	54.75	54.75	159.41[a]	155.41
Variance predicted data	20.52	20.29	2.58	1.66	38.92	44.66	39.54	39.96
Maximum observed concentration ($\mu g/m^3$)	14.60	14.60	8.92	8.92	30.13	30.13	69.17	69.17
Maximum predicted concentration at monitoring sites ($\mu g/m^3$)	21.83	14.90	8.74	7.31	23.35	25.20	23.99	45.69
Frequency of concentrations within a factor of 2 (%)	70	59	100.00	89	73	78	62	62
Frequency of concentrations within a factor of 3 (%)	88	72	100.00	99	99	86	79	89

[a]Apparent bias by a local influence at Johnstown, PA.

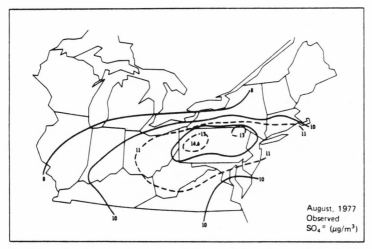

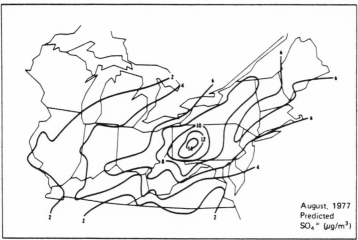

Figure 5-1.   Comparison of observed SO$_4^=$ concentration fields to
              PNL model predictions (Case 2) for August 1977.[34]

TABLE 5-3. PNL MODEL EVALUATION STATISTICS FOR MONTHLY WET DEPOSITION
OF SULFUR (AS $SO_4^=$ IN $g\ m^{-2}\ h^{-1}$)[35]

Station	August 1977			October 1977		
	Observed	Case 1	Case 2	Observed	Case 1	Case 2
Whiteface, NY	5.96	6.90	4.83	3.45	2.03	1.30
State College, PA	5.35	6.71	3.67	4.28	4.34	1.47
Charlottesville, VA	5.02	6.92	3.41	0.69	0.66	0.31
Ithaca, NY	1.56	0.59	0.49			
Mean $\dfrac{Predicted}{Observed}$		1.04	0.62		0.85	0.39

In the model simulation, $SO_2/SO_4^=$ emissions consisted of the 1977 emission data base prepared for the SURE program by GCA Corporation. The months of January and August 1977 were chosen for the analysis, and the results were compared with SURE, NEDS, and SAROAD air quality data. The calculated and measured concentration fields of $SO_4^=$ are compared in Figures 5-2 and 5-3.[12] In January, ENAMAP-1 predicts high sulfate in the northeastern states and relatively low values elsewhere. The observed concentration field is similar in the East, but measured values are much higher than predicted in the Midwest. The model results for August are in better agreement with observations. Wet deposition patterns were calculated, but, unfortunately, they were not compared with actual data.

The ENAMAP-1 approach is similar to the PNL model formulation; the largest difference is in how they parameterize wet deposition. The month-averaged $SO_4^=$ concentration field calculated by ENAMAP-1 for August 1977, Figure 5-3, shows a distribution similar to results of the PNL, Figure 5-1. The magnitude of the PNL concentrations is closer to the observed values.

The AES-LRT Regional Model

The Atmospheric Environment Service of Canada (AES) has developed and applied an event simulation model to simulate ambient concentrations and deposition patterns of sulfur over eastern North America.[14] The AES Long Range Transport (LRT) model is based on trajectories, at about 600 meters above the ground, which are calculated using analyzed wind fields from standard observations. As air parcels follow the trajectories towards a receptor, sulfur dioxide emissions, mixing heights, and precipitation amounts along the path are analyzed.

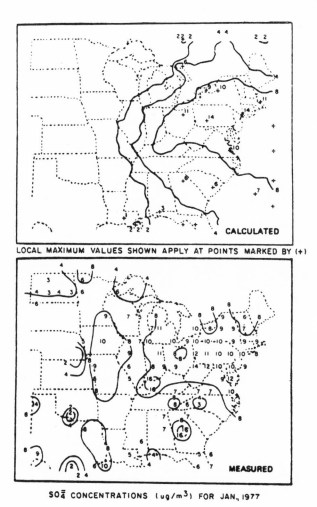

LOCAL MAXIMUM VALUES SHOWN APPLY AT POINTS MARKED BY (+)

SO$_4^=$ CONCENTRATIONS (ug/m^3) FOR JAN., 1977

Figure 5-2.   ENAMAP-1 calculated SO$_4^=$ concentration field and the corresponding measured field for January 1977 (Bhumralkar et al.).[12]

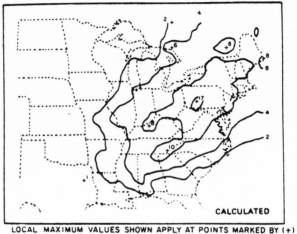

LOCAL MAXIMUM VALUES SHOWN APPLY AT POINTS MARKED BY (+)

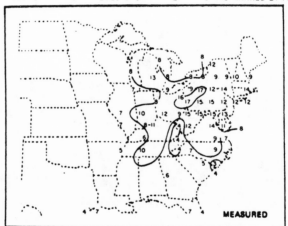

$SO_4^=$ CONCENTRATIONS (ug/m^3) FOR AUGUST

Figure 5-3.   ENAMAP-1 calculated $SO_4^=$ concentration field and the
corresponding measured field for August 1977
(Bhumralkar et al.).[12]

The transformation and deposition processes are parameterized linearly. Wet deposition is parameterized by using a scavenging ratio approach and the 24-hour precipitation amount. Dry deposition is parameterized through the use of fixed deposition velocities. Trajectories are calculated using wind data interpolated to the 925-millibar level and using computed vertical motions. The concentrations at each receptor are averaged to provide daily, monthly, and annual concentration and deposition values and related directly to acid rain.

Figures 5-4 and 5-5 present ratios of computed to measured monthly concentrations.[14] Analysis of the data indicates some overprediction of sulfur dioxide concentrations and some underprediction of wet deposition, but generally the overall concentration patterns and episode occurrences agree quite well with measurements.[14]

STATISTICAL MODELS

The results of several of the most often cited statistical simulation models prepared for eastern Canada and the northeastern United States are presented below.

The ASTRAP Regional Model

Argonne National Laboratory has developed the Advanced Statistical Trajectory Regional Air Pollution (ASTRAP) model for sulfur under the MAP3S program initiated by the U.S. Department of Energy. The Model was developed by Sheih[37] from a concept introduced by Durst et al.[38] and applied by Shannon.[6] As its name suggests, this model takes a statistical approach to long-term regional modeling rather than the event simulation technique discussed earlier. The ASTRAP model is based on the assumption that, for long-term averaging (periods of 1 month or longer), horizontal and vertical dispersion processes can be separated. Based on this assumption, the model consists of three independent subprograms. First, the long-term horizontal dispersion statistics (mean position and spread as a function of plume age) for simulated tracers released from a grid of virtual sources are calculated. Individual puffs are not tracked; instead, the month-long emissions are represented by the dispersion statistics. During this step of the modeling procedure, statistics of tracer removal by precipitation are also evaluated. Next, a vertical dispersion subprogram numerically integrates the standard one-dimensional diffusion equation allowing for surface dry deposition and transformation of SO_2 to $SO_4^=$. Finally, the normalized results of the first two subprograms are used to produce fields of SO_2 and $SO_4^=$ concentrations and wet and dry deposition of total sulfur.

Seasonal and diurnal variations in SO_2 to $SO_4^=$ transformation rates as noted by Husar et al.[39] are taken into account. Based on the work of Wesely and Hicks[40] and Wesely et al.,[41] there are seasonal and diurnal cycles in the deposition velocities of SO_2 and $SO_4^=$. Sulfate deposition velocities are on the same order of magnitude as SO_2 velocities rather than an order of magnitude less, as found in other modeling studies.

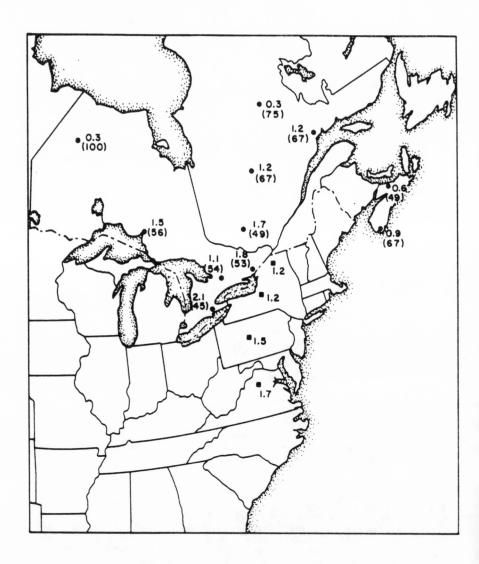

Figure 5-4.   Ratios of AES—LRT computed to measured monthly
precipitation weighted sulfate concentrations in
the rain and percent contribution from direct
sulfate scavenging (in parentheses) for October 1977.[14]

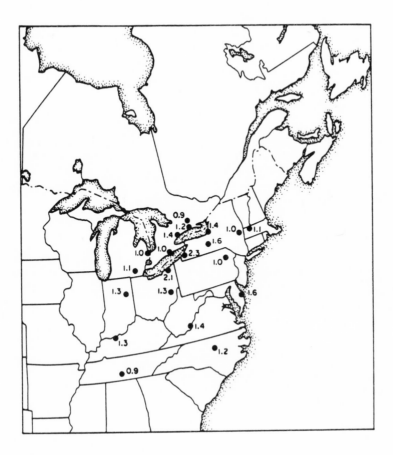

Figure 5-5.   Ratios of AES-LRT computed to measured monthly mean
              sulfate concentrations in the air for October 1977.[14]

Wet removal is taken into account using the scavenging ratio approach. This method relates wet deposition to the ratio of field measurements of concentration of pollutant measured in the air to that measured in rainfall at the same time. Argonne National Laboratory has found scavenging rates to be relatively constant,[42] and sulfur deposition by wet processes is found to be a function of the half power of the amount of precipitation.

The mixed layer is assumed to be 2100 meters in depth and is divided into 11 layers for the vertical numerical integration. A wind field is developed at a specified level in the atmosphere based on NWS data. The 1000-meter level winds are used for simulation of winter conditions and 1800-meter level winds are used for summer. Winds are interpolated between data points using a radius of influence inverse-squared relationship.

Preliminary model runs have been made in the eastern United States and Canada using 1974 and 1975 meteorological data. The emission inventory consisted of both point and area source emissions in the eastern United States and Canada. The model results were then compared with measurements from the SURE data network for 1977 and 1978. The average 2-month summer and winter sulfate fields are compared with data in Figures 5-6 and 5-7.[6] As these figures show, there are major deviations between model predictions and measured data. The ASTRAP model noticeably underpredicted sulfate concentrations, especially in the winter scenario as shown in Figure 5-7. These differences are most notable in the western portion of the modeling region, but also occur generally. A probable reason for these differences is that the meteorological data used were for 1974 and 1975, while the measured data represent 1977 and 1978. Significant differences in the statistical representation of the meteorological data between these two time periods could account for a large portion of the variations in the results. The ASTRAP simulations of wet deposition of total sulfur were scaled to a 1-year period and compared in Figure 5-8 with observations during 1977 of annual accumulations of sulfate in precipitation, expressed as total sulfur.[43] There is some general agreement, but the data show a more complex distribution than that indicated by the ASTRAP model results. On an annual basis, an estimated 5.4 million metric tons were deposited in the eastern United States. Wet and dry removal were approximately equally important. By season dry deposition was equal to wet deposition in the summer, but wet removal was approximately twice dry removal in the winter.

The OME-LRT Regional Model

The Ontario Ministry of the Environment (OME) has developed a statistical model which uses a Lagrangian grid system to simulate long-term ambient concentration and wet deposition patterns on a regional basis over eastern North America.[15] The dispersion and removal of pollutants and the required meteorological parameters in the OME model are specified in terms of the statistics of these physical processes from wind and precipitation data.

The horizontal dispersion of pollutants is based on a Gaussian puff whose mean motion follows that of large-scale synoptic flows. The standard deviations of the Gaussian puff are related to the statistics of trajectories

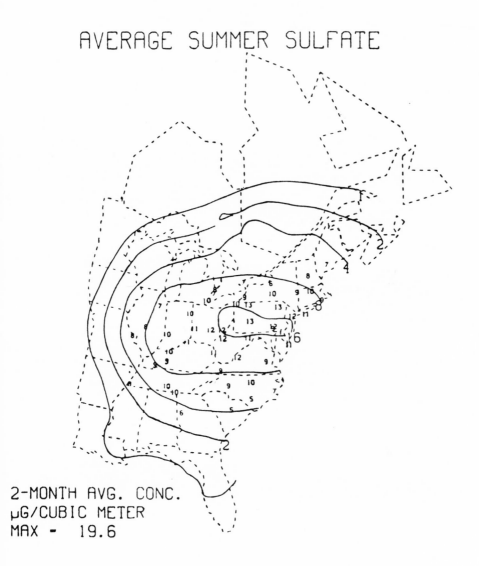

Figure 5-6. Comparison of August 1977 SURE average sulfate measurements
(numbers) with ASTRAP simulations (isopleths) using July–
August 1975 meteorology.[6]

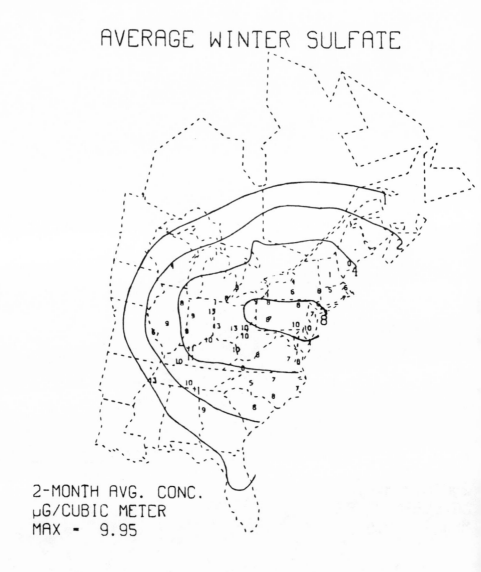

AVERAGE WINTER SULFATE

2-MONTH AVG. CONC.
µG/CUBIC METER
MAX - 9.95

Figure 5-7. Comparison of January-February 1977 SURE average sulfate measurements (numbers) with ASTRAP simulations (isopleths) using January-
February 1975 meteorology.[6]

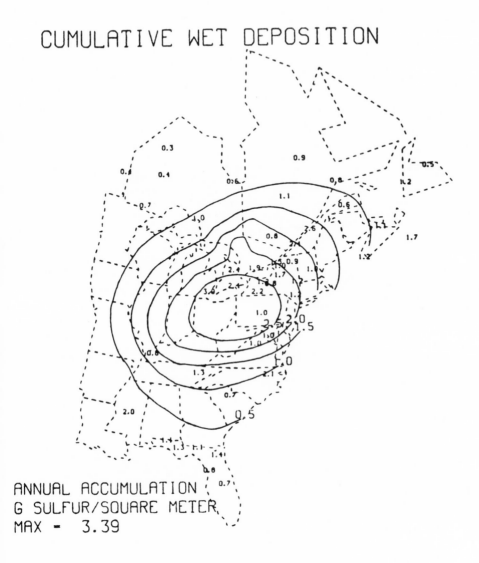

CUMULATIVE WET DEPOSITION

ANNUAL ACCUMULATION
G SULFUR/SQUARE METER
MAX - 3.39

Figure 5-8.   Comparison of cumulative sulfate in rain, expressed as total
               sulfur (numbers) for 1977 with ASTRAP simulations (isopleths).[43]

from the source(s) under consideration. Scavenging of pollutants is treated
with a stochastic model which accounts for the distinctly different
probabilities of rain in synoptically dry and wet regions. The model also
allows for different SO_2 to $SO_4^=$ conversion rates in wet and dry periods.

Figure 5-9 shows modeled total wet deposition of sulfur for 1977.[15]
The model estimates compare quite well with measurements of annual wet
deposition taken from Canadian and United States networks for 1977.[15]

The RCDM Regional Model

The Regional Climatological Dispersion Model (RCDM) uses analytical
solutions to the diffusion equations to simulate sulfur dioxide and sulfate
concentrations through the use of simplifying assumptions. Temporal and
spatial averaging of the wind data are applied to eliminate most of the
detailed fluctuations while maintaining the mean transport field. Seasonal
and annual resultant wind vectors are derived by averaging available upper air
wind data for the eastern United States and Canada.[9]

The RCDM model uses a simple deposition velocity technique to calculate
dry and wet depositions of sulfur dioxide, sulfate, and total sulfur. The
model has been evaluated against historical data as well as current sulfur
dioxide and sulfate data and wet deposition measurements.[9] Figures 5-10 and
5-11 present predicted annual concentrations for SO_2 and $SO_4^=$, respectively.
Figure 5-12 shows predicted wet sulfur deposition from the RCDM model.
Figure 5-13 presents the 3-year average sulfate concentrations from the
eastern United States.

RCDM annual predictions are in generally good agreement with regional
SO_2 and $SO_4^=$ concentrations.[9] The model also gives generally good
agreement with seasonal concentrations when the seasonal mixing height is used
and the inverse chemical conversion rate is decreased slightly for summer and
increased slightly for winter.[9] The predicted wet sulfur deposition values
are in general agreement with those computed from the MAP3S and EPRI
precipitation chemistry networks in the areas of highest SO_2 emissions.[9]

STATE-OF-THE-ART OF REGIONAL MODELING

As demonstrated by the modeling results presented above, the accuracy of
acid rain modeling results varies greatly with each modeling approach and is
limited by a lack of detailed understanding of the complex processes
controlling the transport, diffusion, chemical transformation, and deposition
of pollutants; by the spatial and temporal variations of these processes; and
by the inadequacy of the input data bases. At this time, there are no
long-range transport models officially approved for use in regulatory
applications.

Little consensus exists among modelers concerning the use of the wind
data and there are several technical approaches presently used to simulate
regional-scale transport. Transport mechanisms based on the wind from a
constant level in the atmosphere or winds averaged throughout a fixed layer

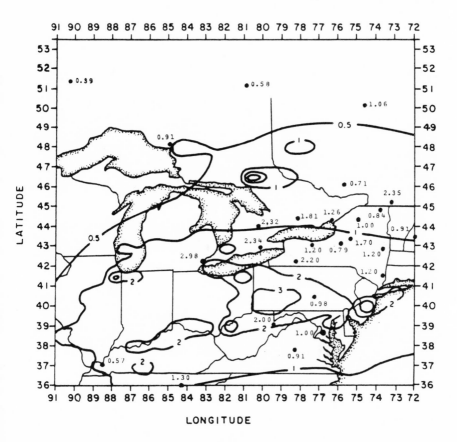

Figure 5-9.   Comparison of OME-LRT model predictions (isopleths) of annual wet
              deposition of sulfur with observed values (numbers) from CANSAP
              network (g/m²/yr).[15]

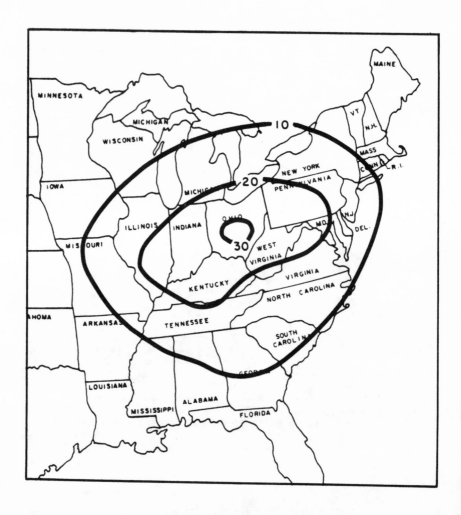

Figure 5-10. Isopleths of annual SO₂ concentrations
(µg/m³) simulated by the RCDM.[9]

Figure 5-11.   Isopleths of annual sulfate concentrations
($\mu g/m^3$) simulated by the RCDM.[9]

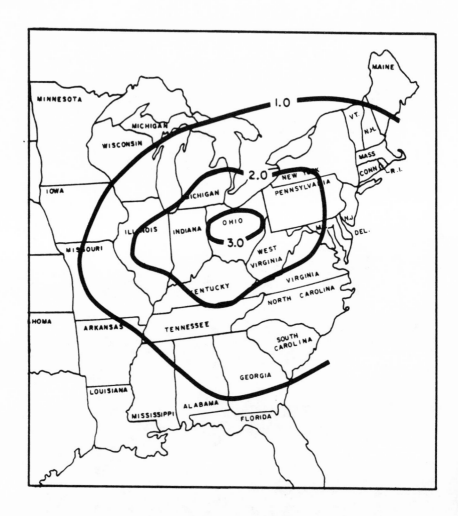

Figure 5-12.   Isopleths of wet sulfur deposition
                ($\mu g/m^2/yr$) simulated by the RCDM.[9]

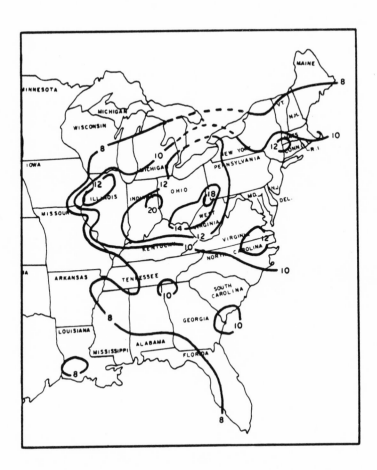

Figure 5-13.   Three-year average (1975-1977) of
sulfate concentrations ($\mu g/m^3$).[9]

are most commonly used. There is uncertainty as to the magnitude of the variations in long-term average transport paths, such that significant errors in determining the wind field may produce serious inaccuracies in determining long-term impacts.[44]

Most transport models tend to ignore vertical atmospheric motion, diurnal cycles in the height of the mixing layer, pollutant versus height profiles, and some pollutant scavenging mechanisms. Neglecting vertical air motions can lead to large horizontal deviations from the mean plume path. This may be especially true during nighttime stable conditions.

It is believed that winds at cloud levels may provide a more realistic representation of the transport of acid precursors than low-level winds do. Some researchers maintain that the incloud wet removal process is of greater importance than below-cloud processes and that aqueous-phase chemical transformation processes within a cloud are also important. Therefore, it appears that a wind field for modeling acid rain transport would more appropriately be based on upper level (cloud height) winds then on surface winds or winds averaged over a shallow layer.

Horizontal diffusion on a regional scale is generally regarded to be of lesser importance than transport. In many models it is assumed that long-term dispersion is primarily controlled by variations in the position of a plume centerline due to changes in the regional wind patterns and not by small-scale dispersion about the plume centerline. A large number of individual plume trajectories from a single source is required to develop the horizontal dispersion statistics and this is only just being attempted.[44]

Vertical diffusion can be treated using one of many possible approaches in a model. Layered models in which vertical diffusion is described more specifically may offer some advantages over single-layer models. A multilayered model allows for a better treatment of wet and dry deposition and chemical transformation both of which vary with altitude.

Most existing models only treat sulfur chemistry while ignoring nitrogen and other compounds; however, the acidity of precipitation is governed by a delicate balance of many ions in solution. It is generally assumed that variations in precipitation pH may be due to changes in sulfate and nitrate concentrations, to which anthropogenic sources contribute greatly in industrialized regions (see Section 2). It is therefore important to note that most current models do not treat total acid formation (including nitrates) or acid neutralization processes. In addition, most models commonly treat sulfur chemistry in an unsophisticated, linearly parameterized manner. This treatment limits the ability of the models to accurately predict the changes in atmospheric acid formation and deposition caused by variations in the magnitude of the emission of acidifying compounds and their precursors.

The modeling of wet deposition is currently treated in a number of ways. A large variation in the empirical relationships to describe the transformation and removal processes exists. In some models washout coefficients are used, while in others a power law relationship is assumed. In the area of modeling incloud scavenging processes, Scott[45] has devised a chemical and dynamical model to describe SO_2 transformation processes which could be quite useful.

Some controversy exists among modelers concerning the velocity of dry deposition of sulfate particles. Most modeling estimates range from 0.1 to 1.0 centimeters per second. Comparatively little measurement data on particle impaction exists. Similarly, little information is available on the deposition velocities of important nitrogen compounds, such as HNO_3, NO, and NO_2.

In summary, while computational and monetary constraints require that the transport and diffusion models be simple, it is necessary that the most important processes be taken into account before the models can be expected to provide a realistic evaluation of possible control strategies. It has been estimated that current models may provide only order-of-magnitude results, even for time-averaged values.[46] The atmosphere is a very complex system, and further evaluations may well show that more sophisticated models are required to obtain useful results.

INTERNATIONAL ASPECTS OF TRANSPORT

The effects of air pollution were at one time considered local problems, occurring near large emission sources. This idea is no longer valid. The increase in anthropogenic emissions coupled with increases in the height and amount of emissions have served to exacerbate the impacts of air pollution by increasing the potential for acid rain formation via long-range transport/transformation processes. Therefore, air pollution, which was once thought of as a local phenomenon, is now an international and even global concern due to the large distances involved in the transport of acid rain precursors.

In Europe, where many countries are located in a relatively small area, the international aspect of the long-range transport of pollutants is obvious. Emissions from sources in the south and west create acid rain, which deposits over many areas of northern Europe. Recent model calculations of wet and dry deposition patterns in Europe show that in Scandinavia, and particularly in Norway, the wet deposition (acid rain) outweighs the estimated dry deposition (from ambient air concentrations). For southern Norway, dry deposition is estimated to account for about 30 percent of the total deposition of excess sulfur. The remainder is attributed to acid precipitation.

International Research

During the last several years significant efforts have been made in developing mathematical models which are capable of estimating long-range transport of acid rain precursors. In the United States over 15 different organizations have developed models; while at least three in Canada, one in

Mexico, and several others in Europe are also working on model development projects. The models are continually being refined to improve their treatment of the transport, transformation, and removal processes.

In conjunction with modeling studies, acid precipitation monitoring programs have been established in many countries. In the United States there are 50 different measurement and analysis programs currently underway or recently completed, while there are 20 programs in progress in Canada, and one in Mexico.

European Studies

Long-range transport studies in Europe have been limited by the magnitude of the problem and international relations. As pointed out earlier, SRI International has developed a long-term regional transport model for the Federal Environmental Agency of the Federal Republic of Germany and named it EURMAP-1.[36] EURMAP-1 is the forerunner of the SRI model developed for North America named ENAMAP-1. The ENAMAP-1 applications to North America have been presented earlier in this section. SRI has also developed a short-term model called EURMAP-2.

A study on the Fate of Atmospheric Emission Plume Trajectory over the North Sea was carried out by the Central Electricity Research Laboratory of Great Britain and may include model development, but the results have not yet been published.[47]

Modeling research efforts are underway by the Norwegian Institute for Air Research,[48] the Organization for Economic Cooperation and Development (OECD),[49] and the Economic Commission for Europe, who originated the Cooperative Programme for Monitoring and Evaluating the Longe-Range Transmission of Air Pollutants in Europe.[47]

United States-Canadian Border Flux Estimates

The pollutant fluxes across the United States-Canadian border have been estimated by either correlating available air quality and meteorological data or using the transport and deposition models. Some initial work has been done with air quality data. For example, Fleming[50] used the Ontario Hydro network to show that high background SO_2 in Ontario, observed primarily in the winter, coincided with winds favoring transport from the United States. At this time, however, the primary source of transboundary flux estimates has been from models.

Preliminary estimates of the transboundary flux by the ASTRAP model, described earlier, indicate that the United States contributes 4 to 5 times as much sulfur to Canada as it receives. As would be expected from the seasonal wind patterns, the summer flux is greater than the winter flux. Galloway and Whelpdale[43] estimate that the inflow to Canada from the United States exceeds the sulfur flux in the opposite direction by a factor of three. The actual annual flux estimates are shown in Table 5-4. In addition, seasonal

transport estimates based on the ENAMAP-1 model indicate that the ratio of
United States-Canada transport to Canada-United States transport is 1.3 in the
winter and 3.2 in the summer.[36]

TABLE 5-4.   TRANSBOUNDARY FLUX ESTIMATES,[a] U.S.-CANADA RESEARCH
             CONSULTATION GROUP[51] (Tg S y^{-1}, MILLIONS OF METRIC
             TONS OF S PER YEAR)

Method of estimation	Canada to USA flux	USA to Canada flux
I Statistical trajectory model (ASTRAP) (Shannon, 1980)[6]	0.5	2.
II Simple advection and decay model (Galloway and Whelpdale, 1980)[43]	0.7	2.

[a]Based on emissions east of approximately 92°W.

Insight into transboundary transport can be gained from estimates of the
contribution from sources in the United States and Canada to each other's
total sulfur deposition. In Table 5-5, ENAMAP-1 and ASTRAP estimates of the
amount of sulfur deposited in eastern United States and Canada are broken down
into incremental contributions by United States and Canadian sources.[43]

Both models indicate that Canadian source emissions contribute less than
5 percent of the total sulfur deposited in the United States, although they do
show that Canadian sources make a significant contribution in northern New
York and northern New England. The model results also indicate that United
States sources contribute about the same portion of total sulfur deposited in
Canada as do Canadian sources. The Galloway and Whelpdale[43] deposition
estimates, based on measurements, are included for comparison. The model
total deposition estimates for Canada are well below the observed values, and
the ENAMAP-1 estimates for United States deposition are a factor of two
greater than the Galloway and Whelpdale estimates.

SUMMARY

There are two basic types of acid precipitation models which describe
long-range transport and chemical transformation. One uses a reference system
which moves with the air parcel (Lagrangian) and the other uses a fixed
coordinate system through which air parcels are moved (Eulerian). These
models attempt to quantify the impacts of sources on receptors which are
several thousands of kilometers away.

There are several ways in which long-range transport models can attempt
to calculate pollutant concentrations. Event simulation models predict plume
transport with an hour-by-hour update of the wind field and are especially
well-suited to the calculation of short-term (episodes of a few days)

TABLE 5-5. TOTAL SULFUR DEPOSITION ESTIMATES (MILLION METRIC TONS)[43]

Source	Region		Eastern U.S. sources	Eastern Canada sources	Total
			Contribution from		
ENAMAP-1	Eastern U.S.	wet	-	-	-
		dry	-	-	-
		total	10.8	0.4	11.2
	Eastern Canada	wet	-	-	-
		dry	-	-	-
		total	0.7	1.2	1.9
ASTRAP (2 summer months)	Eastern U.S.	wet	0.554	0.019	0.573
		dry	0.455	0.017	0.472
		total	1.009	0.036	1.045
	Eastern Canada	wet	0.132	0.109	0.241
		dry	0.048	0.064	0.112
		total	0.180	0.173	0.353
Galloway and Whelpdale[43] based on measurements	Eastern U.S.	wet	-	-	2.5
		dry	-	-	3.3
		total	-	-	5.8
	Eastern Canada	wet	-	-	3.0
		dry	-	-	1.2
		total	-	-	4.2

averages. Statistical models use long-term (seasonal or yearly) averages of
meteorological data to describe mean plume position and spread, and are more
efficient for simulating long time periods. Both model types use additional
formulas to define chemical transformation and deposition processes.

The monthly-averaged SO_2 and SO_4^- concentration fields predicted by
most models are generally within 30 percent of measured values in the vicinity
of large point sources. However, predictions were off by a factor of two or
more in rural areas.

Preliminary estimates of the transboundary flux of acid components have
been made by the ASTRAP model (described earlier). These results indicate
that the United States contributes 4 to 5 times as much sulfur to Canada as it
receives. Based on the seasonal wind patterns, the summer flux is greater
than the winter flux. Other studies have found that the ratio of the United
States-to-Canada sulfur flux to the Canada-to-United States sulfur flux is
3 to 1.

Model results indicate that Canadian source emissions contribute less
than 5 percent of the total sulfur deposited in the United States. However,
Canadian sources make a significant contribution to northern New York State
and northern New England. These results also indicate that the United States
sources contribute about the same magnitude of total sulfur deposited in
Canada as do Canadian sources.

With regard to modeling uncertainties, little consensus exists among
modelers concerning the specification of the wind field, and the methods
employed generally ignore vertical motions, wind shears, diurnal mixing height
variations, vertical pollutant contributions, thermal structure of the
atmosphere, precipitating cloud type, and certain scavenging mechanisms.

As in all air pollution modeling, definition of the wind fields is
crucial to obtain correct transport patterns. Most models rely on objective
analysis of available National Weather Service (NWS) wind data.
Unfortunately, the NWS network is designed for use in synoptic- (continental)
scale modeling, and the spatial scale is not fine enough to capture the
variation from synoptic-scale motion that is important in regional-scale
modeling. One alternative is to use basic thermodynamic and hydrodynamic
equations to predict atmospheric behavior using real initial and boundary
conditions.

The problems inherent in assuming linear relationships when
parameterizing non-linear variables can vary from significant overprediction
to severe underprediction of pollutant concentrations. Most models treat
sulfur chemistry as a highly parameterized, linear process generally as a
function of solar radiation, while ignoring other aspects of acid rain
formation chemistry and neutralization processes. The models have provided
only limited preliminary simulations of SO_2 and SO_4 transport and
chemistry. The nitrogen cycle has not yet been simulated and could be very
important. At this time, because of a lack of understanding of the complex
chemical processes taking place, particularly within clouds, and a limited

knowledge of the wet removal processes, the models must rely heavily on empirical relationships to describe transformation and removal processes. The greatest disagreement among model parameterizations relates to wet removal mechanisms.

Although the use of long-range transport models is considered to be the best currently available methodology for investigating the transport, transformation, and deposition of atmospheric pollutants on a regional scale, their accuracy and reliability are restricted. This is due to our limited understanding of all of the physical and chemical processes involved, and to a lesser extent, to the computational and monetary constraints which historically have dictated that the transport and diffusion models be simple. However, the atmosphere is a very complex system and further evaluations may show that more sophisticated models are required to obtain realistic estimates of air quality changes associated with emission control scenarios or policy options.

REFERENCES

1. Hilst, G. R. SURE Findings and Conclusions. EPRI Journal, July/August
    1982.

2. Atmospheric Modeling Committee of the Utility Air Regulatory Group.
    Quoted in the Regional Implications of Transported Air Pollutants--An
    Assessment of Acidic Deposition and Ozone. Interim Draft. Office of
    Technology Assessment. July 1982.

3. Bass, A. Modeling Long-Range Transport and Diffusion. Preprint,
    Proceedings of the Second Joint AMS/APAC Conference on Applications of
    Air Pollution Meteorology. March 24 to 27, New Orleans, LA, 1980.

4. McNaughton, D. J. Time Series Comparisons of Regional Model Predictions
    with Sulfur Oxide Observations from the SURE Program. Paper 80-54.5,
    Presented at the 73rd Annual Meeting of the Air Pollution Control
    Association, Montreal, Quebec, June 22 to 27, 1980.

5. Kleinman, L. J., J. G. Carney, and R. E. Meyers. Time Dependence on
    Average Regional Sulfur Oxide Concentrations, Proceedings of the Second
    Joint AMS/APCA Conference on Applications of Air Pollution Meteorology.
    March 24 to 27, New Orleans, LA, 1980.

6. Shannon, J. Examination of Surface Removal and Horizontal Transport of
    Atmospheric Sulfur on a Regional Scale. In: Proceedings of the Second
    Joint AMS/APCA Conference on Applications of Air Pollution Meteorology.
    March 24 to 27, New Orleans, LA, 1980.

7. Lavery, T. L., et al. Development and Validation of a Regional Model to
    Simulate Atmospheric Concentrations of Sulfur Dioxide and Sulfate.
    In: Proceedings of the Second Joint AMS/APCA Conference on Air Pollution
    Meteorology. March 24 to 27, New Orleans, LA, 236-247, 1980.

8. Fay, J. A., and J. J. Rosenzweig. An Analytical Diffusion Model for Long
    Distance Transport of Air Pollutants. Atmos. Environ., 14:355-365, 1980.

9. Niemann, B. L., A. A. Hirata, B. R. Hall, M. T. Mills, P. M. Mayerhofer,
    and L. F. Smith. Initial Evaluation of Regional Transport and
    Subregional Dispersion Models for Sulfur Dioxide and Fine Particulates.
    In: Proceedings of the Second Joint AMS/APCA Conference on Applications
    of Air Pollution Meteorology. March 24 to 27, New Orleans, LA, 1980.

10. Prahm, L. V. and O. Christensen. Long-Range Transmission of Pollutants
    Simulated by a Two-Dimensional Pseudo-Spectral Dispersion Model. Appl.
    Meteor. J., 16(9):896-910, 1977.

11. Patterson, D. E., R. B. Husar, W. E. Wilson, Ir., and L. F. Smith. Monte
    Carlo Simulation of a Daily Regional Sulfur Distribution: Comparison
    with SURE Sulfate Data and Visibility Observations During August 1977.
    Paper submitted to Appl. Meteor. J., June 1980.

12. Bhumralkar, C. M., W. B. Johnson, R. L. Mancusco, R. H. Thuillier, and D. E. Wolf. Interregional Exchanges of Airborne Sulfur Pollution and Deposition in Eastern North America. In: Proceedings of the Second Joint AMS/APCA Conference on Applications of Air Pollution Meteorology. March 24 to 27, New Orleans, LA, 1980.

13. Lamb, R. G. A Regional Scale (1000 km) Model of Photochemical Air Pollution - Part I: Theoretical Formulation. Draft report from the Meteorology and Assessment Division, EPA Environmental Sciences Laboratory, 1980.

14. Voldner, E. C., M. P. Olson, K. Oikawa, and M. Loiselle. Comparison Between Measured and Computed Concentrations of Sulfur Compounds in Eastern North America. To appear in Journal of Geophysical Research Proceedings of CACGP Symposium on Trace Gases and Aerosols, August 1979, 1980.

15. Venkatram, H. A., B. E. Ley, and S. Y. Wong. A Statistical Model to Estimate Long-Term Concentrations of Pollutants Associated with Long Range Transport. Atmos. Environ., 16(2): 249-257, 1982.

16. Heffter, J. L. Transport Layer Depth Calculations. In: Proceedings of the Second Joint AMS/APCA Conference on Air Pollution Meteorology, March 24 to 27, New Orleans, LA, 1980.

17. Henmi, J. Long-Range Transport Model of SO_2 and Sulfate and Its Application to the Eastern United States. Geophys. Res. J., 85(C8):4436-4442, August 20, 1980.

18. Wilkening, K. E. and K. W. Ragland. Users Guide for the University of Wisconsin Atmospheric Sulfur Computer Model (UWATM-SO_x). Draft report prepared for the EPA Environmental Research Laboratory, Duluth, MN, November 12, 1980.

19. Weisman, B. Long-Range Transport Model for Sulfur. Paper 80-54.6 presented at the 73rd Annual Meeting of the Air Pollution Control Association, Montreal, Quebec, June 22 to 27, 1980.

20. Lelievre, C. Modele Simple de Transformation Chimique du Soufre Lors de Son Transport Dans L'atmosphere. Rapport Interns, Service de la Meteorologie, Ministere de l'Environment du Quebec, 1981.

21. Hales, J. M., D. C. Powell and T. D. Fox. STRAM - An Air Pollution Model Incorporating Nonlinear Chemistry, Variable Trajectories, and Plume Segment Diffusion. EPA-450/3-77-012. 1977.

22. Benkley, C. W. and A. Bass. Development of Mesoscale Air Quality Simulation Models. Volume 2. User's Guide to MESOPLUME (Mesoscale Plume Segment) Model. Prepared by Environmental Research and Technology, Inc. for the Environmental Protection Agency, 1979.

23. Liu, M. K. and D. Durran. The Development of a Regional Air Pollution Model and Its Application to the Northern Great Plains. EPA-908/1-77-002. Systems Applications, Inc., 1977.

24. Morris, C. S., C. W. Benkley, and A. Bass. Development of Mesoscale Air Quality Simulation Models. Volume 4. User's Guide to MESOGRID (Mesoscale Grid) Model. Prepared by Environmental Research and Technology, Inc. for the Environmental Protection Agency, 1979.

25. Pendergast, M. M. Model Evaluation for Travel Distances 30 to 140 km. Preprint Volume, Fourth Symposium on Turbulence, Diffusion, and Air Pollution. January 15-19, 1979, Reno, NV. pp. 648-651, 1979.

26. Lange, R. ADPIC - A Three-Dimensional Transport-Diffusion Model for the Dispersal of Atmospheric Pollutants and its Validation Against Regional Tracer Studies. Appl. Meteor. J., 17:320-329, 1978.

27. Kreitzberg, C. W. and M. J. Leach. Diagnosis and Prediction of Tropospheric Trajectories and Cleansing. In: Proceedings, 85th National Meeting, American Institute of Chemical Engineers. Philadelphia, PA, June 4 to 8, 1978.

28. Powell, D. C., D. J. McNaughton, L. L. Wendell, an R. L. Drake. A Variable Trajectory Model for Regional Assessments of Air Pollution from Sulfur Compounds. PNL-2734, Battelle, Pacific Northwest Laboratory, Richland, Washington, 1978.

29. Scott, B. C. Parameterization of Sulfate Removal by Precipitation. Appl. Meteor. J., 17:1375:1389, 1978.

30. Scott, B. C., and N. S. Laulainen. On the Concentration of Sulfate in Precipitation. Appl. Meteor. J., 18:138-147, 1979.

31. Dana, M. T., J. M. Hales, and M. A. Wolf. Rain Scavenging of SO_2 and Sulfate from Power Plant Plume. Geophys. Res. J., 80:4119-4129, 1975.

32. U.S. Environmental Protection Agency. 1973 National Emissions Report. EPA-450/2-75-007, 1976.

33. U.S. Federal Power Commission. Steam Electric Plant Air and Water Quality Control Data, 1973. FPC-5-253, 1976.

34. McNaughton, D. J., and B. C. Scott. Modeling Evidence of Incloud Transformation of Sulfur Dioxide to Sulfate. J. Air Pollution Control Assoc., 30(3):272-273, 1980.

35. Dana, M. T. The MAP3S Precipitation Chemistry Network: Second Periodic Summary Report (July 1977 to June 1978). PNL 2829, Battelle Pacific Northwest Laboratory, Richland, Washington, 1979.

36. Johnson, W. B., D. E. Wolf, and R. L. Mancuso. Long Term Regional Patterns and Transfrontier Exchanges of Airborne Sulfur Pollution in Europe. Atmos. Environ., 12:511-527, 1978.

37. Sheih, C. M. Application of a Statistical Trajectory Model to the Simulation of Sulfur Pollution Over Northeastern United States. Atmos. Environ., 11:173-178, 1977.

38. Durst, C. S., A. F. Crossley, and N. E. Davies. Horizontal Diffusion in the Atmosphere as Determined by Geostrophic Trajectories. Fluid Mech. J., 6:401-422, 1959.

39. Husar, R. B., D. E. Patterson, J. D. Husar, N. V. Gillani, and W. E. Wilson. Sulfur Budget of a Power Plant Plume. Atmos. Environ., 12:549-568, 1978.

40. Wesely, M. L., and B. B. Hicks. Some Factors that Affect the Deposition Rates of Sulfur Dioxide and Similar Gases on Vegetation. J. Air Pollution Control Assoc., 27:1110-1116, 1977.

41. Wesely, M. L., B. B. Hicks, W. P. Dannevik, S. Frisella, and R. B. Husar. An Eddy-Correlation Measurement of Particulate Deposition from the Atmosphere. Atmos. Environ., 11:561-563, 1977.

42. Hicks, B. B. An Evaluation of Precipitation Scavenging Rates of Background Aerosol. Appl. Meteorol. J., 17:161-165.

43. Galloway, J. N., and D. M. Whelpdale. An Atmospheric Sulfur Budget for North America. Atmos. Environ., 14(14):409-417, 1980.

44. Dittenhoeffer, H. C. A Critical Review of Long Range Transport/Acid Precipitation Models. Paper 82-10.8 presented at the 75th Meeting of the Air Pollution Control Association, New Orleans, LA, June 20 to 25, 1982.

45. Scott, B. C. Predictions of In-Cloud Conversion Rates of SO_2 to SO_4 Based Upon a Simple Chemical and Dynamical Model. In: Second Joint Conference on Applications of Air Pollution Meteorology, American Meteorological Society. 389-396 pp, 1980.

46. Hosker, R. P. Jr. Practical Application of Air Pollutant Deposition Models - Current Status, Data Requirements, and Research Needs. In: Proceedings of the International Conference of Air Pollutants and Their Effects on the Terrestrial Ecosystem, Banff, Alberta, Canada, May 10-17, 1980.

47. Cowling, E. B. Acid Precipitation in Historical Perspective. Env. Sci. and Tech., 16(2)110A-123A, 1982.

48. Eliassen, A. and J. Saltbones. A Two-Layer Dispersion Model; Description and a Few Results. Internal report from the Norwegian Institute for Air Research, 1975.

49. OECD Programme on Long Range Transport of Air Pollutants, Measurements and Findings, Paris: Organization for Economic Cooperation and Development, 1977.

50. Fleming, R. A. Long Range Transport of Sulfur Dioxide. Paper No. 80-54.1 presented at the 73rd Meeting of the Air Pollution Control Association, Montreal, Quebec, Canada, June 22-27, 1980.

51. United States - Canada Research Consultation Group on the Long-Range Transport of Air Pollutants. The LRTAP Problem in North America: A Preliminary Overview, 1980.

6

Adverse and Beneficial Effects of
Acid Precipitation

INTRODUCTION

As discussed in detail in earlier sections of this report, recent studies have reported a pH of 4.0 to 5.0 for rain and snow in the United States, particularly in the Northeast.[1-11] It has been suggested that this acidic precipitation, by acidification of lakes, has been responsible for extinction of acid-sensitive aquatic species and disruption of primary production and the food web within the affected ecosystems. Direct and indirect injury to crops and other vegetation by acidic precipitation has been postulated based on laboratory, greenhouse, and field experiments. However, some studies have revealed beneficial responses of crops exposed to acidic precipitation. There is also concern about the potential indirect impact of acidic precipitation on human health and wildlife. In addition, acidic precipitation has the potential to produce deterioration of stone buildings, monuments, and a variety of other materials.

This section discusses the potential impacts of acidification on the environment. It must be recognized throughout the discussion that there are broad gaps in the data on which many of the assumed impacts are based, and there should be a clear distinction between what is known and what is unresolved.

Generalizations about the effects of acid precipitation on the ecosystem without reference to the amount and type of acidic input, the nutrient conditions of the system, and the pathway by which acidifying materials enter the ecosystem are unwise. For example, in experiments where acid is added directly to water bodies, the possibility of metals leaching from the soil or watershed is not accounted for in the simulation.

Most of the data available to date on impacts of acidic precipitation are derived from studies of the effects of increased acidity on aquatic organisms. The effects of lowering pH on fish, plant species, and other members of freshwater ecosystems are well documented; therefore, the manner and severity of disruption of the affected aquatic ecosystems produced by acidification may be postulated with some confidence.

Discussion of potential impacts of acidic precipitation on terrestrial ecology rests on more tenuous evidence. Most of these data were generated under laboratory or greenhouse conditions using simulations of exposure of terrestrial species to acidic precipitation. Therefore, any conclusions drawn

from these data suffer by extrapolation from the laboratory to the field.
This is not a refutation or condemnation of laboratory-generated data;
however, the limitations of extrapolating these data, especially to as complex
a system as a forest or other terrestrial ecosystems, must be recognized.
Also, any generalizations or postulations on the impacts of acidic
precipitation suffer from the lack of unequivocal or detectable damage to
terrestrial ecosystems outside the laboratory. This may be contrasted with
the aquatic ecosystems where actual acidification-induced impacts have been
observed and measured in situ.

Finally, it must be recognized that there has been no clear agreement
among researchers regarding quantification of the magnitude of the potential
adverse impacts of acidic precipitation, and whether the observed effects are
a local or regional phenomenon caused by poor buffering capacity of the
affected lakes or soils or whether the effects are more widespread.[12] This
question is difficult to resolve at present because research has centered on
those areas where effects, especially aquatic effects, have been observed.
Such research has therefore involved the most acid-sensitive regions, systems,
and organisms. Implied impacts of acid precipitation on more highly buffered
areas whose acid resistance is higher are somewhat speculative at this point.

IMPACTS OF ACIDIC PRECIPITATION ON AQUATIC ECOSYSTEMS

Acidification of Lakes

The increasing acidity of freshwater lakes and streams appears to be an
environmental factor stressing aquatic ecosystems in Europe and North
America.[13] However, the trend toward increased acidity of lakes has not
been demonstrated in controlled studies.

The chemical composition of lakes is largely determined by the
composition of influents from precipitation and watershed drainage. The
complex pathways contributing to acidic inputs to lakes and streams are
illustrated in Figure 6-1. Soft water lakes are usually produced by drainage
over acidic igneous rocks, whereas hard waters contain large concentrations of
alkaline earths derived from drainage of calcareous deposits.[14] Naturally
acidic lakes have been studied in Alaska.[15] Organic acids (pH $<$4.7)
produced in surface soils and bog soils increase the susceptibility of these
lakes to the effects of acid precipitation compared to nearly neutral lakes.
The bog moss Sphagnum generates polyuronic acids which release hydrogen ions
in exchange for metal cations, thereby acidifying bog waters. During dry
periods, bogs also generate sulfuric acid by oxidizing sulfur compounds.[16]
Acidification is also achieved by the nitrification of ammonia from
atmospheric deposition or from the decomposition of organic matter.[16]

The acidity of freshwater lakes reflects both the acidity of
precipitation and the capability of the watershed and the lake itself to
neutralize incoming acid.[17] Most of the acid ultimately deposited in lakes
comes from water that percolates through the surrounding watershed.
Figure 6-2 demonstrates the response of two individual lakes at different
levels of sensitivity as atmospheric sulfate loading is increased. The result
of sulfate loading past the lake's threshold for buffering the acid is

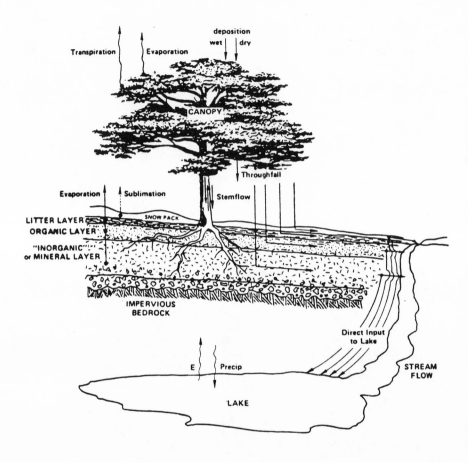

Figure 6-1. Definition sketch for the pathways of a water
tributary to a lake.

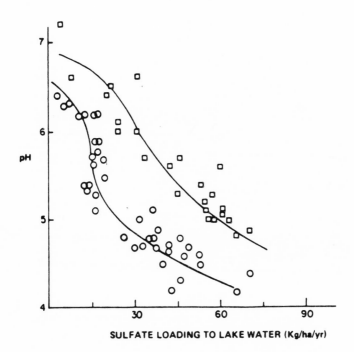

Figure 6-2.   Relationship between acid loading and pH change for:[18]

    ○ very sensitive, and

    □ moderately sensitive surroundings.

demonstrated by the sharp drop in pH.[18] The moderately sensitive lake
starts at a pH 0.4 higher than the very sensitive lake and will accept 1.5 to
2.0 times more sulfate per year to reach the same pH. It should be noted,
however, that these curves were developed for acid-sensitive Scandinavian
lakes and do not necessarily reflect the response of lakes in most of the
United States and Canada. Each lake has its own response curve based on its
watershed characteristics. Application of these curves to groups of lakes in
northeastern North America provides useful qualitative information on lake
acidification. Factors which control the shape and displacement of these
curves include watershed-lake area/volume ratio, soil geology, vegetative
cover, ground water input, and displacement of toxic metals. Although
uncertainties such as the lack of effects caused by nitric acid inputs or the
absence of response time or short-term effects exist, quantitative prediction
of bicarbonate lakes can be made with a reasonably high level of accuracy.
However, application of this approach to the more important prediction of
transition to acid lakes does not yield as high a level of predictive accuracy.

Schofield and Henricksen have remarked[19-21] that lake acidification is
analogous to a large-scale chemical titration. For each lake affected by
acidification, its location on the alkalinity titration curve is determined by:
the watershed hydrology; the capacity of the soils, bedrock, and sediments in
the watershed to neutralize incoming acid; and the rate of acid deposition and
generation.[22] Figure 6-3 is a titration curve for a bicarbonate solution at
100 µeq/liter, illustrating the acidification process of a lake.[21] As noted,
hardness of water is associated with alkalinity and, therefore, with the
increased capacity of the water to neutralize or buffer the acidity entering a
lake.[17] Chemical weathering and ion exchange are two mechanisms in
watersheds that act to neutralize incoming acidity. The rate at which these
processes proceed is dependent on the physical and chemical nature of the
bedrock and soils.

The bicarbonate ion provides most of the buffering capacity of soft water
lakes. The concentration of bicarbonate in soft waters is highly
pH-dependent, and as the pH of precipitation and runoff decreases, the
bicarbonate concentration also decreases. In acidified soft water lakes,
sulfate, largely supplied by acidic precipitation, replaces bicarbonate as the
major anion[17,23,24] (see Figure 6-2). Bicarbonate in these lakes is
essentially eliminated, and no effective buffering capacity remains. High
alkaline waters are acidified based on the accumulation of acidic materials
until a threshold level is reached in the watershed. Schindler et al.[25]
experimentally acidified a small lake and found that 70 percent of the lake's
alkalinity had been depleted before pH values decreased. Damage to the lake
had occurred before the detection of a drop in pH.[16,26] Poorly buffered
waters are subject to large fluctuations in acidity, especially in response to
the large influxes of acidic species observed following melting of ice and
snow.[17,19,20,27,28] These sudden episodes of acidic input have been the
cause of fish kills that have occurred in Europe during the late winter and
early spring thaw; fish are often unable to adapt to the abrupt change in
pH.[17,19,24,28-31] In areas where the watersheds or lake waters have no
capability to neutralize incoming acid, acidic precipitation causes the pH of
the lake to drop permanently below 5.0.

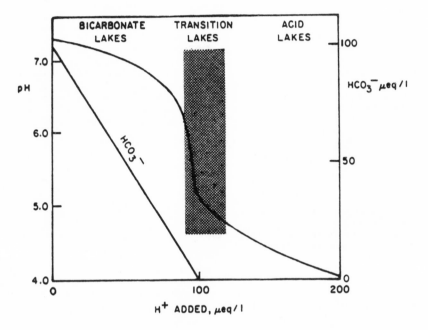

Figure 6-3.   Titration curve for bicarbonate solution at a concentration of 100 µeq/1, illustrating the acidification process.[21]

Measurement techniques are needed to monitor alkalinity levels through all seasons to differentiate between seasonal and long-term trends.[16] Researchers have investigated various parameters to predict the effect of acid precipitation on the aquatic ecosystem. These variables have included measurements of pH, alkalinity or bicarbonate concentrations, sulfate loadings, and calcium and/or magnesium ion concentrations. All of these variables have been discussed except for calcium and/or magnesium ion concentrations. Nonmarine calcium and magnesium ions result from the dissociation of carbonate. Alkalinity levels and calcium and/or magnesium ion levels will normally be found in equal amounts in unpolluted areas. Figure 6-4 shows that by measuring calcium and/or magnesium ions and alkalinity in a lake, one can predict the sulfate load to the area. Therefore, as lakes become acidified, a solution dominated by calcium and/or magnesium ions and bicarbonate ions shifts to one dominated by calcium and/or magnesium ions and sulfate.[32]

Depending on various factors, therefore, lakes exhibit a range of sensitivity to acidification. Included are the acidity of both wet and dry atmospheric deposition, the hydrology of the lake, the soil system, and the resultant chemistry of the surface water. Among these factors, the most important in assessing the impact of acidic precipitation on lake acidification appears to be the soil system and associated canopy effects relative to the lake in question. Studies indicate that the capability of a lake and its drainage basin to neutralize the acidic inputs of precipitation is largely predicted by the composition of the bedrock of the watershed.[14,17,33,34] Lakes vulnerable to acidic precipitation have been shown to have watersheds whose geological composition makes them resistant to chemical weathering.[17,33,35] Also, watersheds of acid-sensitive lakes generally have soils which are shallow in depth, low in base saturation, and naturally acidic. The cation-ion exchange capacity of these soils is poor. Weathering and ion exchange have been shown to be two crucial mechanisms by which acidity input to lakes may be neutralized.[19,33]

Bedrock geology, therefore, is generally a good indicator of the susceptibility of an area to acidification caused by acidic precipitation. Using bedrock geology as an indicator, Galloway and Cowling[35] mapped those areas of North America that have the potential for being sensitive to acidic precipitation (see Figure 6-5).

The shaded areas in Figure 6-5 indicate bedrock composed of igneous or metamorphic rock, whereas unshaded areas are calcareous or sedimentary rock. Igneous or metamorphic bedrock weathers slowly; therefore lakes in these areas would be assumed to have low alkalinity and low buffering capacity. Galloway and Cowling verified this assumption by compiling alkalinity data; lakes with low alkalinity were consistently found in regions having igneous and metamorphic bedrock.[35] Glass et al.[36] classified rock formations by their abilities to neutralize acid. Table 6-1 lists the four major types of rock formations.[36] Alkalinity levels of less than 200 μeq/liter have been associated with Types I and II rock formations. A study by the Institute of Ecology, in which alkalinity data from acid-sensitive lakes and streams in 27 states were collected, resulted in the following classification system of alkalinity values:[37]

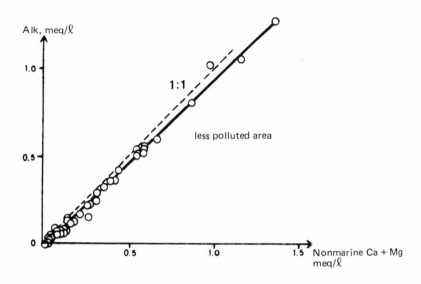

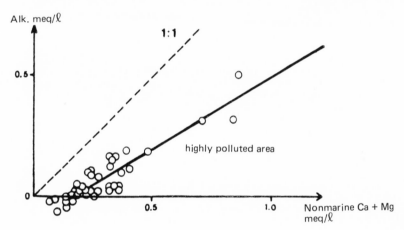

Figure 6-4.   Alkalinities and contents of calcium and magnesium
of nonmarine origin in lakes in two regions in
Sweden with different sulfur loads.[32]

Figure 6-5.   Regions in North America with lakes which may be
              sensitive to acid precipitation, using bedrock
              geology as an indicator.[35]

Class	Alkalinity (μeq/1)
1 Acidified	0
2 Extreme Sensitivity	0-39
3 Moderate Sensitivity	40-199
4 Low Sensitivity	200-499
5 Not Sensitive	≥500

TABLE 6-1.   CLASSIFICATION OF ROCK FORMATIONS ACCORDING TO THEIR ABILITY TO NEUTRALIZE ACID[36]

Type I-- Low or no buffering capacity, overlying waters very sensitive to acidification (granite/syenite, granitic gneisses, quartz sandstones, or equivalents)

Type II-- Medium-to-low buffering capacity, acidification restricted to first and second order streams and small lakes (sandstones, shales, conglomerates, high grade metamorphic to intermediate volcanic rock, intermediate igneous rocks, calc-silicate gneisses)

Type III--High-to-medium buffering capacity, no acidification except in cases of overland runoff in areas of frozen ground (slightly calcareous, low grade intermediate to mafic volcanic, ultramafic, glassy volcanic rocks)

Type IV-- "Infinite" buffering capacity, no acid precipitation effect of any kind (highly fossiliferous sediments or metamorphic equivalants, limestones, dolostones)

Although bedrock geology is a good indicator of susceptibility of an area to acidification, other factors exert an influence as well. As an example, there are areas in Maine with granite bedrock, which commonly have a low capacity for buffering, where lakes have not become acidified despite receiving precipitation with an average pH of about 4.3. It is believed that acidification has not occurred because drainage basins feeding these lakes contain lime-bearing till and marine clay. Small quantities of limestone in a drainage basin can apparently exert a strong influence on water quality in areas that would otherwise be assumed susceptible to acidic precipitation. Attempts to classify regions by sensitivity to acidic precipitation must take into account the potential buffering capacity of rock mixtures (bedrock geology) and the types of soils overlying the rock formations; as the soils do not necessarily have the same composition as the bedrock below. The soils cation exchange capacity and the ability to retain sulfates are good indicators of an area's sensitivity to acid precipitation. The flushing of sulfates from low sulfate retention soils has been associated with increased acidity.[26,38] The cation exchange capacity, which is defined as the capacity of soil to absorb and hold hydrogen ions or their equivalent, and the corresponding level of soil sensitivity are listed in Table 6-2.[36]

TABLE 6-2. SOIL SENSITIVITY TO ACID PRECIPITATION[a,36]

Sensitivity	Cation exchange capacity (CEC)[b] meq/100 g	Other relevant conditions
Nonsensitive	Any value or >15.4	Free carbonate present or subject to frequent flooding None
Slightly sensitive	6.2 ≤ CEC ≤ 15.4	Free carbonates absent; not subject to frequent flooding
Sensitive	<6.2	Free carbonates absent; not subject to frequent flooding

[a]Sensitivity is predicted from the chemical characteristics of the top 25 cm of soil and cation input.

[b]CEC is the fraction of exchangeable cations that can be leached.

It must be emphasized that although the mechanisms of acidic input into freshwater lakes and streams have been recognized, the magnitude of the contribution of acidic precipitation to lake acidification is far from resolved. A study recently completed by the U.S. Geological Survey in New York found the evidence linking precipitation acidity and stream flow quality in nine water basins to be inconclusive using data compiled from 1965.[39] Many studies have emphasized the complex nature of the interactions between precipitation and resultant water quality. Some authors caution that water quality effects, i.e., acidification, usually attributed directly to the input of acidic precipitation, could possibly be the result of lithospheric or ecosystem changes not caused by acid deposition.[40] Some European investigators assign a secondary role to acidic precipitation in water quality changes. Rosenqvist concluded that the acidity of soil leachate and resulting acidic water was a factor determined more by patterns of agricultural land use than by acidic precipitation.[41] This theory has been discounted by the work of Drablös et al. in Norway.[42,43] Watersheds with and without changing land-use patterns were shown over several years to become acidified at equal rates. Other investigators also maintain that acidic precipitation is the causative factor.[44]

These differences remain to be resolved, and a complete assessment of the magnitude of the effects of acidic precipitation on freshwater quality is needed. This assessment requires detailed modeling as well as field and laboratory investigation. The study would have to consider all other factors potentially responsible, including the impacts of changing land use patterns, agricultural fertilizer runoff, and waste treatment plant effluents. Such a study would also require detailed chemical analyses and the chemical history of the water bodies surveyed. Finally, a quantification of the extent of the determined impacts of acidic precipitation has to be attempted. Is it a truly regional problem only affecting areas particularly sensitive, or is the impact more widespread, economically or otherwise? These areas all await systematic scientific investigation.

Effects on Fish ✓

The death of fish in acidified freshwater lakes and streams has been more thoroughly studied, both in the laboratory and in the field, than any other aspect of lake and stream acidification. Various factors that affect the tolerance of fish to acidic waters have been identified, among which are species, strain, age, and size of the fish and physical factors including temperature, season, and hydrology.[1] Species of fish vary in their tolerance to low pH. Among the salmonids, rainbow trout appear to be most sensitive, salmon are next, and brown and brook trout are least sensitive.[1,45] These data are based on experiments conducted with fish maintained at constant pH. Data are not presently available on species' response to transient pH changes such as spring snow melt surges.

Strains of the same species have demonstrated differing survival times either through variation in acclimative ability or genetics. Laboratory data reveal that older fish are more tolerant than those which are younger.[1,46] The sensitivity of fish eggs has also been shown to vary with species.[1]

Laboratory studies have indicated that the higher the water temperature, the shorter the survival time. Survival of a species has also been found to vary with the season. Thus, acid episodes occurring at differing times of the year or at different water temperatures may differ in toxic effects.[1]

Chemical factors also influence fish survival in acidic waters. These factors include the ionic composition of the water, synergism or antagonism of toxic ions, and the presence of toxic organics. Table 6-3 presents a summary of effects of pH changes on fish (adapted from Reference 47).

The decline of fish populations in acidified lakes and streams has been reported in Scandinavia,[29,48-53] Canada,[54] and more recently in the United States.[30] Although the disappearance of fish populations in Scandinavia was initially reported as long as 50 years ago, the rate of such disappearances has sharply increased during the past 15 years.[29] Surveys conducted in southern Norway indicate large portions of the fish populations, especially trout and salmon, have been adversely affected by acidification.[29] Similar changes have been observed in Sweden.[50,53] Beamish and co-workers have documented the acidification of lakes and the loss of fish in Sudbury, Ontario.[23,54] Surveys conducted in New York State's Adirondack Mountains[55,56] have indicated an increase in the number of lakes and streams with acid pH (less than 5) over time with reduced fish populations.

TABLE 6-3. SUMMARY OF EFFECTS OF pH CHANGES IN FISH[a]

pH	Effects
11.5 - 11.0	Lethal to all fish.
11.5 - 10.5	Lethal to salmonids; lethal to carp, tench, goldfish, pike if prolonged.
10.5 - 10.0	Roach, salmonids survive short periods, but lethal if prolonged.
10.0 - 9.5	Slowly lethal to salmonids.
9.5 - 9.0	Harmful to salmonids, perch if persistent.
9.0 - 6.5	Harmless to most fish.
6.5 - 6.0	Significant reductions in egg hatchability and growth in brook trout under continued exposure.
6.0 - 5.0	Rainbow trout do not occur. Small populations of relatively few fish species found. Fathead minnow spawning reduced. Molluscs rare. Declines in a salmonid fishery can be expected. High aluminum concentrations may be present in certain waters causing fish toxicity.
5.0 - 4.5	Harmful to salmonid eggs and fry; harmful to common carp.
4.5 - 4.0	Harmful to salmonids, tench, bream, roach, goldfish, common carp; resistance increases with age. Pike can breed, but perch, bream, and roach cannot.
4.0 - 3.5	Lethal to salmonids. Roach, tench, perch, pike survive.
3.5 - 3.0	Toxic to most fish; some plants and invertebrates survive.

[a]Adapted from Reference 47.

Upon reanalysis of original data, one study which attempted to correlate a decrease in pH with decreasing fish populations found that the data provide no indication of any significant correlation between changes in pH and changes in number of fish species.[57] This study goes on to refute the potential link between alleged trends in decreasing pH and decreasing numbers of fish species and acid precipitation. Furthermore, it concludes that there is some documentation that, to a limited degree, past and present use of pesticides, particularly DDT and methoxychlor, are having a detrimental effect upon fish stocks in the Adirondack region. The toxic effects of these compounds tend to vary with temperature, age of fish, duration of exposure, persistence of pesticide, and the ability of the pesticide to bioaccumulate.

Although the effects attributed to the extensive past usage of DDT should continue to diminish with the passage of time, the present use of methoxychlor appears to remain a problem. The magnitude of pesticide effects upon fish stocks cannot be quantified without further research. However, it appears that pesticide effects as well as decreased stocking efforts and shifts in land use activity may be contributing to the decline in fish stocks in the Adirondack lakes.[57]

Field surveys in Norway,[48,52] Sweden,[50] Canada,[47] and the United States[19,55] have indicated that most fish species disappear from acidified lakes when the pH drops below 5. This is probably caused, as indicated by laboratory data, by reproductive inhibition.[19,51,52,55,58-62] Experimentation has indicated that fish eggs and fry are sensitive to acidic water.[51] Both inhibition of gonad maturation[23,58] and mortality of eggs and larvae[48,60,61] can contribute to reproductive failure in fish populations inhabiting acidified waters.

Disappearance of fish from affected bodies of water usually may be the result of two patterns. A sudden, short-term shift in pH resulting in acid shock may cause fish mortality. Sudden drops in pH could cause fish kills at pH levels above those normally toxic to fish.[31,52,61] Such pH shocks often occur in early spring when snow melt releases acidic constituents accumulated during the winter.

A gradual decrease in pH with time, rather than sudden acid shock, is a second mechanism whereby acidification of water bodies could result in elimination of fish populations. Based on field observations and laboratory experimentation, as noted above, prolonged acidity interferes with fish reproduction and spawning so that, over time, there is a decrease in fish population density and a shift in the size and age of the population to older and larger fish.[53] This pattern has been observed in Norway,[30,31] Sweden,[50] Canada,[23,54] and the United States.[30,55] It is important to note that even small increases (5 to 50 percent) in mortality of fish eggs and fry can significantly decrease fish populations and eventually bring about the extinction of the species in the affected water body.[55]

Recent studies in fish suggest that impairment of reproduction, embryonic abnormality (skeletal deformities),[63] and high embryonic mortality rates occur at pH levels below 6.5.[64,65] Embryonic morbidity and mortality appear to result from the disruption of calcium metabolism and deposition of protein in the egg cell.[64] Kennedy[65,66] studied an indigenous population of trout inhabiting a lake experimentally acidified over 3 years to a pH of 5.84. Examination of eggs prior to hatching revealed that only 6 percent contained embryos and all were anatomically malformed compared to the controls, where 92.9 percent of the eggs contained normal embryos. The authors assumed that fertilization in the study group was successful. When fish went through gametogenesis and fertilization in the acidified lake, but embryogenesis occurred in untreated water in the laboratory, only one fish experienced a 50 percent reduction in viability of eggs compared to controls.[66] Thus, it appears that the mature sex cells are more sensitive to the effects of acidification than the embryo.

The physiological mechanisms responsible for mortality of fish in acidic waters may vary in response to levels of acidity and the presence of such components as heavy metals and CO_2. At the pH levels usually encountered in acidified waters (4 to 5), disruption of osmoregulatory functions is the most likely cause of fish death.[29,55] Laboratory studies have revealed impaired sodium uptake and loss of plasma sodium and chloride in fish at the pH range present when lakes become acidified.[22,27,46,64,67-69] Blood pH also decreases resulting in a reduced capacity to transport oxygen.[25]

Though the electrolyte homeostasis of fish is upset by acidified water, it is not known how this effect relates to the permeability of the gills and/or the gills' ion exchange mechanism. In an experiment with isolated perfused rainbow trout gills exposed to acute acid stress (i.e., pH was dropped from 7.2 to 3.5), no significant effect on the transfer capacity of the gills was observed, although some vascular resistance was noted.[70] Other physiological effects of reduced pH levels are impaired energy metabolsim and altered behavioral functions, such as, hyperactivity of Gulf Killifish during normal diurnal active periods in water at pH 5.0 and 4.0.[71]

Studies in the Adirondacks have indicated that mobilization of toxic metals, such as, nickel, manganese, cadmium, zinc, and especially aluminum, is an additional factor that may contribute to mortality of fish at low pH values.[16,19,45,47,63] Experiments conducted to determine the pH levels at which lead is released from the sediments at two lakes in the Adirondacks found significant lead desorption at pH values of less than 3.0 and less than 2.0; acidity levels below those most commonly found in monitoring results.[72] Soil leaching and mineral weathering by acidic precipitation may result in high concentrations of aluminum in surface and ground waters. Also, increased transport of aluminum into aquatic systems may affect phosphorous availability.[73] Aluminum has been observed to be toxic at pH levels as low as 4.0. Aluminum and hydrogen ions together appear to cause gill damage and the resulting disruption of osmoregulation by clogging the gills with irritation-induced mucus discharges. Severe respiratory distress may ensue.[68,69]

Manganese is also believed to be mobilized by acidic precipitation, but its toxic effects at low pH, if any, are unknown.[22] Several studies in Sweden,[74] Canada,[75,76] and the United States,[75] have revealed high mercury concentrations in fish from acidified regions. Tomlinson[75] has reported that precipitation is the source of high mercury levels in the Bell

River area of Canada. The mercury content of precipitation was between 100 and 200 parts per trillion (ppt) and occasionally values were measured as high as 300 ppt. The results of at least one study suggest that acid stress and terrestrial impacts of mercury on several lakes have enhanced mercury uptake in fish.[16,77] Elevated mercury levels in fish or freshwater lakes could pose potential concern for both aquatic species and human health impacts if large numbers of fish were consumed. However, studies done to date are far from comprehensive, and reports of results are still controversial.

Effects on Plant Life and the Food Chain

Elimination or reduction of a fish population is the most obvious biological impact associated with acidification of freshwater lakes and streams. Less obvious, but of great importance, however, are the effects of acidification on other aquatic organisms. Organisms at all trophic levels within the food chain may be affected. Species can be reduced in number and variety, and primary production and decomposition may be impaired with a resultant disruption of the entire ecosystem.

Within the aquatic ecosystem, energy moves along two pathways, the grazing food chain and the detrital food chain.[78,79] The green plants, the primary producers (phytoplankton, mosses, algae, etc.), are the food base of the grazing food chain where plants are eaten by animals and animals by other animals. Decomposers (bacteria, fungi, some protozoa, etc.) use dead plant and animal matter as food and release minerals and other compounds back into the environment. Thus, in the detrital food chain, the base is dead organic matter. Disruption of either of these pathways could result in a large-scale disruption within the ecosystem.

Changes in pH have caused changes in the composition and structure of the aquatic plant communities involved in primary production. Experimental lowering of the pH of lakes studied in Ontario resulted in changes in species' composition and in the standing crop and production of the phytoplankton community. In these lakes, for example, the species of Chlorophyta (green algae) were reduced in number from 26 to 5, the Chrysophyta (golden brown) from 22 to 5, and the Cyanophyta (blue-green) from 22 species to 10.[25,80,81] In addition, the relative abundance of the algal flora also changed. Differences in nutrient levels (phosphorous and nitrogen) were not responsible for these changes in primary productivity; acidity appeared to be the limiting factor.

A study of phytoplankton populations in 115 lakes in Sweden supports the findings of the Ontario study.[29] The species composition of lakes with a pH less than 5 lacked diversity, and the size of the population was restricted.[50] Similar data were reported in a regional survey of 55 lakes in southern Norway.[31]

As discussed above, aluminum is leached into surface water by acid precipitation. In lakes, aluminum precipitates humates, which are natural complex salts of humic acid, the acid component of the decomposition of humus. Lakes become transparent as humates are precipitated allowing increased light penetration and increased phytoplankton production deep in the water column.[32] Therefore, while the number of species is decreased due to acidification, phytoplankton biomass and production may remain the same.[63,82]

Acidification of lakes also results in reduction in productivity and species diversity of the macrophyte community. Studies of macrophyte communities in six lakes in Sweden have indicated that in five of the six lakes, Lobelia communities are being replaced by Sphagnum.[83,84] The abundance of Sphagnum mats covering the lake bottoms, which chokes out Lobelia, has been positively correlated with decreasing pH. The consequences of the Sphagnum occupying increasing areas of these lake bottoms are several. Basic ions (e.g., Ca^{++}) that are necessary for biological production are bound to the moss tissue because of its strong ion exchange capacity and are, therefore, unavailable because the Sphagnum filamentous algae such as Mougestia proliferate. This has been verified under laboratory conditions at pH 4.0.[25,29,32]

In contrast to the study in Ontario, Hendrey et al.[82] found that a decrease in number of species could not be proven directly causal to a decreased pH. They suggest that aluminum toxicity or aluminum removing inorganic phosphorus could account for the elimination of some species. Thus, the biomass and productivity appear to be controlled by nutrient levels of phosphorous rather than hydrogen ion concentration.[86] Hendrey attributed an increased biomass in acidified waters to the lowered activities or removal of predators.[82,85] Müller[81] had similar results for the accumulation of algae, but this study showed the same biomass at all hydrogen ion concentrations.

Heavy growths of these filamentous algae and mosses have also been reported in Norwegian streams affected by acidification. These effects have been observed in artificial stream channels in which water and naturally seeded algae from an acidified brook (pH 4.3 to 5.5) were used. Lowering the pH to 4.0 increased algae growth when compared to controls.[83,87]

There appear to be many contradictions on the trends of primary production and biomass in acidified aquatic ecosystems. Very little quantitative information is available and most data are collected from experiments conducted in laboratories where artificial acidification occurred abruptly versus a quasi-steady state condition found in the environment.[85] Generally, though, reductions in the diversity of the plant communities in lakes and streams and subsequent disruption in primary production reduce the supply and variety of food and, therefore, the energy flow within the affected ecosystem. Changes in these communities also reduce the supply of nutrients. These factors limit the number of organisms that can exist within the ecosystem.

Effects on Microorganisms and Decomposition

Microbiological activity in lakes affects the rates of decomposition and the accumulation of organic matter in aquatic ecosystems. Organic matter (detritus) in lakes plays a major role in the energetics of lake ecosystems.[14] The biochemical transformations of detrital organic matter by microbial metabolism are fundamental to nutrient cycling and energy flux within the system, and the trophic relationships within lake ecosystems are almost entirely dependent on detrital structure.[14]

Bacteria are central to the food relationships in a lake. Experiment has shown that the populations of decomposer organisms change from predominantly bacteria to predominantly fungi as pH is lowered.[29,63,83,88] Interference with nutrient cycling through disruption of the detrital trophic structure could, therefore, be a major result of changes in microdecomposer populations caused by acidification.[83] Accumulation of organic litter observed in acidified Swedish lakes, produced by extensive mats of fungal growth, seals off nutrients that would otherwise be available if normal decomposition occurred.[89]

Recent studies indicate that microbiota are unaffected by acidification and the resulting increased concentrations of hydrogen ions.[25,81] Schindler et al.[25] found no evidence that decomposition of organic detritus was reduced when the pH of a lake was lowered from 6.7 to 5.7 by the addition of sulfuric acid. In fact, the number of sulfate-reducing bacteria increased with the lowered pH and increased sulfate present in the water. It was suggested that the sulfate-reducing bacteria may partially counteract the effects of acidification.[25]

The effects of acidification on the microorganism community of aquatic ecosystems has received insufficient study as is evident from the contradicting results from studies discussed above.

Effects on Other Aquatic Organisms

Invertebrate communities are also affected by acidification of freshwater lakes and streams. Surveys conducted at sites in Scandinavia and North America have shown that acidified lakes and streams have fewer species of benthic invertebrates than do waters with higher pH.[31,90-92] Zooplankton analyzed from samples collected from 84 Swedish lakes showed that acidification had caused limitation of many species and led to simplification of zooplankton communities.[50] The distributions of crustacean zooplankton in acidified lakes in Ontario were shown to be strongly related to pH. As acidity increased, the complexities of zooplankton communities decreased.[82,93] At a pH of about 5, an abrupt change from complex to simple zooplankton communities occurred. The Daphnia species and the fairy shrimp Branchinecta paludosa are very sensitive to small declines below pH 5.5. Daphnia magna and Daphnia middendurfiana are susceptible to fungal infections at low pH levels.[94] Since heavy metals are negligible at these pH levels, the observed effects in these organisms have been implicated directly to the toxicity of the hydrogen ion. Reduced diversity in zooplankton communities affects the food supply and thus causes changes in the community structure of organisms dependent on the zooplankton as a food source.

Gastropods are also affected by acidic water conditions. In a survey of Norwegian lakes no snails were found when the pH was less than 5.2.[29,95-97] The amphipod Gammarus lacustris, an important element in the diet of trout in Norwegian lakes where it occurs, is not found in lakes with a pH below 6.0.[29,83,96,97] Experiments have revealed that adults of this species cannot tolerate 2 days of exposure to a pH of 5.0.[29,83] The short-term acidification which often occurs during spring snow melt could eliminate these species from small lakes.

The tolerance of aquatic invertebrates to low pH varies during their life cycle. Many invertebrates are unaffected by increased hydrogen ion concentration.[81] Adult insects such as mayflies, stoneflies, and some trueflies,[45] seem to be particularly sensitive at emergence. In general, although there is broad variation, available data indicate a pH value of 5.5 or higher is necessary for 50 percent viable emergence.[98] Insect larvae that inhabit sediments survive well in acidified lakes.[16]

Amphibians may be the species most directly affected by acidic precipitation. They may be affected by acid stress in the same way as fish.[63] The reproductive habits of amphibians make them especially susceptible to the pH changes of the ponds where they lay their eggs. Frogs, toads, and most salamanders in the United States lay eggs in ponds.[99] In addition, many species breed in shallow, temporary pools that are strongly affected by the pH of the precipitation that fills them.[99]

Frog embryos have been observed to develop abnormally at pH 3.7 to 4.6, and pH less than 4.0 is usually lethal.[100] A pH lower than 6.0 can inhibit the development and increase egg mortality of spotted salamanders.[101] Amphibian embryos are more sensitive to acidity in the later stages of development versus the initial cleavage of the embryo. The acidity appears to cause teratogenic effects by damaging the superficial tissues of the embryo.[102] Based on available data, it appears that reproduction in amphibians, as in fish, is primarily affected first when pH is lowered.[103]

Frogs and salamanders are important predators of invertebrates (mosquitoes, etc.) and they themselves are important prey for higher trophic levels in the ecosystem. Increasing acidity in freshwater habitats results in shifts in species, populations, and communities. Any specie that depends on aquatic organisms (plant or animal) for a portion of their food will be affected. A summary of the changes most likely to occur in aquatic biota with decreasing pH is presented in Table 6-4.[104] Table 6-5 lists effects of decreasing pH on aquatic organisms.[104]

IMPACTS OF ACIDIC PRECIPITATION ON TERRESTRIAL ECOSYSTEMS

Assessing the impacts of acid precipitation on terrestrial ecosystems is extremely difficult. In aquatic systems, it has been possible to measure pH changes and correlate the observed effects on aquatic species with the pH shift. To date, it appears that no component of terrestrial ecosystems is as sensitive to the impacts, if any, of acidic precipitation as is a poorly buffered aquatic system. In fact, at present, it has not been possible to observe or measure changes in natural terrestrial ecosystems that could be unequivocally attributed to acidic precipitation;[105] however, such changes have been observed under controlled laboratory and field conditions.[106] Therefore, it may be postulated that such effects could occur. Although this postulation is somewhat tenuous, assuming as it does extrapolation from the laboratory to the natural situation, it is probably prudent to view these potential effects as possible, even as a worst case. Such worst-case assumptions are frequently made to assess potential impacts on health or the environment, especially where the capability of the observer to measure the

TABLE 6-4.   CHANGES IN AQUATIC BIOTA THAT COULD OCCUR
WITH INCREASING ACIDITY[104]

1.   Bacterial decomposition is reduced and fungi dominate saprotrophic
communities. Organic debris accumulates rapidly.

2.   The ciliate fauna is greatly inhibited.

3.   Nutrient salts are taken up by plants tolerant of low pH (mosses,
filamentous algae) and by fungi. Thick mats of these materials may
develop, inhibiting sediment-to-water nutrient exchange and choking out
other aquatic plants.

4.   Phytoplankton species diversity, biomass, and production are reduced.

5.   Zooplankton and benthic invertebrate species diversity and biomass are
reduced. Remaining benthic fauna consists of tubificids and Chironomus
(midge) larvae in the sediments. Some tolerant species of stoneflies and
mayflies persist as does the alderfly. Air-breathing bugs
(water-boatman, backswimmer, water strider) may become abundant.

6.   Fish populations are reduced or eliminated.

7.   Changes in populations and communities occur at virtually all trophic
levels.

TABLE 6-5. SUMMARY OF EFFECTS ON AQUATIC ORGANISMS WITH DECREASING pH[104]

pH range	Effects
8.0-6.0	• Long-term changes of less than 0.5 pH units in the range 8.0 to 6.0 are very likely to alter the biotic composition of freshwaters to some degree. The significance of these slight changes is, however, not great.
	• A decrease of 0.5 to 1.0 pH units in the range 8.0 to 6.0 may cause detectable alterations in community composition. Productivity of competing organisms will vary. Some species will be eliminated.
6.0-5.5	• Decreasing pH from 6.0 to 5.5 will cause a reduction in species numbers and, among remaining species, significant alterations in ability to withstand stress. Reproduction of some salamander species is impaired.
5.5-5.0	• Below pH 5.5, numbers and diversity of species will be reduced. Many species will be eliminated. Crustacean zooplankton, phytoplankton, molluscs, amphipods, most mayfly species, and many stonefly species will begin to drop out. In contrast, several pH-tolerant invertebrates will become abundant, especially the air-breathing forms (e.g., Gyrinidae, Notonctidae, Corixidae), those with tough cuticles that prevent ion losses (e.g., Sialis lutaria, and some forms that live within the sediments (Oligochaeta, Chiromomidae, and Tubificidae). Overall, invertebrate biomass will be greatly reduced.
5.0-4.5	• Below pH 5.0, decomposition of organic detritus will be severely impaired. Autochthonous and allochthonous debris will accumulate rapidly. Most fish species will be eliminated.
4.5 and below	• Below pH 4.5 all of the above changes will be greatly exacerbated. Lower limit for many algal species.

effect is limited by the complexity of the natural situation or because the impact is only fully realized after a long time (e.g., decades).

Effects on Vegetation

Chemical species in the atmosphere reach plant surfaces through wet and dry deposition. Although sulfates, nitrates, and other water-soluble species may be assimilated through plant leaves, it has generally been assumed that the free hydrogen ion concentration in acidic precipitation is the component most likely to cause direct, harmful effects on vegetation.[107] Experimental studies have supported this assumption, but, as noted above, there have been no reports of foliar symptoms on field-grown vegetation in the continental United States that could be attributed to exposure to ambient acidic precipitation.[108] The most frequently reported response of vegetation to experimental exposure of simulated acidic rain is the formation of lesions or areas of dead tissue on leaf surfaces.[108-110] A large percentage of the leaf area may exhibit such lesions after repeated exposures to simulated acid rain at pH levels of 3.7, 3.0, 2.5, and 2.3.[111,112] Pinto bean leaves exhibited pronounced leaf injury.[111,113,114] Most leaf injury caused by exposure to simulated acid rain has been observed to occur on expanding or recently expanding leaves.

A recent study (May 1981) measured the effects of acid precipitation on 28 major crops. Crops were grown under controlled environmental conditions (field chambers) and exposed to simulated (sulfuric) acid rain of pH; 3.0, 3.5, and 4.0, in addition to a control rain of pH 5.6. Injury to foliage and roots and effects on yield of edible portion were then determined.[115] The marketable yield production (statistically significant) was inhibited for the radish, pepper, carrot, mustard greens, and broccoli; stimulated for the tomato, green pepper, strawberry, alfalfa, orchardgrass, corn, and timothy; ambiguously affected for the potato; and, no effects were reported for the other 15 crops. The part of plant marketed and the species of plant grown will affect the impacts of acid rain on yield. Generally, dicotyledons were more susceptible to foliar injury from simulated acid rain than monocotyledons, but this did not necessarily affect marketable yields. Observed inhibited root growth was also not associated with a decreased marketable yield. For example, at pH 3.0, the roots of tomatoes weighed 15 percent less than controls, while the fruit weighed 30 percent more than controls. Though the study was conducted for a single growing season with a particular soil, the effects of acid rain appear to be the result of competing stimulatory and inhibitory effects. The results imply that an optimum rain pH or sulfate concentration may exist for maximum productivity.[115]

It should be mentioned that exposure of crops to pH less than 3.5 represents a situation which probably would not exist in crop-growing areas.

In leaves injured by simulated acidic rain exposure, collapse and distortion of cells on the upper leaf surface is frequently followed by further injury until all leaf surfaces are affected.[116] Although foliar injury is commonly observed, reductions in growth and crop yield have not been unequivocally associated with leaf injury. In addition, foliar response to exposure to acidic precipitation has been shown to be dependent on numerous factors. Duration and frequency of exposure, acid content and size of rain drops, and the intensity of rainfall all influence the development and extent of foliar symptoms.[117] Environmental conditions during and after precipitation may affect the response of plants. Fresh rain deposited on leaves with previously deposited dry particles results in concentrations of elements in solution orders of magnitude above the levels of constituents in the rain alone. Decomposition of some components of the leaf cuticle, factors affecting particle retention on leaf surfaces, and the interactions of pollutants are critical parameters in the evaluation of the effects of acid rain on vegetation.[107] Variation in such conditions could alter physiological processes, the amount of liquid remaining on leaf surfaces, the rate of evaporation after the rainfall has stopped, etc.[117] Recognition and appreciation of these variables accentuate the difficulties in extrapolating laboratory results to the natural condition. Table 6-6 summarizes available results on direct injury to vegetation by exposure to simulated acidic precipitation.

Acidic precipitation can also cause indirect effects on plants and vegetation, some of them beneficial. Wood and Bormann reported an increase in needle length and the weight of seedlings of Eastern white pine with increasing acidity of simulated precipitation.[109] Investigators at the Argonne National Laboratory have reported no harmful effects on soybean productivity following exposure to simulated acidic rain. In fact, they observed a positive effect on productivity as reflected by seed growth.[125] Table 6-7 summarizes the results of experiments on the effects of simulated acidic precipitation on field grown crops where only slight, none or positive effects were observed.[110]

Most vegetation requires a symbiotic association with soil fungi for adequate mineral uptake.[105,126] Shriner[127] reported on the effects of acidic precipitation on host-parasite interactions. Simulated acid rain with a pH of 3.4 inhibited the development of bean rust. Response of other diseases such as halo blight of bean seedlings was observed to vary depending on the time in the disease cycle during which simulated acidic rain was applied. An area requiring research is the potential effects of acid precipitation on foliar susceptibility of fungal attack and of roots to infection by fungal pathogens.

The effects of acidic precipitation on forest tree growth have been investigated. Studies have been conducted using simulated acid rain and by comparing development of the rings in the past with present ring formation.[128] Jonsson and Sundberg[129] used this tree ring method to analyze forest growth in southern Sweden from 1896 to 1965. They report a 2 to 7 percent decrease in growth between 1950 and 1965, which they attribute to increases in acidification. Professor Folke Andersson, Swedish University of Agriculture, has reported that these ring studies have recently been updated, and the trends that were previously reported are no longer observed. Studies in Norway and North America could not corroborate their findings, however.[119,130,131] Tree ring chronology of pine tree species in New Jersey were studied for 25 years and compared to pH levels in a nearby stream. Eliminating factors such as drought, fire, pests, and atmospheric oxidants from consideration, abnormally slow growth rates had a strong statistical

TABLE 6-6. SUMMARY OF DIRECT FOLIAR INJURY FOLLOWING EXPOSURE TO
SIMULATED ACIDIC PRECIPITATION

Effect	Receptor	pH value	Reference
Foliar lesions	Eastern white pine	2.3	112
Foliar aberrations, decrease in growth	Bean	2.5	118
Foliar lesions, plasmolysis of cells, reduction in dry weight	Bean	2.5	112
Foliar necrotic spots	Scots pine birch (Bethula pubescens Ehrb)	2.5	119
Necrotic lesions and chlorotic areas in leaves	Soybean	3.0	120
Foliar lesions, decrease in growth	Yellow birch (Betula alleghaniensis Britt)	3.1	121
Foliar lesions	Bean, sunflower	3.1	111
Bifacial necrosis	Oak (Quercus phellos)	3.2	122
Foliar lesions	Hybrid poplar	3.4	119
Foliar lesions	Sunflower	3.4	108
Reduction in dry weight	Bean	4.0	123
Reduction in dry weight	Mustard greens	3.0	124
Reduction in dry weight	Broccoli	3.0	124
Reduction in dry weight	Radishes	3.0	124
Foliar lesions, reduction in dry weight	Spinach	3.0	124
Decrease in growth	Mustard greens, radishes	3.5-4.0	124

TABLE 6-7.   RESULTS OF RECENT EXPERIMENTS ON EFFECTS OF SIMULATED ACIDIC PRECIPITATION
ON FIELD-GROWN CROPS[110]

Laboratory	Crop	Effect	pH
Argonne National Laboratory (rain and simulated rain)	Soybean "Wells"	No effect on seed mass Increase in seed size No foliar symptoms or effects on growth	3.1
Boyce Thompson Institute (simulated rain only)	Soybean "Beeson" and "Williams"	Decreased growth, yield, and seed quality (germination) Increased yield No foliar symptoms	2.8 (high ambient ozone) 2.8, 3.4 (low ozone) 2.8, 3.4, 4.0 (low ozone)
Brookhaven National Laboratory (rain and simulated rain)	Soybean "Amsoy"	Decreased yield and quality (protein content), foliar symptoms	2.3, 2.7
Cornell University (rain and simulated rain)	Tomato, pepper, snap-bean, cucumber	No effect on growth or yield, reduced quality	3.0
North Carolina State University (rain and simulated rain)	Soybean "Davis"	Slight foliar injury No effect on growth or yeild	2.8 2.8, 3.2, 4.0

relationship with stream pH.[132] Conversely, simulated acidic precipitation was observed to increase the growth of pine saplings in experiments conducted in Norway.[128] Saplings in test plots watered with acidic rain of pH 3.0, 2.5, and 2.0 grew more rapidly than did control trees. Additional research is necessary to determine if acid rain has an adverse effect on the growth of trees.

The American Electric Power Company funded the University of Vermont to study acid rain and forest productivity.[133] The 3-year study concluded that evidence indicates acid precipitation may be adversely effecting forest productivity even though much of the evidence is circumstantial and large data gaps exist. The study was conducted on Camels Hump, a high peak in the northern Green Mountains of Vermont. This area has been extensively studied since the mid-1960's and researchers have noted a nearly 50 percent decline of spruce trees in the forest. After discounting normal causes of tree death such as insect infestation, long-term population cycles or climatic changes, acid rain appears to be the prime causative agent. The University of Vermont also conducted experiments to demonstrate declines in plant growth from the synergistic effects of acid rain and heavy metals. Fungi that exist in a symbiotic association with tree roots were found to decline in laboratory tests and have been absent from young roots examined on Camels Hump. In another concomitant study, aluminum content in tree cores was measured. Aluminum has been implicated in the death of young roots of trees that supply the tree with water. The study indicates that the aluminum content changed little from 1900 to 1950, but increased thereafter; the period associated with the start of acid rain.[133]

Among other effects of acidic precipitation on terrestrial systems are increased leaching of chemical elements from exposed plant surfaces and/or forest soils. Leaching of organic and inorganic materials from vegetation to the soil is part of the natural functioning of terrestrial ecosystems and forms an integral phase in nutrient cycling. Plant leachates affect soil texture, aeration, permeability, and ion-exchange capacity. These leachates influence the number and behavior of soil microorganisms and thereby soil fertility and the immunity of plants to pests and disease.[134]

Research to date on the effects of acidic precipitation on the leaching of chemical constituents from vegetation has resulted in equivocal and often contradictory results. It has been demonstrated that acidic precipitation can increase the leaching of various cations and organic carbon from the tree canopy.[105,119,135,136] There is a wide diversity of leaf and cell permeability responses to various ions after acid precipitation. One study found an increased rate of nutrient leaching at increased pH levels correlated with a lower adaxial leaf resistance during leaf development.[136] Foliar losses of nutrient cations from bean plants and maple seedlings were found to increase as acidity of the artificial mist to which they were exposed increased. However, in experiments using Norway spruce, researchers found no evidence of change in the foliar cation content although increased leaching was observed.[128] It has been stated that increased leaching of nutrients from foliage can actually accelerate their uptake by plants.[134] The impact of the increased leaching of chemical substances from vegetation by acidic precipitation is still unresolved.[105]

Increased acidic precipitation may cause a decrease in the fertility of forest soils. Laboratory studies have shown that leaching of the important nutrients--potassium, magnesium, and calcium--is accelerated by increased acidity.[137] However, other investigators contend that soil fertility may be increased as a result of deposition of nitrates and sulfates (typical components of chemical fertilizers) in acidic rain. Finally, another major uncertainty in estimating effects of increased acidic precipitation on forest fertility and productivity is the as-yet unquantified capability of forest soils to buffer against leaching by hydrogen ions.

Many researchers have concluded that acid rain affects vegetation by altering the nutrient conditions of the ecosystem. Forest productivity can be increased, decreased or remain the same depending on the site, nutrient status, and the duration and rate of inputs. Short-term accumulation of sulfur and nitrogen have been observed to have beneficial effects on vegetation, whereas the long-term effects of accumulation and cycling of these nutrients is less understood. The long-term effect of sulfur input is least understood due to the broad plateau between sulfur sufficiency and toxicity and the ability of excess sulfur as sulfate to exist in the forest ecosystem without apparent detriment. A critical level must exist between nutrient sufficiency and toxicity, where heavy metals accumulate, cation depletion occurs, and hydrogen ion concentrations increase.[138]

Effects on Soil

Another area that suffers from limited investigation and equivocal results is the effects or consequences of increased acidity on soil and the subterranean ecosystem. Effects have been postulated, but the picture is far from clear. It is especially difficult to factor out the impacts of acid precipitation on soil, if any, as compared to natural or anthropogenic mechanisms resulting in soil acidification, such as agricultural fertilization.[139] Some authors contend that acid precipitation inputs to date are low compared to the possible influences of agricultural fertilization or liming practices.[140-142]

Soils may be exposed to: (1) the process of modified cation exchange, which results from the penetration of acidic precipitation, resulting in the losses of such species as Ca^{++}, Mg^{++}, K^+, and Na^+; and, (2) the collection of metals that could result in soil contamination and potential phytotoxicity. As water containing H^+ moves through soil, some of the hydrogen cations replace adsorbed exchangeable cations such as Ca^{++}, Mg^{++}, K^+, and Na^+, which may eventually be leached into ground water.[138] All soils are not equally susceptible to acidification. The buffering capacity of soil depends on mineral content, texture, structure, pH, base saturaton, salt content, and soil permeability. Buffering capacity is greatest in soils derived from sedimentary rocks, especially those containing carbonates, and least in soils derived from crystalline rocks such as granites and quartzites.[143] The spodosol, ultisol, and inceptisol soil classes have a low alkalinity potential and are thus more sensitive to the effects of acid rain.[34] A summary of soil class characteristics is provided in Table 6-8.[34] Soil buffering capacity varies widely in different regions of

TABLE 6-8. GENERAL PROPERTIES AND USES OF SOIL CLASSES[34]

Soil class	Relative age	Characteristics
Inceptisols	Relatively new	Often formed from volcanic ash Found in steep lands and depressions Extensive leaching Poorly drained, fine sand Resistant parent material Low organic matter
Spodosols	Intermediate	Significant weatherability (carbonate leaching) with replacement of exchangeable cations (Ca, Mg, K, Na) Accumulation of Fe, Al pH less than 5 not uncommon Low base status High moisture content
Alfisols	Old	High clay and moisture content High cation and exchangeability Plant nutrients Medium to high base status
Ultisols	Oldest	Extensive clay content Extensive leaching leads to severe removal of bases Tendency toward large slopes and low fertility Tendency toward water saturation

the country. The sensitivity of different soils based on pH, texture, and calcite content is summarized in Table 6-9.[144]

Few comprehensive studies have been conducted to assess the potential impacts of acidic precipitation on cation exchange and leaching of nutrients. Those that have been conducted tend to concur that increases in acidification of precipitation lead to reduced cation exchange capacity and increased rates of mineral loss (especially Ca^{++}).[137,138,144-146] A study in model forest plots with a hardwood canopy and a litter layer monitored water samples below the litter layer and from 20 centimeters and 1 meter depths below the surface of the soil after simulated sulfuric acid rain (pH 4.0, 3.5, 3.0) was applied. At the 20 cm level the rain did not cause a significant increase in sulfate concentration until the ability of the soil to adsorb sulfate was exhausted, about 1 to 2 years. Concentrations of Mg^{++}, Ca^{++}, and K^+ were elevated simultaneously with increased sulfate levels. No acid rain related effects were observed at 1 meter after 2.5 years. The results indicate that acidic precipitation can alter the chemical composition of the root zone within a few years.[147] Other studies have found significant depletion of cation exchange capacity and declining quantities of Ca^{++}, Mg^{++}, and K^+.[21,22,146,148]

TABLE 6-9. THE SENSITIVITY TO ACID PRECIPITATION BASED ON BUFFER CAPACITY AGAINST pH CHANGE, RETENTION OF H^+, AND ADVERSE EFFECTS ON SOILS[144]

| | | Noncalcareous | | |
	Calcareous soils	Clays pH >6	Sandy soils pH >6	Cultivated soils pH >5	Acid soils pH >5
Buffering	Very high	High	Low	High	Moderate
H^+ retention	Maximal	Great	Great	Great	Slight
Adverse effects	None	Moderate	Considerable	None-slight	Slight

Although the potential effects of acidic precipitation on soil could be long lasting, researchers note that many counteracting forces could mitigate the overall final effects, including the release of new cations to exchange sites by weathering or through nutrient recycling by vegetation.[149] Leaching of soil nutrients is efficiently inhibited by vegetation growing in and on the soil. Plant roots frequently absorb nutrients in amounts larger than the plants require. Large amounts of these nutrients will be deposited later on the soil surface as litter or as leachate from the vegetation canopy.[128] Mites and springtails present in soil breakdown litter and humus releasing nutrients, even under low pH conditions.[67]

Lowered soil pH can also affect the mobility and availability to plants of toxic metallic species. In general, the availability of toxic metals increases as pH decreases. Very low soil pH has been associated with the mobility of toxic aluminum compounds in soil.[138,139] Ulrich[150] has reported that aluminum released by acidified soils could, in time, reach levels that would be phytotoxic. The effects of acidification on release of toxic metals is an area that is currently receiving increased research effort. Biological processes in the soil necessary for plant growth could also potentially be affected by soil acidification, including nitrogen fixation.[128] However, there are few data available in this area.

Soil microorganisms are important to the ecosystem because: (1) they carry out reactions essential to plant growth; (2) they carry out biochemical processes below ground which contribute to soil structure for root development and soil aeration; (3) they decompose organic matter releasing nutrients; and, (4) they have biochemical processes that destroy synthetic manmade pollutants.[151] It is difficult to generalize about potential effects of soil acidification on microorganisms. Many microbial processes that are essential for plant growth are suppressed as acidity increases; however, the inhibition observed in one soil at a given pH may not be seen at the same pH in another soil.[151,152] Also, laboratory studies performed to date have typically tested soils maintained for short periods of time at very low pH. Brookhaven National Laboratory studied the effects of acid rain on microbial processes in forest soil at a pH of 3.0. The results showed decreased rates of organic matter decomposition, nitrification, denitrification, ammonification, nitrogen fixation by free-living bacteria, bacterial enzyme activities, and degradation of pesticides.[153] To date, no direct field evidence exists that acidification negatively effects microbial nitrification, denitrification, and ammonification in terrestrial ecosystems.[16]

In summary, at present, there is little evidence of visible or even detectable damage to terrestrial ecosystems, as measured in the field, that can be attributed to acidic precipitation. Terrestrial ecology is a complicated biological system, and deposition of acidic precipitation exerts a complex influence on the functioning of that ecology. The evaluation of potential impacts is complicated by the apparent trade-offs between benefits from nutrient enhancement and the possibility of inhibition of plant growth or other detrimental effects. Although results to date have been generated in the laboratory under controlled conditions and no evidence of crop damage in the field has been observed, it is possible that acidic precipitation is producing or will produce some responses within the ecosystem even though it is not possible at the present time to observe, record, or evaluate them. The determination of what these changes are, their quantification, and the determination of whether they are harmful or beneficial can only be accomplished with certainty through systematic scientific investigation over a long period of time.

EFFECTS OF ACIDIC PRECIPITATION ON ANIMAL AND HUMAN HEALTH

As previously observed, mobility of metallic compounds in soil is increased at low pH values. Given this fact, there exists a potential indirect impact on human health through contamination of edible fish and drinking water supplies by these metallic species. Although this impact is highly speculative, and data are scarce or nonexistent, the potential does exist and thus should not be ignored.

Changes in the concentrations of heavy metals have been observed in waters and aquatic species in acidified regions.[74-76] Increased concentrations of aluminum, manganese, zinc, copper, cadmium, and nickel have been reported.[16,17,23,45,63,154,155] Elevated mercury concentrations have also been observed.[16,77] Beamish[23] has suggested that increased concentrations of nickel and copper in Canadian lakes studied could be the result of increased acidic precipitation, although copper concentrations measured in acidified lakes were not significantly different from those in nonacidified lakes. Likewise, although zinc concentrations measured were higher in acidified lakes as compared to nonacidified, the levels were well within the range reported from analysis of samples obtained from 1500 water bodies within the United States.[23]

Aluminum appears to be the primary element mobilized by acidic precipitation in regions characterized by soils with poor acid-buffering capacity. Cronan et al.[73] found that acid deposition triggers the release of aluminum from soil horizons that would normally immobilize this element. Such releases of aluminum could have detrimental effects on fish populations in acidified lakes. In addition, there is a possibility that ingestion of fish contaminated by aluminum or other metals could represent a health hazard to both animals and humans. However, comprehensive study and analysis of toxic metals in commercial or recreational fish catches has yet to be conducted. Also, reported concentration levels of these metallic species in waters analyzed have been orders of magnitude below public health drinking water standards. The bioaccumulative potential of fish for these metallic species is unknown.

Wildlife may be indirectly impacted by acid precipitation by feeding on heavy metal contaminated vegetation or prey or by the elimination of a major prey.

Another possible human health impact is the potential that, as drinking water supplies acidify through increased input from acid precipitation, levels of metal concentrations in drinking waters could approach health standards. This increase in the concentrations of metallic species could be caused by increased watershed weathering or by leaching of metals such as copper and lead from household plumbing. A study on the impacts of acid precipitation on roof catchment-cistern water supplies found heavy metals deposited on the bottom of the cistern's masonry structure.[156] The water was less acidic, but still corrosive enough to leach additional heavy metals from the plumbing system; posing a potential health threat to those ingesting the water.

The major component of acid precipitation, sulfuric acid, has been studied for potential health effects in man and animals from inhalation exposure. Observed excess morbidity and mortality following the London smog incident of 1962 has been attributed to high levels of sulfuric acid by some authorities, but synergistic effects with other pollutants could account for the increased illnesses and deaths. To date, results from experimentation with low levels of sulfuric acid have been contradictory.[157,158] Kerr et al.[158] exposed 14 smokers and 14 nonsmokers to 0.1 mg/m^3 H$_2$SO$_4$ aerosol in the respirable particle size range of 0.1 to 0.3 μm for 4 hours in an environmentally-controlled exposure chamber. The dose of 0.1 mg/m^3 was chosen because this concentration is commonly encountered in the atmosphere during severe pollution episodes. The results showed no significant differences in pulmonary function up to 24 hours post-exposure.[158] Conversely, Leikauf et al.[159] observed increased bronchial clearance rates in healthy nonsmokers exposed to sulfuric acid mist (0.5 μm) at levels below 1 mg/m^3) for 1 hour. At 1 mg/m^3, the bronchial clearance rates were depressed. Other pulmonary indices tested at 1 mg/m^3 or less were negative.[159] In experiments with donkeys and monkeys, sulfuric acid mist induced pulmonary function impairment.[157,160]

Only preliminary and inconclusive investigations of these areas have been made thus far. However, it should be noted that no direct evidence exists to support the speculation that animals and humans are adversely affected by direct or indirect exposure to acidified rain. Clearly, additional research is needed to substantiate observations of adverse health effects in animals and humans from the indirect exposure of acid rain via heavy metal contamination of drinking water and food supplies to direct exposure from inhalation of sulfuric acid mists.

EFFECTS OF ACIDIC PRECIPITATION ON MATERIALS

Acidic precipitation can damage natural and manmade materials, structures, and manmade artifacts. It has the potential to accelerate corrosion of metals and erosion of stone. However, because a dominant factor in the formation of acidic precipitation is sulfur species (especially SO_2), it is difficult to distinguish effects of acidic precipitation from damage induced by sulfur pollution in general. Laboratory and field studies that attempted to assess the effects of single pollutants and combinations of pollutants on materials at various concentrations have been conducted. Although physical damage functions for some pollutant species have been developed, most are based on exposure data collected at relatively high pollutant levels. Data from exposures to pollutants at ambient levels are generally unavailable. Generalizations based on laboratory data must, therefore, be regarded as somewhat tenuous. Field observations and measurements may be of greater value in determining the impact of acid pollutants on materials and structures, but isolation of these impacts from the impacts associated with other constituents of the ambient atmosphere is extremely difficult.

The influence of acidic precipitation on corrosion of metals has been investigated.[161,162] Precipitation, as rain, can have a variable influence on corrosion. Rain may accelerate corrosion by forming a layer of moisture on the metallic surface and by adding hydrogen and sulfate ions. However, rain may also wash away sulfates deposited during dry deposition and can, therefore, retard corrosion.[161] Kucera[162] has investigated this problem and has concluded, as indicated, that mode of deposition complicates analysis of the impact of acid precipitation. It has been observed that in an area where dry deposition of hydrogen and sulfate ions exceeded that by wet deposition, flat steel plates corroded more rapidly on their undersides than on their upper, rain-exposed surfaces. This illustrates the washing effect of rainfall. However, in areas where wet and dry deposition were equivalent, the upper sides of the plates corroded more rapidly, indicating the predominance of rainfall's corrosive effects. Other variables were also observed to influence the impact of acid precipitation on corrosion, including amount and frequency of precipitation, pH, relative humidity, and temperature.[54]

High acidity in rainfall is believed to promote corrosion because the hydrogen ions present act as a sink for the electrons liberated during the corrosion process.[163] The metals most likely to be corroded by precipitation with low pH are those whose corrosion resistance depends on a layer of carbonates, sulfates, or oxides, such as zinc or copper. A pH of 4 or less in rainfall could accelerate the dissolution of these protective layers.[162]

Besides metals, limestone, sandstone, concrete, cement-lime, and lime plaster are reported to be adversely affected by acidic precipitation.[164] Sulfur compounds in the ambient atmosphere react with the carbonates in limestones and dolomites, calcareous sandstone, and mortars to form calcium sulfate. This reaction results in blistering, scaling, and loss of surface cohesion.[161,165]

Acidic precipitation may leach chemical constituents from stonework just as acidic water leaches ions from soils and bedrock. However, at the present time, it is not possible to attribute observed effects of atmospheric sulfur compounds in general, or acidic precipitation in particular, to specific chemical compounds.[161] The precise chemical mechanisms involved in such deteriorations are, likewise, unresolved. However, the effects are evident on buildings, monuments, and statuary.[164,165]

MODELS TO DETERMINE ACCEPTABLE LOADINGS OF ACIDIC MATERIALS TO THE ECOSYSTEM

Developing acidic tolerance models for lakes, crops, or materials is very difficult due to interference from other pollutants or due to direct introduction of chemicals by man, such as fertilizer application. However, the following models for relating deposition of sulfur compounds to adverse aquatic effects have been described in the literature. All of the models are based on empirical reports.

The model proposed by Dickson[166] is based on an empirical relationship between sulfate loading to lake water (in kilograms per hectare per year), and pH. The U.S.-Canadian report interpreting Dickson's material suggested tolerable sulfate loadings between 9 and 17 kg/ha/yr depending on lake sensitivity. The report advised caution in applying these data from Sweden to North America.[166]

An aquatic tolerance model, developed in Sweden by Henriksen involves two relationships. The first is the relationship between calcium ions and pH of lake water. The other relationship is between excess calcium and magnesium ions in lakes, pH of rainwater, and excess sulfate in lake water. Using these relationships, the U.S.-Canadian report tentatively concluded a precipitation sulfate concentration of about 40 µeq/l or 10 to 20 kg/ha/yr would protect most sensitive lakes. The report noted that Henriksen's equations have not been validated for North America, that the method does not consider pulse episodes such as snow melts, and that nitrates (which represent about one-third of the acidity of some eastern North American precipitation) are not included in the analysis.[166]

Thompson and others[166] in Canada are focusing their acidic tolerance model on the depletion of all positive ions, or cations, in watersheds. Hence, this model also relates calcium ions and pH of water bodies. This model is particularly interesting because it addresses short-term effects of storm events or snow melts which are believed to have shock effects on fish reproduction and fish fry. The U.S.-Canadian group cited above summarized Thompson's work, which indicates that an annual sulfate loading not exceeding 5 to 7 kg/ha is necessary to protect the most sensitive lakes. They also concluded that more work is required to evaluate Thompson's assumptions and model relationships.[166]

The setting of quantitative levels of acceptable maximum deposition of sulfate in precipitation for sensitive surface water bodies is, to date, scientifically unsupportable. This judgement is based on the following two points:

- "The field studies to date have provided too few data from which to derive a quantitative loading/response relationship.

- Our knowledge about soil and water physical, chemical, and biological processes that influence acidification in susceptible watersheds is too limited to allow one to derive quantitative loading/response relationships from theory."[166]

The multifaceted Integrated Lake-Watershed Acidification Study (ILWAS), sponsored by the Electric Power Research Institute, is developing models to simulate the physical and chemical transformations occurring in lakes and watersheds due to acid precipitation and natural acid production in the ecosystem.[167] They are using data from the Woods and Panther Lakes basins in the Adirondack Park region of New York. The hydrologic module performs five functions to follow the flow paths of rain and snow melt water through the terrestrial ecosystem into the aquatic ecosystem. These functions include: (1) canopy interception, storage, and evapotranspiration; (2) snow accumulation and melting; (3) ground water movement; (4) overland flow; and (5) freezing and thawing of soil. The model simulates concentrations of the major cations, anions, total inorganic carbon, and alkalinity. The model indicates the importance of including water flow through vertical (canopy, snow pack, and soil layers) and horizontal (terrestrial subcatchments, stream segments, and to a lake) subcatchments in determining lake acidity.[167]

Models to determine the effects of short-term acute episodes of low pH and related heavy metal flushing on lake acidity and biota are being developed. Flushing events have been defined by the U.S.-Canadian Group as an acidic input caused by the equivalent of a 2 to 4 cm rainfall or snow melt into streams of 0.2 to 5 m^3/s flow, following a period of accumulation of acid deposition in snow or surface litter and foliage.[166] Two to 4 days of short-term acute exposure to as small a pH change as 0.5 to 1.5 has resulted in effects in waters with a broad range of pH values above those at which chronic effects are observed. These relationships were developed from the recurring pattern observed in recent experiments.[166]

It should be noted that all of the above models attempt to relate sulfate deposition to critical changes in lake pH. No similar relationships for nitrogen compound deposition were found in the literature. To date, there are no scientifically accepted models to project future trends in lake acidification or recovery.

SUMMARY

The data presented and discussed in this section suggest that acidic precipitation, by acidification of several lakes, has been responsible for elimination of acid-sensitive aquatic species and has disrupted primary production and the nutritional food web within these selected ecosystems. These conclusions rely on an extensive data base relating the death of fish and other aquatic organisms to increased acidification of freshwater lakes and streams. The acidification of lakes has been extensively studied and modeled by monitoring the lake and watershed's ability to neutralize incoming acid. The sensitivity of lakes to acidification is dependent on the acidity of wet and dry atmospheric deposition, the hydrology of the lake, the soil system, and the resultant chemistry of the surface water. There are no widely accepted models to predict future trends in lake acidification or recovery.

The effects of pH changes on aquatic organisms vary from total devastation to no observed effects to proliferation depending on the physical condition of the organism, the ion composition of the water, synergism or antagonism of toxic ions, and the presence of toxic organics. Reproductive and pulmonary physiology appear to be most adversely affected by acidic waters. Reductions in the diversity of the plant communities in lakes and streams and subsequent disruption in primary production reduces the supply and variety of food and, therefore, the energy flow within the ecosystem. The specific mechanisms for the toxic effects of acid precipitation on aquatic ecosystems have not received a scientific consensus.

Discussion of potential impacts of acidic precipitation on terrestrial ecology rests on more tenuous evidence. To date, there has been no visible or detectable damage to terrestrial ecosystems outside the laboratory. In fact, some studies have indicated indirect beneficial responses due to exposure of vegetation to acidic precipitation. The most common response of vegetation to simulated acid rain is the formation of lesions on leaf surfaces. Studies measuring the effects of simulated acid rain on major United States crops found some crops to be inhibited, others stimulated, and still others had no

effects. The results suggested that an optimum pH or sulfate concentration
may exist for maximum crop productivity since acid rain resulted in competing
stimulatory and inhibitory effects. Contradictory observations have been
reported on the increased leaching of chemical elements from exposed plant
surfaces and/or forest soils from acid precipitation. A consensus has been
reached on the fact that acid rain affects vegetation by altering the nutrient
conditions of the ecosystem. The reduced cation exchange capacity and
increased rates of mineral loss are generally agreed to be the major effects
of acid precipitation on soils. Terrestrial ecology is a complicated
biological system, and deposition of acidic precipitation exerts a complex
influence on the functioning of the ecosystem. Since acid rain appears to
impact differently on the various layers of the ecosystem, studies
encompassing an entire ecosystem need to be conducted to adequately address
the effects of acid rain.

Although the possibility exists that acid precipitation may have indirect
or direct, adverse impacts on animal and human health, little data are
available, and any proposed relationships are currently considered speculative.

Acid precipitation has been associated with damage to natural materials,
structures, and manmade artifacts, although it is difficult to factor out the
effects of acidic precipitation on structures and materials from those of
sulfur air pollutants in general.

Finally, it must be recognized that there remain broad gaps in the data
on which many of the impacts of acidification are based. Also, there has been
no clear agreement among researchers regarding the magnitude of the potential
adverse impacts of acidic precipitation, nor whether observed effects are a
local or regional phenomenon caused by poor buffering capacity of the affected
lakes or soils, or whether the effects are more widespread.

REFERENCES

1. Wood, T. Acid Precipitation. In: Sulfur in the Environment, Missouri
    Botanical Garden in cooperation with Union Electric Company. St. Louis,
    Missouri, 1975, pp. 39-50.

2. Likens, G. E., R. F. Wright, J. N. Galloway, and T. J. Butler. Acid
    Rain. Scientific American, 241:43-51, 1979.

3. Glass, N. R., G. E. Glass, and P. I. Rennie. Effects of Acid
    Precipitation. Env. Sci. and Tech., 13:1350-1355, 1979.

4. Likens, G. E. Acid Precipitation. Chem. Eng. News, 54:(48):29-44, 1976.

5. Likens, G. E., F. H. Bormann, and N. M. Johnson. Acid Rain.
    Environment, 14:33-40, 1972.

6. Braekke, F. H., ed. Impact of Acid Precipitation on Forest and
    Freshwater Ecosystems in Norway. SNSF Project, Research Report FR 6/76,
    Oslo, Norway, 1976.

7. Cogbill, C. V., and G. E. Likens. Acid Precipitation in the Northeastern
    United States. Water Resource Res., 10:1133-1137, 1974.

8. Cogbill, C. V. The History and Character of Acid Precipitation in
    Eastern North America. In: Proceedings of the First International
    Conference on Acid Precipitation and the Forest Ecosystem, May 12-15,
    1975, Columbus, Ohio, L. S. Dochinger and T. A. Seliga, eds., U.S.
    Forest Service General Technical Report NE-23, U.S. Department of
    Agriculture, Forest Service, Northeastern Forest Experiment Station,
    Upper Darby, Pennsylvania, 1976. pp. 363-379.

9. Likens, G. E. The Chemistry of Precipitation in the Central Finger
    Lakes Region. Technical Report No. 50, Water Resources and Marine
    Science Center, Cornell University, Ithaca, New York, 1972.

10. National Research Council. Air Quality and Stationary Source Emission
    Control. Commission on Natural Resources, National Academy of Sciences,
    for the Committee on Public Works, U.S. Senate, 94th Congress, 1st
    Session, Committee Serial No. 94-4, U.S. Government Printing Office,
    Washington, D.C., 1975.

11. Matheson, D. H., and F. C. Elder, eds. Proceedings of Symposium on
    Atmospheric Contribution to Chemistry of Lake Waters. J. Great Lakes
    Res., 2 (Suppl. 1):1-225, 1976.

12. Hidy, G. M., D. A. Hansen, and R. C. Henry. Comments on External Review
    Draft No. 1 of the Air Quality Criteria for Particulate Matter and
    Sulfur Oxides. Prepared by Environmental Research and Technology,
    Westlake Village, Calif. for Prather, Seeger, Doolittle, and Farmer,
    Washington, D.C., July 1980.

13. Hendrey, G. R. (ed.). Limnological Aspects of Acid Precipitation. Proceedings of the International Workshop held at the Sagamore Lake Conference Center, September 25-28, 1978. Co-sponsored by Corvallis Environmental Research Laboratory (U.S. Environmental Protection Agency) and Brookhaven National Laboratory. Report No. BNL 51074.

14. Wetzel, R. G. Limnology. W. B. Saunders Co., Philadelphia, Pennsylvania, pp. 287-521, 1975.

15. Johnson, D. W. The Natural Acidity of Some Unpolluted Waters in Southeastern Alaska and Potential Impacts of Acid Rain. Water, Air and Soil Pollution, 16(2):243-252, 1981.

16. National Research Council. Atmosphere-Biosphere Interactions: Toward a Better Understanding of the Ecological Consequences of Fossil Fuel Combustion. National Academy Press, Washington, D.C., 1981. pp. 140-182.

17. Wright, R. F., and E. T. Gjessing. Changes in the Chemical Composition of Lakes. Ambio., 5:219-223, 1976.

18. Glass, N. R., G. E. Glass, and P. J. Rennie. Environmental Effects of Acid Precipitation. EPA Decision Series - Energy/Environ. June 7-8, 1979. (4th National Conference on Interagency Energy//Env. R&D Program).

19. Schofield, C. L. The Acid Precipitation Phenomenon and its Impact in the Adirondack Mountains of New York State. In: Scientific Paper from the Public Meeting on Acid Precipitation, May 4-5, 1978, Lake Placid, New York. Science and Technology Staff, New York State Assembly, Albany, New York, March 1979. pp. 86-91.

20. Schofield, C. L. Acid Precipitation's Destructive Effects on Fish in the Adirondacks. New York Food Life Sci. Q., 10(3):12-15, 1977.

21. Henriksen, A. Acidification of Freshwaters--A Large Scale Titration. In: Ecological Impact of Acid Precipitation. Proceedings of an International Conference, Sandefjord, Norway, March 11-14, 1980, edited by D. Drablös an A. Tollan. Oslo-Aas, Norway: SNS project. pp. 68-74.

22. Pottes, W. T. W., and D. J. A. Brown. Study Group 5 Discussions. D.5.1-D.5.5. In: Ecological Effects of Acid Precipitation, M. J. Wood, ed. Report of workshop held at Cally Hotel, Gatehouse-of-Fleet, Galloway, United Kingdom, 4-7 Sept. 1978. EPRI SOA77-403, Report No. EA-79-6-LD, December 1979.

23. Beamish, R. J. Acidification of Lakes in Canada by Acid Precipitation and the Resulting Effects on Fish. Water, Air and Soil Poll., 6:501-514, 1976.

24. Schofield, C. Effects of Acid Rain on Lakes. Presented at the American Society of Civil Eng. Convention, Boston, April 2, 1979.

25. Schindler, D. W., R. Wagemann, R. B. Cook, T. Ruszczynski, and J. Prokopowich. Experimental Acidification of Lake 223, Experimental Lake Area: Background Data and the First Three Years of Acidification. Can. J. Fish. Aquat. Sci., 37:342-354, 1980.

26. Johnson, D. W. Site Susceptibility to Leaching by H_2SO_4 in Acid Rainfall. In: T. C. Hutchinson and M. Havas (eds.) Effects of Acid Precipitation on Terrestrial Ecosystems. Plenum Press, New York. pp. 525-535, 1980.

27. Leivestard, H., and I. P. Muniz. Fish Kill at Low pH in a Norwegian River. Nature, 259:391-392, 1976.

28. Hagen, A., and A. Langeland. Polluted Snow in Southern Norway and the Effect of the Meltwater on Freshwater and Aquatic Organisms. Env. Pollut., 5:45-57, 1973.

29. Leivestad, H., G. Hendrey, I. P. Muniz, and E. Snekviki. Effects of Acid Precipitation on Freshwater Organisms. In: Impact of Acid Precipitation on Forest and Freshwater Ecosystems in Norway, F. H. Braekke, ed. Research Report FF 6/76, 1432 Aas - NLH, Norway: SNSF Project Secretariat, 1976. pp. 87-111.

30. Schofield, C. L. Lake Acidification in the Adirondack Mountains of New York: Causes and Consequences. In: Proceedings of the First International Symposium on Acid Precipitation and the Forest Ecosystem, May 12-15, 1975, Columbus, Ohio, L. S. Dochinger and T. A. Seliga, eds. U.S. Forest Service General Technical Report NE-23, U.S. Department of Agriculture, Forest Service, Northeastern Forest Experiment Station, Upper Darby, Pennsylvania, 1976. p. 477. (Abstract).

31. Hendrey, G. R., and R. F. Wright. Acid Precipitation in Norway: Effects on Aquatic Fauna. J. Great Lakes Res., 2 (Suppl. 1):192-207, 1976.

32. Almer, B., W. Dickson, C. Ekström, and E. Hörnstöm. Sulfur Pollution and the Aquatic Ecosystem. Sulfur in the Environment, Part II, edited by J. O. Nriagu. New York John Wiley & Sons, 1978, pp. 271-311.

33. Wright, R. F., and A. Henksen. Chemistry of Small Norwegian Lakes with Special Reference to Acid Precipitation. Limnol. Oceanog., 23:487-498, 1978.

34. Kaplan E., H. C. Thode, Jr., and A. Protas. Rocks, Soils, and Water Quality. Relationships and Implications for Effects of Acid Precipitation on Surface Water in the Northeastern United States. Env. Sci. and Tech., 15(5):539-544, 1981.

35. Galloway, J. N., and E. B. Cowling. The Effects of Precipitation on
     Aquatic and Terrestrial Ecosystems: A Proposed Precipitation Network.
     J. Air Pollution Control Assoc., 28:229-235, 1978.

36. Glass, N. R., D. E. Arnold, J. N. Galloway, G. R. Hendrey, J. J. Lee,
     W. W. McFee, S. A. Norton, C. F. Powers, D. L. Rambo, and
     C. L. Schofield. Effects of Acid Precipitation. Env. Sci. and Tech.,
     16(3):162A-169A, 1982.

37. Office of Technology Assessment. OTA Summary of "Regional Assessment of
     Aquatic Resources at Risk from Acidic Deposition." Washington, D.C.
     1982.

38. Johnson, D. W., G. S. Henderson, and D. E. Todd. Evidence of Modern
     Accumulations of Adsorbed Sulfate in an East Tennessee Forested
     Ultisol. 1981.

39. Peters, N., R. Schroeder, and D. Troutman. Temporal Trends in the
     Acidity of Precipitation and Surface Waters of New York. USGS
     Water-Supply Paper 2188, 1982.

40. Davis, R. B., M. O. Smith, J. H. Baily, and S. A. Norton. Acidification
     of Maine (U.S.A.) Lakes by Acidic Precipitation. Verh. Internat. Verein
     Limnol., 20:532-537, 1978.

41. Rosenqvist, I. T. A Contribution Towards Analysis of Buffer Properties
     of Geological Materials Against Strong Acids in Precipitation Water.
     Norwegian General Sci. Res. Council for Res. and Natural Sci., Oslo,
     Norway, 1976. p. 99.

42. Drablös, D., and I. H. Sevaldrud. Lake Acidification, Fish Damage and
     Utilization of Outfields. A Comparative Survey of Six Highland Areas,
     Southeastern Norway. Ecological Impact of Acid Precipitation.
     Proceedings of an International Conference, Sandefjord, Norway, March
     11-14, 1980, edited by D. Drablös and A. Tollan. Oslo-Aas, Norway:
     SNSF project. pp. 354-355.

43. Drablös, D., I. H. Sevaldrud, and J. A. Timberlid. Historical Land-Use
     Changes Related to Fish Status Development in Different Areas in
     Southern Norway. Ecological Impact of Acid Precipitation. Proceedings
     of an International Conference, Sandefjord, Norway, March 11-14, 1980,
     edited by D. Drablös and A. Tollan. Oslo-Aas, Norway: SNSF project.
     pp. 367-369.

44. Holden, A. V., and J. F. Spencer. Study Group 4 Discussions.
     D4.1-D4.5. In: Ecological Effects of Acid Precipitation. M. J. Wood,
     ed. Report of workshop held at Calley Hotel, Gatehouse-of-Fleet,
     Galloway, United Kingdom, 4-7 September 1978, EPRI SOA77-403 Report
     No. EA-79-6-LD, December 1979.

45. Hall, R., G. Likens, S. Fiance and G. Hendrey. Experimental
     Acidification of a Stream in the Hubbard Brook Experimental Forest, New
     Hampshire. Ecology, 61(4):976-989, August 1980.

46. McDonald, D. G., H. Hobe, and C. M. Wood. The Influence of Calcium on
     the Physiological Responses of the Rainbow Trout, Salmo gairdneri, to
     Low Environmental pH. J. Exp. Biol., 88:109-131, 1980.

47. European Inland Fisheries Advisory Committee (EIFAC). Water Quality
     Criteria for European Freshwater Fish. Water Res., 3:596-611, 1969.

48. Wright, R. F., and E. Snekvik. Acid Precipitation: Chemistry and Fish
     Populations in 700 Lakes in Southernmost Norway. Verh. Inte. Ver.
     Theor. Angew. Limnol., 20:765-775, 1978.

49. National Research Council. Sulfur Oxides. In: Effects of Sulfur
     Oxides on Aquatic Ecosystems, National Academy of Sciences, Washington,
     D.C., 1978.

50. Almer, B., W. Dickson, C. Ekstrom, E. Hornstrom, and U. Miller. Effects
     of Acidification on Swedish Lakes. Ambio., 3:30-36, 1974.

51. Jensen, K. W., and E. Snekvik. Low pH Levels Wipe Out Salmon and Trout
     Populations in Southeasternmost Norway. Ambio., 1:223-225, 1972.

52. Wright, R. F., T. Dale, E. T. Gjessing, G. R. Hendrey, A. Henriksen,
     M. Johannessen, and I. P. Muniz. Impact of Acid Precipiation on
     Freshwater Ecosystems in Norway. Water, Air and Soil Poll., 6:483-499,
     1976.

53. Dickson, W. The Acidification of Swedish Lakes. Fishery Board of
     Sweden, Institute of Freshwater Research, Drottningholm, Sweden. Report
     No. 54, Lund, Sweden, Carl Bloms Boktryckeru A.OB, 1975. pp. 8-20.

54. Beamish, R. J., and H. H. Harvey. Acidification of the LaCloche
     Mountain Lakes, Ontario, and Resulting Fish Mortalities. J. Fisheries
     Res. Board Canada, 29:1131-1143, 1972.

55. Schofield, C. L. Acid Precipitation: Effects on Fish. Ambio.,
     5:228-230, 1976.

56. Pfeiffer, M. List and Summary of Acidified Adirondack Waters Based on
     Data Available as of April 1979. New York State Department of
     Environmental Conservation, Albany, New York, May 1979.

57. Comments of the American Petroleum Institute on the Revised Air Quality
     Criteria for Oxides of Nitrogen. Appendix C titled, "Reinterpretation
     of Data Used to Evaluate Effects of Acidic Precipitation Upon Fish
     Stocks in Pennsylvania Streams," November 1980.

58. Beamish, R. J., W. L. Lockhart, J. C. Van Loon, and H. H. Harvey. Long-Term Acidification of a Lake and Resulting Effects on Fishes. Ambio., 4:98-102, 1975.

59. Menendex, R. Chronic Effects of Reduced pH on Brook Trout (Salvelinus fontinalis). J. Fish. Res. Board Can., 23:118-123, 1976.

60. Trojnar, J. R. Egg and Larval Survival of White Suckers (Catostomus commersoni) at Low pH. J. Fish Res. Board Can., 34:262-266, 1977.

61. Trojnar, J. R. Egg Hatchability and Tolerance of Brook Trout (Salvelinus fontinalis) Fry at Low pH. J. Fish. Res. Board Can., 34:574-579, 1977.

62. Schofield, C. L. Lake Acidification in the Adirondack Mountains of New York: Causes and Consequences. In: First International Symposium on Acid Precipitation and the Forest Ecosystem, USDA Forest Service, Northeastern Forest Experiment Station and Ohio State University Atmospheric Science Program, Columbus, Ohio, 1975. pp. 25.

63. Haines, T. A. Acidic Precipitation and Its Consequences for Aquatic Ecosystems: A Review, (Aquatic Biology and Ecology, Biota, Fish, Water Pollution, Europe, North America). Transactions of the American Fisheries Society, 110(6): 669-707, November 1981.

64. Fromm, P.O. A Review of Some Physiological and Toxicological Responses of Freshwater Fish to Acid Stress. Env. Biol. Fish., 5:79-93, 1980.

65. Kennedy, L. A. The Effects of Lake Acidification on Embryonic Development of the Lake Trout, Salvelinus mamycush. In: Proceedings of the 6th Annual Aquatic Toxicology Workshop. Fisheries and Marine Service Technical Report No. 975. Ottawa: Fisheries and Marine Service, 1981. pp. 49-54.

66. Kennedy, L. A. Teratogenesis in Lake Trout (Salvelinus mamycush) in an Experimentally Acidified Lake. Can. J. Fish. Aquat. Sci., 37:2355-2358, 1980.

67. Hagvar, S. Effects of Acid Precipitation on Soil and Forest Soil Animals. In: Ecological Impact of Acid Precipitation. Proceedings of the International Conference March 11-14, 1980. pp. 202-203.

68. Muniz, I. P., and H. Leivestad. Acidification—Effects on Freshwater Fish. In: Ecological Impact of Acid Precipitation. Proceedings of an International Conference, Sandefjord, Norway, March 11-14, 1980, edited by Dr. Drablös and A. Tollan. Oslo-Aas, Norway: SNSF project. pp. 84-92.

69. Rosseland, B. O. Physiological Responses to Acid Water in Fish. 2. Effects of Acid Water on Metabolism and Gill Ventilation in Brown Trout, Salmo trutta L., and brook trout, Salvelinus fontinalis Mitchell. In:

Ecological Impact of Acid Precipitation. Proceedings of an International Conference, Sandefjord, Norway, March 11-14, 1980, edited by D. Drablös and A. Tollan. Oslo-Aas, Norway: SNSF project. pp. 348-349.

70. Jackson, W. and P. Fromm. Effect of Acute Acid Stress on Isolated Perfused Gills of Rainbow Trout. Comparative Biochemistry and Physiology, 670(2):141-145, 1980.

71. MacFarlane, R. B. Effects of Low pH Water on the Adenine Nucleotide Pool and Locomotor Activity of the Gulf Killifish, Fundulus Grandis Thesis, Florida State University, Tallahassee, FL, 1980.

72. Davis, A. O., J. N. Galloway, and D. K. Nordstrom. Lake Acidification: Its Effects on Lead in the Sediment of Two Adirondack Lakes. Limnol. Oceanogr., 27(1):163-167, 1982.

73. Cronan, C. S., and C. L. Schofield. Aluminum Leaching Response to Acid Precipitation: Effects on High-Elevation Watersheds in the Northeast. Science, 204:304-305, 1979.

74. Landner, L., and P. O. Larsson. Biological Effects of Mercury Fall-Out in Lakes from the Atmosphere. IUL Report B115. Institute for Water and Air Research, Stockholm, Sweden, 1972. 18 pp. (In Swedish, translated by H. Altosaar, Domtar Research Centre, December 25, 1975).

75. Tomlinson, G. H. Acidic Precipitation and Mercury in Canadian Lakes and Fish. In: Public Meeting on Acid Precipitation, May 4-5, 1978, Lake Placid, New York. Sponsored by the Committee on Environmental Conservation, New York State Assembly. Pub. by Science and Technology Staff, New York State Assembly, March 1979. pp. 104-118.

76. Prouzes, R. J. P., R. A. N. McLean, and G. H. Tomlinson. Mercury - The Link Between pH of Natural Waters and the Mercury Content of Fish. Paper presented at a meeting of the Panel on Mercury of the Coordinating Committee for Sciencific and Technical Assessments of Environmental Pollutants, National Academy of Sciences, National Research Council, Washington, D.C., May 3, 1977. Montreal, Quebec: Domtar Research Center, 1977.

77. Jackson, T. A., G. Kipphut, R. H. Hesslein, and D. W. Schindler. Experimental Study of Trace Metal Chemistry in Soft-Water Lakes at Different pH Levels. Can. J. Fish Aquat. Sci., 37:387-420, 1980.

78. Billings, W. D. Plants and the Ecosystem. Third ed. Wadsworth Publishing Company, Inc., Belmont, Pennsylvania, 1978. pp. 1-62.

79. Odum, E. P. Fundamentals of Ecology. Third Ed. W. B. Saunders Co., Philadelphia, Pennsylvania, 1971. pp. 5, 8-139.

80. Kwiatkowski, R. E., and J. C. Roff. Effects of Acidity on the Phytoplankton and Primary Productivity of Selected Northern Ontario Lakes. Can. J. Bot., 54:2546-2561, 1976.

81. Müller, P. Effects of Artificial Acidification on the Growth of Periphyton. Can. J. Fish. Aquat. Sci., 37:355-363, 1980.

82. Hendrey, G. R., N. D. Yan, and K. J. Baumgartner. Responses of Freshwater Plants and Invertebrates to Acidification. Brookhaven National Laboratory, Upton, New York, 1980.

83. Hendrey, G. R., K. Baalstrud, T. S. Traaen, M. Laake, and G. Raddum. Acid Precipitation: Some Hydrobiological Changes. Ambio., 5:224-227, 1976.

84. Grahn, O. Macrophyte Succession in Swedish Lakes Caused by Deposition of Airborne Acid Substances. In: Proceedings of the First International Symposium on Acid Precipitation and the Forest Ecosystem, L. S. Cochinger and T. A. Seliga, eds. Ohio State University, May 12-15, 1975. USDA Forest Service General Technical Report NE-23, Upper Darby, Pennsylvania, Forest Service, U.S. Department of Agriculture, Northeastern Forest Experiment Station, 1976. pp. 519-530.

85. Conway, H. L., and G. R. Hendrey. Ecological Effects of Acid Precipitation on Primary Producers. Brookhaven National Laboratory, Upton, New York, 1981.

86. Shellito, G. A., and J. Decosta. Primary Production in a Eutrophic Acid Lake. Water, Air and Soil Pollution, 16:415-431, 1981.

87. Hendrey, G. R. Effects of pH on the Growth of Periphytic Algae in Artificial Stream Channels. Research Report IR 25/76. 1432 Aas-NLH. Norway: SNSF Project Secretariat, 1976.

88. Singer, R. Effects of Acid Precipitation on Benthos. In: Acid Precipitation: Effects on Ecological Systems. F. M. Ditri, Ed., Ann Arbor Science Publishers, Ann Arbor, Michigan, 1982.

89. Grahn, O., H. Hultberg, and L. Landner. Oligotrophication—A Self-accelerating Process in Lakes Subjected to Excessive Supply of Acid Substances. Ambio., 3:93-94, 1974.

90. Conroy, N., K. Hawley, W. Keller, and C. Lafrance. Influences of the Atmosphere on Lakes in the Sudbury Area. J. Great Lakes Res., 2 (Suppl. 1):146-165, 1976.

91. Anderson, I., O. Grahn, H. Hultberg, and L. Landner. Jamforande Undersokning av Olika Tekniker for Terstallende av Forsurade sjoar. STU Report 73-3651. Stockholm: Institute for Water and Air Research, 1975. Cited In: National Research Council, Sulfur Oxides, National Academy of Sciences, Washington, D.C., 1978.

92. Borgstrom R., J. Brittain, and A. Lillehammer. Evertebrater og Surt Vann: Oversikt over Innsamplingslokaliteter. Research Report IR 21/76. 1432 Aas-NLH, Norway: SNSF Project Secretariat, 1976. Cited In: National Research Council, Sulfur Oxides, National Academy of Scieces, Washington, D.C., 1978.

93. Sprules, G. W. Midsummer Crustacean Zooplankton Communities in Acid-stressed lakes. J. Fish Res. Board Can., 32:389-395, 1975.

94. Havas, M. A Study of the Chemistry and Biota of Acid and Alkaline Ponds at the Smoking Hills. N. W. Territories. Ph.D. Thesis. Department of Botany. Toronto: University of Toronto, 1980.

95. Oakland, J. Distribution and Ecology of the Freshwater Snails Gastropoda of Norway. Malacologia, 9:134-151, 1969.

96. Ökland, J. Environment and Snails (Gastropoda): Studies of 1,000 Lakes in Norway. In: Ecological Impact of Acid Precipitation. Proceedings of an International Conference, Sandefjord, Norway, March 11-14, 1980, edited by D. Drablös and A. Tollan. Oslo-Aas, Norway: SNSF project. pp. 322-323.

97. Ökland, J., and K. A. Ökland. pH Level and Food Organisms for Fish: Studies of 1,000 Lakes in Norway. In: Ecological Impact of Acid Precipitation. Proceedings of an International Conference, Sandefjord, Norway, March 11-14, 1980, edited by D. Drablös and A. Tollan. Oslo-Aas, Norway: SNSF project. pp. 326-327.

98. Bell, H. L. Effects of Low pH on the Survival and Emergency of Aquatic Insects. Water Res., 5:313-319, 1971.

99. Pough, F. H., and R. E. Wilson. Acid Precipitation and Reproductive Success of Ambystoma Salamanders. In: Proceedings of the First International Symposium on Acid Precipitation and the Forest Ecosystem, Ohio State University, May 12-15, 1975. U.S. For. Serv. Gen. Tech. Rep. NE-23, 1976. pp. 531-544.

100. Gosner, K. L., and I. H. Black. The Effects of Acidity on the Development and Hatching of New Jersey Frogs. Ecology, 38:256-262, 1975.

101. Pough, F. H. Acid Precipitation and Embryonic Mortality of Spotted Salamanders, Ambystoma Maculatum. Science, 192:68-70, 1976.

102. Pough, F. H. Mechanisms by Which Acid Precipitation Produces Embryonic Death in Aquatic Vertebrates. Cornell University, Ithaca, NY.

103. U.S. Department of the Interior, Fish and Wildlife Service. Impacts of Coal-Fired Power Plants on Fish, Wildlife, and Their Habitats. FWS/OBS-78/29, March 1978. pp. 64-70.

104. Hendrey, G. Aquatics Task Force on Environmental Assessment of the Atikokan Power Plant: Effects on Aquatic Organisms. Land and Fresh Water Environmental Sciences Group, Department of Energy and Environment. Brookhaven National Laboratory Associated Universities, Inc., Upton, New York, 1978.

105. Evans, L. S. Considerations of an Air-Quality Standard to Protect Terrestrial Vegetation from Acidic Precipitation. Manhattan College, New York. BNL-29097. 1981.

106. Lindberg, S. E., D. S. Shriner, and W. A. Hoffman. The Interaction of Wet and Dry Deposition with the Forest Canopy. Oak Ridge National Laboratory, Oak Ridge, TN, 1981.

107. Shriner, D. S. Terrestrial Vegetation-Air Pollutant Interactions: Non-Gaseous Pollutants, Wet Deposition In: Drupa, S. V., and A. Legge (eds.) Air Pollutants and Their Effects on Terrestrial Ecosystems. Wiley Interscience, New York, 1981.

108. Jacobsen, J. S. Experimental Studies on the Phytotoxicity of Acidic Precipitation: The United States Experience. Paper presented at NATO Advanced Research Institute, Effects of Acid Precipitation on Terrestrial Ecosystems, Toronto, May 22-26, 1978.

109. Wood, T., and F. H. Bormann. Short-Term Effects of a Simulated Acid Rain Upon the Growth and Nutrient Relations of Pinus Strobus, L. Water, Air Soil Pollut., 7:479-488, 1977.

110. Jacobson, J. S. The Infuence of Rainfall Composition on the Yield and Quality of Agricultural Crops. In: Ecological Impact of Acid Precipitation. Proceedings of an International Conference, Sandefjord, Norway, March 11-14, 1980, edited by D. Drablös and A. Tollan. Oslo-Aas, Norway: SNSF project. pp. 41-46.

111. Evans, L. S., N. F. Gmur, and F. DaCosta. Leaf Surface and Histological Perturbations of Leaves of Phaseolus vulgaris and Helianthus annus after Exposure to Simulated Acid Rain. Amer. J. Bot., 64:893-913, 1977.

112. Hindawi, I. J., J. A. Rea, and W. L. Griffis. Response of Bush Bean Exposed to Acid Mist. 70th Annual Meeting of the J. Air Pollution Control Assoc. Abstract 77-30.4, 1977.

113. Evans, L. S., and T. M. Curry. Differential Responses of Plant Foliage to Simulated Acid Rain. Amer. J. Bot., 66:953-962, 1979.

114. Evans, L. A., N. F. Gmur, and F. DaCosta. Foliar Response of Six Clones of Hybrid Power Poplar to Simulated Acid Rain. Phytopathology, 68:847-856, 1978.

115. Lee, J., G. Neely, S. Perrigan and L. Grothaws. Effect of Simulated Sulfuric Acid Rain on Yield, Growth and Foliar Injury of Several Crops. Env. and Exp. Bot., 21(2):171-185, May 1981.

116. Evans, K. S., N. F. Gmur, and J. J. Kelsch. Perturbations of Upper Leaf Surface Structures by Simulated Acid Rain. Env. and Exp. Bot., 17:145-149, 1977.

117. Jacobson, J. S., and P. van Leuken. Effects of Acidic Rain on Vegetation. Proc. Fourth Intern. Clean Air Congress, 1977. pp. 124-127.

118. Ferenbaugh, R. W. Effects of Simulated Acid Rain on Phaseolus vulgaris L. (Fabaceae). Amer. J. Bot., 63:283-288, 1976.

119. Abrahamsen, G., K. Bjor, R. Horntvedt, and B. Tveite. Effects of Acid Precipitation on Coniferous Forest. In: Research Report FR-6, F. H. Braekke, ed. SNSF Project, NISK, Aas, Norway, 1976. pp. 36-63.

120. Irving, P. M. Induction of Visible Injury in Chamber-Grown Soybeans Exposed to Acid Precipitation. RER Division Annual Report, ANL-78-65-III, Argone, Illinois, 1978.

121. Wood, T., and F. H. Bormann. The Effects of an Artificial Acid Mist upon the Growth of Betula alleghaniensis. Brit. Env. Pollut., 7:259-268, 1974.

122. Lang, D. S., D. S. Shriner, and S. V. Krupa. Injury to Vegetation Incited by Sulfuric Acid Aerosols and Acidic Rain. Paper 78-7.3, 71st Annual Meeting, Air Pollution Control Association, Houston, Texas, 1978.

123. Shriner, D. S. Atmospheric Deposition: Monitoring the Phenomenon; Studying the Effects. In: Handbook of Methodology for the Assessment of Air Pollutant Effects on Vegetation, W. W. Heck, S. V. Krupa, and S. N. Linzon, ed. Air Pollution Control Association, Pittsburgh, Pennsylvania, 1979.

124. Office of Research and Developmnt. Research Highlights 1979. Report No. EPA-600/9-80-005, U.S. Environmental Protection Agency, 1980. pp. 26-29.

125. Irving, P., and J. E. Miller. The Effects of Acid Precipitation Alone and in Combination with Sulfur Dioxide on Field-Grown Soybeans. RER Division Annual Report, ANL-78-65-III, Argonne, Illinois, 1978.

126. Shriner, D. S., and E. B. Cowling. Effects of Rainfall Acidification on Plant Pathogens. In: Effects of Acid Precipitation on Terrestrial Ecosystems, edited by T. C. Hutchinson and M. Havas. New York: Plenum Press, 1980. pp. 435-442.

127. Shriner, D. S. Effects of Simulated Rain Acidified with Sulfuric Acid on Host-Parasite Interactions. In: Proceedings of the First International Symposium on Acid Precipitation and the Forest Ecosystem, May 12-15, 1975, Columbus, Ohio, L. S. Dochinger and T. A. Seliga, eds., U.S. Forest Service General Technical Report NE-23, U.S. Department of Agriculture, Forest Service, Northeastern Forest Experiment Station, Upper Darby, Pennsylvania, 1976. pp. 919-925.

128. Abrahmsen, G., and G. J. Dollard. Effects of Acid Deposition on Forest Vegetation. In: Ecological Effects of Acid Precipitation, M. J. Wood, ed. Report of Workshop held at Calley Hotel, Gatehouse-of-Fleet, Galloway, United Kingdom, 4-7 Sept. 1978. EPRI SOA77-403, Electric Power Res. Institute, Palo Alto, California, 1979.

129. Jonsson, B., and R. Sundberg. Has the Acidification by Atmospheric Pollution Caused a Growth Reduction in Swedish Forests? Rep. Notes No. 20, Royal College of Forestry, Stockholm, Sweden, 1972.

130. Cogbill, C. V. The Effect of Acid Precipitation on Tree Growth in Eastern North America. Water, Air and Soil Pollution, 8:89-93, 1977.

131. Abrahamsen, G., R. Horntvedt, and B. Tveite. Impacts of Acid Precipitation on Coniferous Forest Ecosystems. Water, Air and Soil Pollution, 8:57-73, 1977.

132. Johnson, A., T. Siccanna, D. Wang, R. Turner and T. Barringer. Recent Changes in Patterns of Tree Growth Rate in the New Jersey Pinelands: A Possible Effect of Acid Rain. J. Env. Qual., 10(4):427-430, 1981.

133. Vogelman, H. W. Catastrophe on Camels Hump. Natural History. 1982. pp. 8-14.

134. Tukey, H. B., Jr. The Leaching of Substances from Plants. Ann. Review of Plant Physiology, 21:305-324, 1970.

135. Wood, T., and F. Bormann. Increases in Foliar Leaching by Acidification of an Artificial Mist. Ambio., 4:169-171, 1975.

136. Evans, L. S., et al. Responses of Leaves of Phaseous Vulgaris L. (Kidney Beans) to Simulated Acidic Rain (Nutrient Penetration, Nutrient Leaching, Cell Permeability). The New Phytocologist, 88(3):403-420, July 1981.

137. Overrein, L. N. Sulphur Pollution Patterns Observed; Leaching of Calcium in Forest Soil Determined. Ambio., 1:145-147, 1972.

138. Johnson, D. W. Acid Rain and Forest Productivity. Oak Ridge National Laboratory, Oak Ridge, TN, 1981.

139. Johnson, D. W., J. Turner, and J. M. Kelly. The Effects of Acid Rain on Forest Nutrient Status. Water Resources Research, 18(3):449-461, 1982.

140. Anderson, R. Acidifying Effects of Nitrogen Fertilizers on Swedish
     Farms. Gruafor Battring, 26:11-24, 1973-1974.

141. McFee, W. W. Effects of Pollutants on Soils. In: Polluted Rain,
     T. Toribara, et al., eds. Pergamon Press, New York, New York, 1980.
     p. 307.

142. Oden, S. The Acidification of Soils Due to Nitrogen Fertilizer and
     Atmospheric Pollutant of Ammonium. Skogsand Cantvenksakad., Tidskar,
     113:445-458, 1974.

143. Gorham, E. The Influence and Importance of Daily Weather Conditions in
     the Supply of Chloride, Sulfate, and Other Ions to Fresh Waters from
     Atmospheric Precipitation. Phil. Tras Roy. Soc. (London) B.,
     247:147-178.

144. Wiklander, L. Leaching and Acidification of Soils. In: Ecological
     Effects of Acid Precipitation. M. J. Wood, ed. Report of Workshop Held
     at Cally Hotel, Gatehouse-of-Fleet, Galloway, United Kingdom,
     4-7 Sept. 1978, EPRI SOA77-403, Electric Power Res. Institute, Palo
     Alto, California, 1979.

145. Malmer, N. Acid Precipitation: Chemical Changes in the Soil. Ambio.,
     5:231-234, 1976.

146. Farrell, E. P., I. Nilsson, C. O. Tamm, and G. Wiklander. Effects of
     Artificial Acidification with Sulfuric Acid on Soil Chemistry in a Scots
     Pine Forest. In: Ecological Impact of Acid Precipitation. Proceedings
     of an International Conference, Sandefjord, Norway, March 11-14, 1980,
     edited by D. Drablös and A. Tollan. Oslo-Aas, Norway: SNSF project.
     pp. 186-187.

147. Lee, J. and D. Weber. Effects of Sulfuric Acid Rain on Major Cation and
     Sulfate Concentrations of Water Percolating Through Two Model Hardwood
     Forests. J. of Env. Qual., 11(1):57-64, Jan/Mar. 1982.

148. Troedsson, T. Ten Years Acidification of Swedish Forest Soils. In:
     Ecological Impact of Acid Precipitation. Proceedings of an
     International Conference, Sandefjord, Norway, March 11-14, 1980, edited
     by D. Drablös and A. Tollan. Oslo-Aas, Norway: SNSF project. p. 184.

149. McFee, W. W., J. M. Kelly, and R. H. Beck. Acid Precipitation: Effects
     on Soil Base pH and Base Saturation of Exchange Sites. In: Proceedings
     of the First International Symposium on Acid Precipitation and the
     Forest Ecosystem, May 12-15, 1975, Columbus, Ohio, L. S. Dochinger and
     T. A. Seliga, eds. U.S. Forest Service General Technical Report NE-23,
     U.S. Department of Agriculture, Forest Service, Northeastern Forest
     Experiment Station, Upper Darby, Pennsylvania, 1976. pp. 725-735.

150. Ulrich, B. Die Umweltbeeinflussung des Nahrstoffhaushaltes eines
     Bodenssauren Buchenwalds. Forstwiss. Centralbl., 94:280-287, 1975.

151. Alexander, M. Effects of Acid Precipitation on Biochemical Activities
     in Soil. In: Ecological Impact of Acid Precipitation. Proceedings of
     an International Conference, Sandefjord, Norway, March 11-14, 1980,
     edited by Dr. Drablös and A. Tollan. Oslo-Aas, Norway: SNSF project.
     pp. 47-52.

152. Alexander, M. Effects of Acidity on Microorganisms and Microbial
     Processes in the Soil. In: Effects of Acid Precipitation on
     Terrestrial Ecosystems, T. C. Hutchinson and M. Havas, eds. Plenum
     Press New York, New York, 1978. pp. 341-362.

153. Francis, A. J., D. Olson, and R. Bernatsky. Effect of Acidity on
     Microbial Processes in a Forest Soil. Brookhaven National Laboratory
     Under Contract No. DE-AC02-76CH00016 with the Department of Energy,
     Upton, New York, 1980.

154. Glass, G. E., and O. L. Loucks, eds. Impacts of Air Pollutants on
     Wilderness Areas of Northern Minnesota. Environmental Research
     Laboratory - Duluth, ORD, U.S. Environmental Protection Agency, Duluth,
     Minnesota, 1979. p. 188.

155. Bowen, H. J. M. Trace Elements in Biochemistry. Academic Press,
     New York, New York, 1966.

156. Sharpe, W. E., and E. S. Young. The Effects of Acid Precipitation on
     Water Quality in Roof Catchment - Cistern Water Supplies. In: Acid
     Precipitation: Effects on Ecological Systems. F. M. Ditri, Ed., Ann
     Arbor Science Publishers, Ann Arbor, Michigan, 1982.

157. Lippman, M. Health Significance of Exposures to Sulfur Oxide Air
     Pollutants. In: Atmospheric Sulfur Deposition. Environmental Impact
     and Health Effects. Shriner, D. S., C. R. Richmond, and S. E. Lindberg
     (eds.). Ann Arbor Science Publishers Inc., Michigan, 1980. pp. 85-97.

158. Kerr, H. D., T. J. Kulle, B. P. Farrell, L. R. Saunder, J. L. Young,
     D. L. Swift, and R. M. Bourshok. Env. Res., 26:42-50, 1981.

159. Leikauf, G., D. B. Yeates, K. A. Wales, D. Spektor, R. E. Albert,
     M. Lippmann. Effects of Sulfuric Acid Aerosol on Respiratory Mechanics
     and Mucociliary Particle Clearance In Healthy Nonsmoking Adults. Am.
     Ind. Hyg. Assoc. J., 4:273-282, 1981.

160. Alarie, Y. C., et al. Long-Term Exposure to Sulfur Dioxide, Sulfuric
     Acid Mist, Fly Ash, and Their Mixtures, Arch. Env. Health, 30:254-262,
     May 1975.

161. Martin, H. C. Materials Performance. 1/82. pp. 36-39.

162. Kucera, V. Effects of Sulfur Dioxide and Acid Precipitation on Metals
     and Anti-Rust Painted Steel. Ambio., 5:243-248, 1976.

163. Nriago, J. Deteriorative Effects of Sulfur Pollution on Materials.
      In: Sulfur in the Environment Part II: Ecological Imports, J. Nriago,
      ed. John Wiley and Sons, New York, 1978. pp. 2-59, 482.

164. Cowling, E. B., and L. S. Dochinger. The Changing Chemistry of
      Precipitation and its Effects on Vegetation and Materials: In: AICHE
      Symposium Series, Control and Dispersion of Air Pollutants: Emphasis on
      NO_x and Particulate Emissions, 7:134-142, 1978.

165. Sereda, P. J. Effects of Sulphur on Building Materials. In: Sulphur
      and its Organic Derivatives in the Canadian Environment, Nat. Res.
      Council of Canada. NRC Associate Committee on Scientific Criteria for
      Environmenal Quality, Ottawa, Canada, 1977. pp. 359-426.

166. Impact Assessment Working Group I. United States--Canada Memorandum of
      Intent on Transboundary Air Pollution. Phase III Report. Volume I.
      November 1982.

167. Chen, C. W., J. D. Dean, S. A. Gherini, and R. A. Goldstein. Acid Rain
      Model: Hydrologic Module. ASCE Environmental Engineering Div.,
      108:455-472, 1982.

7

Regulatory Alternatives and Mitigative Strategies

As the debate over the cause and effect relationships of acid precipitation has intensified, the need for understanding the regulatory alternatives and strategies for controlling anthropogenic emissions of acid rain precursors and mitigating the effects of acid deposition has grown. This section briefly summarizes several recent legislative proposals and regulatory analyses on acid rain. Its purpose is to acquaint the reader with recent work in this rapidly changing area. As such, no attempt has been made to completely synthesize the key legislative, analytical, and policy issues raised by these efforts.

Among the methods suggested to mitigate the possible effects of acid deposition (other than decreased emissions of pollutants), are liming of waterways and soils, management of fisheries, and development of resistant species of biota. Of these, liming has received the most attention, and as such its advantages and disadvantages are fully discussed in this section.

REGULATORY ALTERNATIVES

It is generally acknowledged that most manmade emissions of acid rain precursors in the United States are from power plants, industrial combustion, transportation, and nonferrous smelters. Since smelters are quite remote from the sensitive areas in the northeastern United States, attention has been placed on the remaining three source categories. Table 7-1 summarizes the advantages and disadvantages of several strategies that have been suggested to reduce emissions from these sources. A number of these options have been refined into specific legislative proposals and are currently being considered by Congress as part of the debate over the Clean Air Act Reauthorization.

The discussion below provides a brief overview of the bills that have been introduced into Congress. Its primary focus, however, is the analyses that have been conducted to gauge the impacts of acid rain control measures on industry, consumers, and the high-sulfur coal market. Three studies are discussed. The Acid Rain Mitigation Study, cofunded by DOE and EPA, is designed to examine the impacts of a wide range of alternative regulatory options on SO_2 reduction, control costs, and coal demand. The second study, which is being conducted by the Office of Technology Assessment (OTA), is designed to provide information on a variety of issues relating to the Long Range Transport of Air Pollutants (LRTAP) for use in the Clean Air Act Reauthorization debate. The third study is an analysis performed for EPA by ICF, Inc. of the acid rain control bill recently approved by the Senate

313

TABLE 7-1.   SUMMARY OF POTENTIAL STRATEGIES TO CONTROL ACID RAIN

Strategy	Advantages	Disadvantages
Enforcement of Current SIPs	Major reductions in emissions are possible.	Monitoring and enforcement in terms of personnel and equipment are very great.
Assign Emission Caps on a State Basis (in lb/MMBtu)	Uniform, simplistic, ease of administration; emission reductions would be achieved.	High sulfur coal states might have to devise method to protect local miners (as in NSPS).
Create Economic Incentives for SO_2 and/or NO_x Control through Emission Taxes or Marketable Permits	State equity would be maintained; emission reductions would be achieved.	Implementation and monitoring of this approach would be cumbersome.
Wait Until LIMB (Limestone Injection with Modified Burners) is Available (est. 1986-1988) to Get Control of Both SO_x and NO_x	High SO_2 reduction (60-70%) as well as high NO_x reduction at costs well below those for conventional scrubbers. Major uncertainties regarding the acid rain phenomenon might be resolved as this technology becomes commercially available.	Long lag time before technology is commercially available.
Assign Regional Pollution Reduction Levels	Less costly than most other options.	No state discretion; equity issue would be raised; administrative difficulties.
Specific Percent Reduction in Each State's Emissions	Administratively easy to apply.	Environmentally progressive states would be penalized in that even further emission reductions would be required; more costly than previous option (regional reduction levels).
Utilize Section 115 of the Clean Air Act Which Sets Up an International Agreement to Control Acid Rain	Plenty of state flexibility allowed in the revision of individual State Implementation Plans.	Equity issue would be raised; administrative difficulties.
Require Use of Specific SO_2 Control Strategies Such as Coal Washing	Relatively inexpensive; may help protect markets for high sulfur coal; can also reduce transportation and handling costs.	Results in only modest reductions in SO_2 (10-30%). Requiring specific control strategy reduces flexibility to achieve least-cost mix of controls.

Environment and Public Works Committee. This discussion provides a brief
overview of each study's purpose and results. Readers who are interested in
the methodological techniques and assumptions used in these analyses should
consult the original studies.

Legislative Initiatives to Control Acid Rain

During the past year, several bills containing regulatory proposals to
control acid rain have been introduced in Congress. On July 22, 1982, the
Senate Environment and Public Works Committee approved an amendment to the
Clean Air Act dealing with acid rain. The Senate Bill (S. 3041) has been
revised somewhat from the preliminary version approved in July 1982. The
House of Representatives' Energy and Commerce Committee is still considering
several bills dealing with acid rain. Table 7-2 summarizes the key features
of the Senate plan as well as those of two bills that have been introduced
into the House. It also describes the two most widely-discussed predecessors
to the Senate plan: S. 1706, introduced by Senator George Mitchell (D-Maine),
and S. 1709, introduced by Senator Daniel Patrick Moynihan (D-New York). The
Moynihan bill has also been introduced into the House as H.R. 4936, by
Representative Scheuer.

As Table 7-2 indicates, the bills have many similarities. All of the
bills, for example, focus on SO_2 reductions in the 31 states east of, or
bordering on, the Mississippi River (see Figure 7-1); most allow NO_x
reductions to be traded for SO_2 reductions on a two-for-one basis. Except
for the Senate bill, which provides states with an initial opportunity to
allocate required emission reductions among themselves, all of the bills
contain a formula to allocate required emission reductions to each state based
on current SO_2 emissions from electric utilities. There are also several
important differences among the bills. The version approved by the Senate
Environment and Public Works Committee specifies the total amount of emission
reduction required in the 31-state region as does the Moffett Bill (H.R. 4829)
in the House. In addition, only the Senate version--and its predecessor,
S. 1706--freeze SO_2 emission rates in the region at their 1980 levels.

The National Governors' Association (NGA) has also developed an acid rain
control plan[5] that differs somewhat from the bills already pending in
Congress. The NGA plan outlines a two-phase control strategy designed to
reduce SO_2 emissions by 5 million tons before 1990. Under the NGA proposal,
Congress would establish a regional transport corridor covering 23 states from
Missouri to Maine. In the first phase, states in this corridor would agree on
a plan to allocate emission reductions equivalent to those that could be
achieved through a universal coal-washing program (to reduce approximately
2.5 to 3 million tons of SO_2). In the second phase, states would reduce
emissions by an additional 2 to 2.5 million tons to offset the growth in
emissions anticipated in the region. States would be allowed to trade NO_x
and SO_2 emissions on a one-for-one basis.

DOE/EPA Acid Rain Mitigation Study

One of the earliest analyses of the impacts of regulatory alternatives to
control acid rain precursors was prepared for DOE, EPA, and Argonne National

TABLE 7-2. COMPARISON OF ACID RAIN LEGISLATION PENDING IN CONGRESS[a]

Feature	S.3041	S.1706 (Mitchell Bill)	S.1709 (Moynihan Bill)	H.R.4816 (D'Amours Bill)	H.R.4829 (Moffett Bill)
Impact Region	31 states east of, and bordering, the Mississippi River, and District of Columbia	31 states east of, and bordering, the Mississippi River, and District of Columbia	31 states east of, and bordering, the Mississippi River, and District of Columbia	31 states east of, and bordering, the Mississippi River	31 states east of, and bordering, the Mississippi River, and District of Columbia
Source Emission Increase	• Existing utility and industrial sources must meet January 1, 1981 SIP limits • Existing sources of SO_2 and NO_x—no increase from 1980 emission rate unless offset (exemptions provided for states with all sources below 1.2 lb SO_2/MMBtu rate in 1980 and for "coal-capable" power plants) • New sources (coming on line after 1995) must offset SO_2 emissions unless they meet BACT and most stringent emission limitation for their source type.	No significant increase permitted (SO_2 and NO_x) from major sources unless offset elsewhere within the region	No provision	No provision	No provision
Reduction Required	8 million tons/yr SO_2 from 1980 actual emissions	10 million tons/yr SO_2 from 1980 actual emissions	By 12/31/91, lesser of: 1) 85% of allowable 1980 SO_2 emissions from all non-NSPS utility units emitting >50 KT/yr and having 1980 rate >3 lb/MMBtu, or either: 2a) 50% of allowable 1980 SO_2 emissions from all utility units >1 MW, where 1980 average statewide utility emission rate <2 lb, or 2b) 75% of allowable 1980 SO_2 emissions from all utility units >1 MW where 1980 average statewide utility emission rate >2 lb	Each state must reduce, by 1990, SO_2 in amount equal to sum of: 1) 85% of 1980 level not less than 0.61 lb/MMBtu from those non-NSPS utility plants in states which are the 50 highest 1980 SO_2 utility emitters or .2 lb/MMBtu, whichever is lower, and 2) Application of 1.2 lb/MMBtu limit to all other non-NSPS utility units 100 MW in state	10 million tons/yr from 1980 actual or allowable emissions

(continued)

TABLE 7-2 (continued)

Feature	S.3041	S.1706 (Mitchell Bill)	S.1709 (Moynihan Bill)	H.R.4816 (D'Amours Bill)	H.R.4829 (Moffett Bill)
State Share of Reduction	If Governors cannot agree on an emission allocation plan, emission reductions will be allocated based on utility SO_2 emissions in excess of 1.5 lb/ MMBtu rate	Equal to ratio of state's utility (all) emissions (actual) in excess of 1.2 lb sulfur (SIC)/MMBtu to region's total utility (all) emissions (actual) in excess of 1.2 lb sulfur (SIC)/MMBtu	See reduction required	See reduction required	Equal to ratio of state's actual 1980 utility emissions in excess of 1.2 lb SO_2/MMBtu to region's total actual 1980 utility emissions in excess of 1.2 lb SO_2/MMBtu
Schedule For Reduction	Reductions must be achieved by January 1, 1993, unless an innovative system of continuous emission reduction is employed or existing sources are replaced by new facilities with substantially lower emissions, in which case reductions must be achieved by January 1, 1995	Unspecified phases; completion 10 years from enactment	Only final date (12/31/91) specified	1) Reductions for large units begin 2 years from enactment, completed by 1990 2) Reductions for other units begin 3 years from enactment, completed by 1990	Phased; reduction beginning 5 years from enactment, substantially complete 8 years from enactment; and completed 10 years from enactment
Reduction Approaches Permitted		May be used if enforceable: 1) least emissions dispatch, 2) early retirement, 3) quantifiable reductions from energy conservation investment, and 4) regional trading	1) Trading offsets within region, 2) early retirement, and 3) energy conservation	1) Transferable emission reduction credits within selected subregions, 2) energy conservation investment reductions, and 3) early retirement	If enforceable: 1) least emissions dispatch, 2) early retirement, 3) quantifiable reductions from energy conservation investments, 4) purchase and sale of reduction credits within subregions, 5) precombustion fuel cleaning, 6) fuel switching, 7) FGD, and 8) combustion changes
NO_x Credits		Allowed on basis of two units NO_x for each SO_2 unit, by weight	Allowed on basis of two units NO_x for each SO_2 unit	No provision	Allowed on basis of two units NO_x for each SO_2 unit, by weight

(continued)

TABLE 7-2 (continued)

Feature	S.3041	S.1706 (Mitchell Bill)	S.1709 (Moynihan Bill)	H.R.4816 (D'Amours Bill)	H.R.4829 (Moffett Bill)
Regulatory Deadlines/ State Default Provisions	States have 18 months from date of enactment to agree on an emission allocation plan; within 4 years from date of enactment, State Implementation Plans should be submitted and approved	States have 2 years from enactment to adopt and submit plans to EPA and other states in region; EPA must approve plans within 4 months of submittal; if state defaults, utilities must submit plan to achieve 1.2 lb average within 3 years from enactment	Not specified	State plan required within 16 months; if state defaults, automatic 1.2 lb/MMBtu limit on all non-NSPS utility units >100 MW, to be achieved 5 years from enactment	If state does not submit plan: 1) utility submittal of plan to reduce emissions companywide, within state 1.2 lb average on 5-8-10 year schedule; 2) if utility defaults, each unit to comply with 1.2 lb limit 5 years from enactment
Studies Required	Federal Interagency Task Force on Acid Precipitation required to submit two comprehensive reports to Congress (12/31/85, 12/31/87); National Academy of Sciences to establish an independent scientific review board; also to submit two comprehensive reports to Congress (6/30/86, 6/30/88)	Long Range Transport of Air Pollutants (LRTAP) study of remaining continental U.S. within 2 years of enactment	No provision	No provision	LRTAP study of remaining continental U.S. within 2 years of enactment
Miscellaneous Provisions	Increased funding of $10 million for interagency Task Force from FY 1983 through FY 1987; also authorizes $5 million for 3 years for liming demonstration in lakes containing game fish			Requires continuous monitoring of all utility units 100 MW and all sources where state plan requires reduction	

aBased on information contained in References 1, 2, 3, and 4.

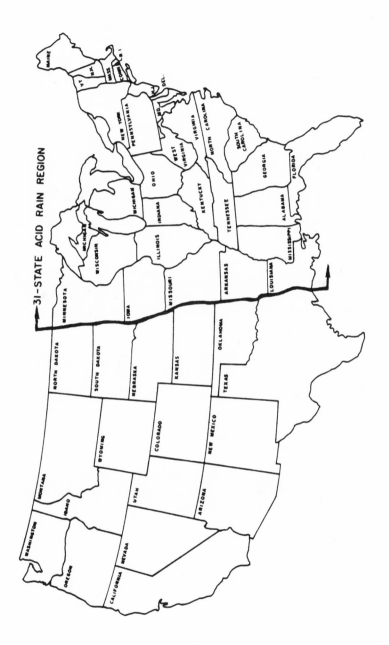

Figure 7-1.   The 31-state acid rain region.

Laboratory by ICF, Inc.[6] This analysis, which predates the specific legislative proposals discussed earlier, focuses on the potential impacts of 22 alternative regulatory scenarios on SO_2 and NO_x emissions and electric utility pollution control costs. Although the study examined impacts for 4 future years (1985, 1990, 1995, and 2000), both the executive summary volume and the volume that presents the study's findings and assumptions focus on impacts in the year 1990.

The basic alternatives examined included:

● 10 and 30 percent SO_2 emission rollbacks—these rollbacks were treated as broad regional emission limits that permitted trading of emission rights among sources within the region being analyzed.

● 2.0 and 4.0 lb SO_2/MMBtu emission limits—these limits provided a "cap" or ceiling on emission rates from individual sources.

Most of the regulatory scenarios that ICF analyzed involved some variation of these basic alternatives. Some scenarios focused on the impacts of these alternatives on only the 31-state Acid Rain Mitigation Study (ARMS) region outlined in Figure 7-1; others looked at impacts on the 45 Coal and Electric Utilities Model (CEUM) demand regions, which roughly encompass the 48 states in the continental U.S. Several scenarios model the impacts of implementing local coal protection policies in conjunction with these basic alternatives; others examine the effects of trading SO_2 and NO_x emissions, or using the Limestone Injected Multistage Burner (LIMB) technology in place of, or in addition to, more conventional control technologies. The study also analyzed an SO_2 emission tax and a "cap" on NO_x emission rates.

Tables 7-3 and 7-4 summarize the changes in utility SO_2 emissions and SO_2 control costs due to each of the four basic alternatives. The impacts of implementing a $0.15 per pound tax on utility SO_2 emissions are also presented. The study results show that only small additional emission reductions can be achieved by implementing any of the basic alternatives outside of the 31-state ARMS region. This report also demonstrates the cost advantages of permitting sources to trade emission rights across a large geographic area.

OTA Analysis

Congress' Office of Technology Assessment has also prepared a report[7] that contains estimates of the costs of regulatory strategies to control acid rain. As the discussion below indicates, the OTA report presents its own analysis of the costs of several different acid rain control measures (including the Mitchell and Moynihan bills described earlier) and also summarizes the results of several previous studies on the same topic. OTA's analysis focuses exclusively on the cost of achieving SO_2 emission reductions from electric utilities in the 31 states east of, or bordering, the Mississippi River.

OTA's analysis, which is summarized in Figure 7-2, focused on the costs of achieving a series of maximum emission limits (termed "caps") ranging from

TABLE 7-3. 1990 UTILITY SO$_2$ EMISSIONS--CHANGES FROM BASE CASE[6] (10^6 tons/yr)

	Base	ARMS region		Each CEUM region		4.0-lb limit	2.0-lb limit	$0.15 tax
		10%	30%	10%	30%			
ARMS Region								
Coal								
Existing	15.2	-1.7	-5.1	-1.7	-5.0	-2.7	-7.0	-6.1
NSPS	0.6	-	-	-	-	-	-	-
RNSPS[a]	0.2							
Total	16.0	-1.7	-5.1	-1.7	-5.0	-2.7	-7.0	-6.1
Oil/Gas	1.1	-	-	-	-0.1	-	-	-
Total	17.1	-1.7	-5.1	-1.7	-5.1	-2.7	-7.0	-6.1
West								
Coal								
Existing	1.1	-	-	-0.1	-0.4	-	-0.2	-0.1
NSPS	0.4	-	-	-0.1	-0.1	-	-	-
RNSPS[a]	0.1							
Total	1.6	-	-	-0.2	-0.5	-	-0.2	-0.1
Oil/Gas	0.1							
Total	1.8	-	-	-0.2	-0.5	-	-0.2	-0.1
Total U.S.								
Coal								
Existing	16.3	-1.7	-5.2	-1.8	-5.4	-2.8	-7.2	-6.2
NSPS	1.0	-	-	-0.1	-0.1	-	+0.1	-
RNSPS[a]	0.3							
Total	17.7	-1.7	-5.1	-1.9	-5.5	-2.7	-7.2	-6.1
Oil/Gas	1.2	-	-	-	-0.1	-	-	-
Total	18.9	-1.7	-5.1	-1.9	-5.7	-2.7	-7.1	-6.1

[a]Revised New Source Performance Standards.

TABLE 7-4. 1990 UTILITY COSTS--CHANGES FROM BASE CASE[6]

	ARMS region		Each CEUM region		4.0-lb limit	2.0-lb limit	$0.15 tax
	10%	30%	10%	30%			
Annualized Costs ($ 1980 x 10^9/yr)							
ARMS	+0.1	+0.9	+0.4	+1.4	+0.7	+2.2	+1.1
West	-	-	+0.9	+2.5	-	+0.4	-
Total	+0.1	+0.9	+1.3	+3.9	+0.8	+2.7	+1.4
Present Value of Costs ($ 1980 x 10^9)	+0.7	+15.2	+6.4	+44.4	+9.7	+46.1	+17.1
Percent Change in Electricity Rate							
ARMS	+0.1	+0.7	+0.3	+1.1	+0.6	+1.8	+0.9
West	-	-	+1.4	+3.9	-	+0.7	-
Total	+0.1	+0.5	+0.7	+2.0	+0.4	+1.4	+0.7
Dollars/Ton Removed (1980 $) Annualized Cost Basis							
ARMS	+80	+180	+210	+270	+270	+320	+180
West	-	-	+4,690	+4,680	-	+2,580	+2,740
Total	+90	+180	+650	+680	+280	+380	+230
Objective Function Basis	+50	+170	+210	+470	+280	+480	+180
Capital Costs ($ 1980 x 10^9)	+0.9	+3.7	+1.3	+8.3	+1.4	+10.0	+3.6
Percent Change in Incremental Capital Requirements	+0.3	+1.2	+0.4	+2.7	+0.5	+3.2	+1.2

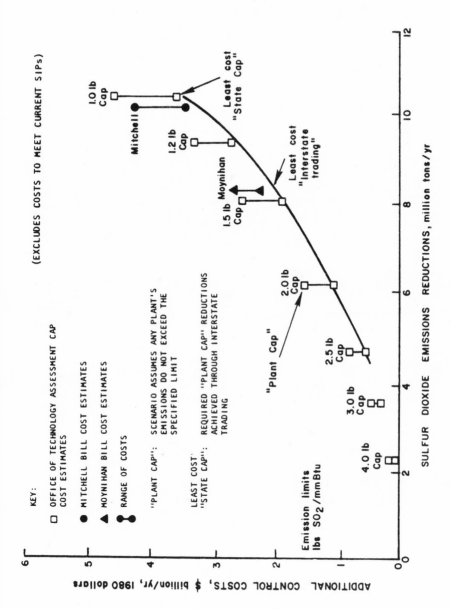

Figure 7-2. Cost of sulfur dioxide controls on electric utilities.[7]

1.0 to 4.0 pounds of sulfur dioxide emitted per million Btu of energy
input.[7] Emission reductions as a result of these "caps" range from 2.2 to
10.3 million tons per year. These emission reductions include 1.5 million
tons of reductions required under current State Implementation Plans (SIPs),
however, the costs presented in the OTA report consider only those reductions
that would be required beyond SIP compliance.

The vertical lines joining each set of symbols indicate the range of
costs that might be associated with the specified emission reduction. The
upper estimate assumes that each state would achieve the required reductions
by imposing uniform emission ceilings on all utility plants (labeled "plant
cap"). The lower estimate assumes that each state will choose the most
cost-effective way of meeting the required emission reductions (labeled "state
cap"). The curve on the graph represents the "regional least cost" that could
be achieved with total freedom to trade emission reduction obligations across
the entire region. For emission reductions less than 2.5 million tons below
SIP compliance (e.g., in the 3.0 to 4.0 pound cap area of the graph), the
"regional least cost" is not significantly different from estimated costs of a
"state cap." For comparison, OTA's estimates of the costs of two legislative
proposals have also been included in the graph. The Moynihan Bill (S. 1709)
would decrease SO_2 emissions by approximately 8 million tons at a cost of
between $2.4 and $2.9 billion annually. The Mitchell Bill (S. 1706) would
decrease annual emissions by 10 million tons at a cost of between $3.7 and
$4.5 billion per year.

Figure 7-3 compares OTA's estimates to estimates of the costs of acid
rain control measures developed by other groups.[7] Only the emission
reductions for which cost estimates were calculated are included on the
graph. The PEDCo study was prepared for DOE, the Teknekron analysis was
prepared for EPA and DOE, and the ICF analyses were performed for EPA, DOE,
Edison Electric Institute, and the National Wildlife Federation. The Peabody,
PEDCo, and DOE estimates represent reductions below actual 1980 emissions, and
the ICF and Teknekron model estimates are shown as emission reductions below
projected 1990 emission levels. Emission reductions and costs (in 1980
dollars) are presented in tabular form in Table 7-5.[7] For an 8-million ton
per year reduction, which is the level specified in the bill reported out of
the Senate Committee on Environment and Public Works, cost estimates range
from slightly under $2 billion per year to almost $4 billion per year. In
most cases, the cost estimates prepared by OTA are higher than the ones
presented in previous studies.

OTA has also analyzed the costs and distributional consequences of a
number of approaches to allocating an 8-million ton reduction in sulfur
dioxide emissions to states. These approaches include:

- Requiring each state to reduce its emissions by 50 percent;

- Allocating emission reductions to states using the formula in
  S. 1709 (Moynihan Bill);

- Requiring power plants in each state to comply with an emission cap
  of 1.5 lb SO_2/MMBtu;

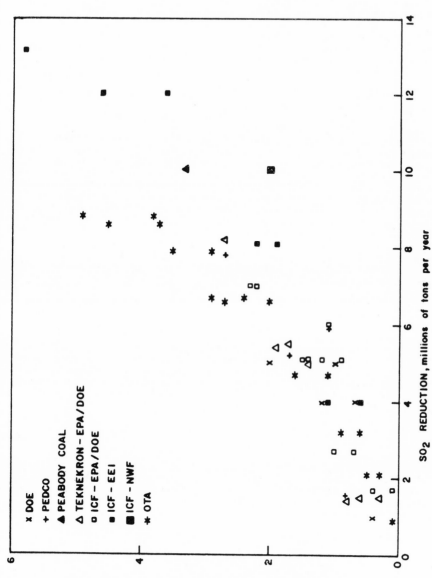

Figure 7-3. Comparison of utility SO$_2$ control cost estimates.[7]

TABLE 7-5.   COMPARISON OF UTILITY SO$_2$ CONTROL COST ESTIMATES[7]

Source	SO$_2$ reduction (millions of tons/year)	Annualized costs ($ billions/year, 1980 dollars)
Reductions Below 1980 Emissions		
DOE[a]		
Coal-Switching	4.0	0.6-1.2
FGD	5.0	1.0-2.0
Coal Cleaning	1.0	0.3-0.4
PEDCO[a]		
Coal-Switching	5.9	1.1
FGD 60%	5.2	1.7
FGD 90%	7.8	2.7
Coal Cleaning	1.5	0.8
Peabody Coal[b]	10.0	3.3
Reductions Below Projected 1990 Emissions		
Teknekron--EPA/DOE[a]		
4 lb Cap	1.5	0.3
4 lb Cap + Local Coal	1.5	0.6
2 lb Cap	5.5	1.7
2 lb Cap + Local Coal	5.4	1.9
30% FGD	5.0	1.4
50% FGD	8.2	2.7
Coal Cleaning	1.4	0.8
ICF--EPA/DOE[a]		
10% Regional	1.7	0.1
10% Each State	1.7	0.4
4 lb Cap	2.7	0.7
4 lb Cap + Local Coal	2.7	1.0
15¢/lb Tax	6.0	1.1
30% Regional	5.1	0.9
30% Regional + Local Coal	5.1	1.2
30% Each State	5.1	1.4
30% Each State + Local Coal	5.1	1.5
2 lb Cap	7.0	2.2
2 lb Cap + Local Coal	7.0	2.3

(continued)

TABLE 7-5 (continued)

Source	SO_x reduction (millions of tons/year)	Annualized costs ($ billions/year, 1980 dollars)
ICF--EEI[c]		
S.1706-Offset Growth	13.1	5.8
S.1706-Offset Growth, NO_x & Ind. Trades	12.0	3.6-4.6
S.1706-SIP Credit, NO_x & Ind. Trades	8.1	1.9-2.2
EEI Rollback	4.0	0.6-1.1
ICF--NWF[c]	10.0	2.0
Reductions Below 1980 SIP Emissions		
Office of Technology Assessment[d]		
1.0 lb Cap	8.8	3.8-4.9
1.2 lb Cap	7.9	2.9-3.5
1.5 lb Cap	6.6	2.0-2.7
2.0 lb Cap	4.7	1.1-1.6
2.5 lb Cap	3.2	0.6-0.9
3.0 lb Cap	2.1	0.3-0.5
4.0 lb Cap	0.9	0.1
Mitchell	8.6	3.7-4.5
Moynihan	6.7	2.4-2.9

[a]Reference 8.

[b]Reference 9.

[c]Reference 10.

[d]Reference 11.

- Requiring power plants in each state to achieve an average emission rate of 1.3 lb SO_2/MMBtu;

- Requiring each state to achieve an average emission rate of 11.3 lb SO_2 per MWh of total electricity output;

- Requiring each state to achieve an average emission rate from all sources (utility, industrial, etc.) of 200 lb SO_2 per capita; and

- Requiring each state to achieve an average emission density of 18 tons SO_2 per square mile.

Table 7-6 presents OTA's estimates of the regional cost of using each of these alternative approaches to allocating reductions to states.[7] The costs vary from formula to formula, ranging from $2.0 billion per year, corresponding to the lower estimate of the 1.5 pound cap, to $3.5 billion per year, corresponding to the higher estimate for the emission density approach. States vary as to the degree to which their costs are affected by alternative approaches. Some states are consistently allocated relatively large costs. These include: Indiana, Kentucky, Missouri, Ohio, Pennsylvania, Tennessee, and West Virginia. However, the control costs for Delaware, Maryland, Massachusetts, and New Hampshire are influenced strongly by the allocation approach used. The control costs for most of the remaining states are relatively low regardless of which allocation approach is used.

The OTA report also contains a discussion of the effects of acid rain control measures on the United States coal market. OTA's analysis is based on estimates of the impact of SO_2 reductions on coal production developed by ICF, Inc. for a variety of clients. OTA combined ICF production projections with coal-miner productivity and income data to project the employment and economic effects of acid rain controls.

ICF's production estimates indicate that although acid rain control measures will not produce changes in nationwide coal production, they will redistribute production among the major coal-producing regions. OTA concludes that in the high-sulfur coal areas of the Midwest (Illinois, Indiana, and western Kentucky) and northern Appalachia (Pennsylvania, Ohio, and northern West Virginia), 1990 coal production is projected to be less than it would have been in 1990 without acid rain controls for all emission reduction scenarios. For emission reductions of 10 million tons and greater, production in these areas is projected to decline 10 to 20 percent below 1979 levels. Estimates of production declines are averaged over these regions, and thus may be greater or less in some states and counties than others. For the low-sulfur coal areas of central Appalachia (eastern Kentucky, southern West Virginia, Tennessee, and Virginia) and the western United States, acid rain control measures are projected to expand coal production beyond what 1990 levels would be, assuming no change in regulations.

Employment changes in general are projected to follow changes in production. Employment effects are most severe in Illinois, Ohio, northern West Virginia, and western Kentucky--for these areas, coal-mining employment is projected to decline more than 10 percent below current levels.

TABLE 7-6.   REGIONAL COSTS OF ALTERNATIVE APPROACHES TO ALLOCATING
AN 8-MILLION TON REDUCTION IN SO_2 EMISSIONS [7]

Allocation approach[a]	State least cost ($ billion/ year)[b]	Average cost ($/ton)[c]	Plant cap ($ billion/ year)[b]	Average cost ($/ton)[c]
50% Each	2.6	390	3.2	480
S.1709	2.5	370	2.9	440
1.5 lb Cap	2.0	310	2.7	410
1.3 lb Average	2.1	320	2.7	400
Total Electricity	2.1	310	2.6	390
Per Capita	2.6	390	2.9	440
Emission Density	3.4	520	3.5	540

[a]Alternative approaches explained in Reference 7.

[b]All costs in 1980 dollars. The allocation formula is used to allocate
emission reductions to states. "State least cost" assumes that each state
will choose the most cost-effective way of meeting the required emissions
reductions. "Plant cap" assumes that each state would achieve its allocated
reductions by imposing uniform emissions ceiling on each utility plant.

[c]Average costs are calculated on the basis of emissions reductions below
SIP compliance levels.

OTA also estimated the impact of employment changes on miner income. Their estimates of direct income effects for a 10-million ton emission reduction are listed below:

- Northern Appalachia: $300 to $400 million per year loss,

- Central Appalachia: $400 to $600 million per year gain,

- Midwest: $300 to $400 million per year loss, and

- West: $200 to $300 million per year gain.

As the report notes, however, at the national level, the monetary effects of coal-market shifts are minimal because benefits to low-sulfur regions are projected to balance out costs to high-sulfur regions.

Analysis of a Senate Emission Reduction Bill (S. 3041)

As discussed previously, the Senate is considering an acid rain amendment to the Clean Air Act. EPA asked ICF, Inc., which had prepared several analyses[4,10,12] of the bill's predecessor (S. 1706, the Mitchell Bill), to estimate the costs of this new bill. The study[4] focuses on the Bill's impact on SO_2 emissions and control costs for both electric utility and industrial sources; it also examines its effect on regional coal production. ICF's analysis indicates that the Senate bill will require sources in the 31-state region identified in Figure 7-1 to reduce SO_2 emissions by 9.5 billion tons (from base case levels) by 1995. Most of these reductions are necessary to meet the Bill's requirement of an 8-million ton reduction in SO_2 emissions; the remaining reductions are necessary primarily to offset growth in emissions between 1980 and 1995. The 1995 annualized cost of achieving these reductions ranges from 3.3 to 4.5 billion (1982) dollars. This variation in costs stems from assumptions about sources' ability to trade emission reductions; the lowest estimate corresponds to the provision included in the bill which permits interstate trading of emission reductions. The industrial sector's share of these costs is relatively small for 1995, totaling only $0.6 billion dollars. By 2010, the results indicate that costs to the industrial sector may actually exceed those to electric utilities.

LIMING

Another option for use in a program to manage acid deposition is to mitigate its harmful effects in susceptible areas. If such an option proved practical, it might be used either alone or in conjunction with emission control strategies. Methods suggested have included increasing the pH of affected lakes, soils, forests, etc.; developing protective coatings for exposed structures and materials; and developing acid-resistant species of crops, trees, and fish. Only the first approach, which involves liming of lakes and/or streams, has received any serious investigation thus far.

The term "liming" applies to any procedure whereby the pH of an acidified lake is raised. Liming can be used to protect sensitive waters that will

continue to receive acidic inputs for the immediate future and to rehabilitate
those waters which have already been impacted by acid precipitation. Various
substances have been used alone or in combination to achieve this purpose
including soda ash, potash, dolomite, calcium hydroxide, calcium oxide,
limestone (calcium carbonate), and olivine. Application of both calcium
hydroxide and calcium carbonate has been found to be the most effective
approach in precipitating metals and humates and increasing the buffering
capacity of lakes.[13] Limestone application has proved to be the least
expensive. Organic carbon addition has recently received attention as a
possible management strategy to mitigate aquatic acidification, but little if
any research has been conducted in this area.

Just as in the agronomic application of limestone, commonly done to
counteract the effects of acidification from fertilizers, the financial cost
of the liming treatment would have to be carefully balanced against the loss
incurred if the treatment were not given. This balance could be a major
consideration in remote or generally inaccessible areas or in areas where the
buffering capacity of the lime applied is rapidly spent, thereby requiring
repeated treatments at increased costs.

Liming of acidified lakes was first attempted in Sweden and effects have
been well documented. Henriksen and Johannessen[14] have presented a survey
of the literature. Swedish studies have also been reported by Grahn and
Hultberg[15,16] and Hultberg and Grahn.[17] Wright[18] has reviewed an early
attempt in which addition of chalk to Swedish lakes increased pH and led to
increased phytoplankton growth and improved fish survival. The reclamation of
acidified lakes in Canada has been discussed by Scheider et al.[19]

The New York State Bureau of Fisheries has added lime to 51 ponds since
the mid-1950's. The emphasis was on maintaining fish populations that were
unique or especially important for recreational activities. However, as
mentioned, the logistical difficulties encountered in attempting to transport
large quantities of limestone to isolated Adirondack ponds often made the
final benefits realized somewhat questionable. Further studies are required
to assess the true feasibility of this approach and the methodologies that
would need to be applied.

Henriksen and Johannessen's report details the forms of calcium that
could be used and options available for application. They also present
methods of calculating the lime required to raise the pH of a given body of
water to 5.5.[14]

Various factors must be considered in attempting to assess the
feasibility of liming acidified waters. The efficiency of liming in terms of
maintenance of elevated pH requires careful consideration of lake turnover
times and the source of acid input to the lake. The addition of lime to
streams has been carried out for many years and often has advantages over the
direct application of lime to lakes, although direct liming of lakes is the
most common and successful approach used to date. Other systems for practical
application of lime include lime wells that consist of a column of lime in a
river bank. Water diverted to the base of this column and subsequently
entering a lake offsets any pH reduction occurring with spring snow melt while

avoiding potential problems associated with sporadic addition of large amounts of lime to treated waters. Table 7-7 compares the advantages and disadvantages of various liming application techniques.[13]

In addition, expected and resulting physical, chemical, biological, and ecological changes occurring in lake waters must be carefully studied subsequent to liming. Although, to date, no observations of long-term detrimental effects of liming have been observed, the true ecological consequences are unknown. Invariably, alkalinity and pH will increase. Phosphorus release from lake sediments may be disrupted and affect the nutrient cycling of the ecosystem. Concentrations of Zn, Mn, and Al will also drop with elevations in pH. Tables 7-8 and 7-9 summarize the physical and chemical changes observed in acidified and limed aquatic ecosystems, respectively.[13]

Among the biological changes that have been reported subsequent to liming are increased phytoplankton and zooplankton diversity and increased bacterial populations. Sphagnum and other acidophilic plants decrease in number. Reported effects of liming on biomass and fish populations are controversial.[13] In some instances, fish species' restoration has occurred due to the precipitation of heavy metals as pH increases. However, the success of liming depends on the initial concentration of metals; i.e., while liming may improve other aspects of water quality, it may not sufficiently reduce metals concentrations to nontoxic levels. In fish populations whose age distribution was skewed toward older groups as a result of acidification, liming resulted in restoration of younger age groups. Addition of $CaCO_3$ and $Ca(OH)_2$ to two acidic lakes in Sudbury, Ontario, increased pH, decreased heavy metal concentrations (although not always to nontoxic levels for some plant life and fish species), and caused a temporary decline in chlorophyll.[13,19,20] A summary of biological changes reported to occur in acidified and limed aquatic ecosystems is presented in Table 7-10.[13]

There are potential problems associated with liming of waters to counteract acidification and data are lacking in these areas. Emmehn[21] has reported that the concentrations of toxic metals in some commercial limestones may pose potential concern. Dickson[22] has reported that aluminum leached from the soil by acid precipitation is especially hazardous to fish populations after liming and several fish kills can be attributed to this cause. Aluminum toxicity is apparently increased at pH levels between 4 and 6. He also states that liming increases cadmium accumulation in lakes. Research obviously is needed to quantify these problems before general liming programs can be initiated.

As mentioned, treatment of affected waters by large-scale liming programs would represent major undertakings that could be logistically difficult and expensive. Detailed evaluation of the economic realities involved in such programs must be made. Several investigators[23,24] have estimated that liming costs in New York State ranged from $55 to $470 per hectare of water surface and averaged $150. R. A. Barnes in an Air Pollution Control Association Acid Rain Panel discussion estimated the cost of liming affected areas in Europe to be $150 million, which he believed was a reasonable cost alternative when compared to the costs of controlling combustion

TABLE 7-7. GENERAL COMPARISON OF THE VARIOUS LIMING APPLICATION TECHNIQUES[13]

Technique	Countries employing various techniques	Advantages	Disadvantages
Trucks and spreaders or blower	Norway Sweden	Can distribute large amounts of lime in a relatively short time period	Can only be applied in areas where the streams and lakes are accessible by roads
Boats	Canada Sweden United States	Simple and relatively inexpensive technique	Application is a relatively slow process
		Widely utilized, therefore comparison of results can be made	Difficult to utilize at remote bodies of water
Aerial applications	Canada Sweden United States	Facilitates access to remote sites	Cost-intensive
		Less labor-intensive	
		Can apply large amounts of lime in a relatively short time period	
Silos	Sweden	Allows for more precise maintenance of pH, since liming material is applied as needed	Need regular maintenance, as existing silos continually break down
			Overall, relatively expensive to build and maintain
Diversion wells	Norway Sweden	Simple and relatively inexpensive technique	May not be adaptable to all streams
			Efficiency not known
Limestone barriers	Canada Sweden United States	Simple and relatively inexpensive technique	Technique only suitable for easily accessible sites
		Once applied, the limestone is present for a relatively long time period	Technique fails during high water flows
			Controversy over low-term buffering capabilities

TABLE 7-8.   SUMMARY OF MAJOR PHYSICAL CHANGES REPORTED TO OCCUR
IN ACIDIFIED AND LIMED AQUATIC ECOSYSTEMS[13]

| Water status | Reported changes | | | |
	Water transparency	Epilimnion	Thermocline	Hypolimnion
Acidified body of water	Increase in transparency	Increase in depth of epilimnion	Increase in depth of thermocline	Increase in temperature
Limed clear water body	Initial increase in transparency (short-term)	Decrease in depth of epilimnion	Decrease in depth of thermocline	Decrease in temperature
	Decrease in water transparency (long-term)			
	No change in transparency (mildly acidic lake)			

TABLE 7-9. SUMMARY OF MAJOR CHEMICAL CHANGES REPORTED TO OCCUR IN ACIDIFIED AND LIMED AQUATIC ECOSYSTEMS[13]

Water status	Buffering capacity	pH and related parameters	Hardness	Metals	Organics	Nutrients	Addition of calcium carbonate
					Reported changes		
Acidified body of water	Loss of HCO₃ buffering	Decrease in pH	Decrease in hardness	Increase in mobilization and concentration of soluble metals	Complexation with soluble metals (e.g., Al)	Reduction in ions important to biological production because they are bound to benthic algae and sphagnum tissue	Mitigates the acidification
		Decrease in alkalinity	Decrease in concentration of calcium	Change in speciation of soluble metals		Possible decrease in phosphorus because it is complexed with Al	
		Increase in acidity					
Limed body of water	Increase in HCO₃ buffering	Increase in pH	Increase in hardness	Change in speciation of soluble metals[a]	Complexation with soluble metals and calcium	Increase, decrease or no change in total phosphorus concentrations[a]	Dissolution over a long period of time (up to 3 years)[a]
		Increase in alkalinity	Increase in concentration of calcium[a]	Decrease in metal concentrations by precipitation or physical settling	Decrease in concentration of dissolved organic matter by precipitation or deposition (e.g., dissolved organic carbon chelated with Al)[a]	Slight increase or no change in total nitrogen concentrations	Becomes nonreactive in a relatively short period of time (as little as 2 weeks) because CaCO₃ is complexed with bottom sediments or coated by insoluble metal compounds[a]
		Decrease in acidity				Changes in the distribution of organic and inorganic nitrogen species	

[a]Changes resulting from liming that need additional research.

TABLE 7-10. SUMMARY OF MAJOR BIOLOGICAL CHANGES REPORTED TO OCCUR IN ACIDIFIED AND LIMED AQUATIC ECOSYSTEMS[13]

Water status	Reported changes				
	Bacteria	Phytoplankton and other primary producers	Zooplankton	Benthic macro-invertebrates	Fish
Acidified body of water	Decrease in numbers	Decrease in species and numbers	Limitation of species and simplification of communities	Limitation of species and simplification of communities	Decline in populations
		Shift in taxonomic composition towards acid-tolerant green algae and flagellates	Shift in taxonomic composition towards acid-tolerant species	Shift in taxonomic composition towards acid-tolerant species	Decrease in recruitment through mortality of eggs and larvae and disturbance of adult reproductive physiology or behavior
		Encroachment of sphagnum moss			Fish mortality due to physiological disturbance in osmoionic regulation of fish
		No change in primary productivity			Fish mortality due to elevated metal concentrations
Limed body of water with preneutralization pH of 4.0 to 5.0 and very high metal concentrations (e.g. Middle (M), Hannah (H), and Lohi (L) Lakes near Sudbury, Ontario)	Aerobic heterotrophic bacteria increased several orders of magnitude (M&L)	Initial decline in phytoplankton biomass (M,H,L)	Immediate decline in biomass (M,H,L)	Immediate decline in biomass (M,H,L)	Stocked smallmouth bass (M) and stocked brook trout (L) were eradicated due to metal toxicity[a]
	Taxonomic composition changed to more acid-tolerant species (M&L)	Phytoplankton biomass recovered in several months almost up to pre-liming levels (M,H,L)	Gradual reestablishment of biomass, up to almost pre-liming levels, in several years (L)		Experiments with stocked rainbow trout also resulted in mortality due to metal toxicity (M&L)[a]
		Species changed from acid-tolerant dino-flagellates to less acid-tolerant chrysophytes (M,H,L)	Species changed from acid-tolerant clado-cerans to less acid-tolerant copepods (M,H,L)		
		Addition of phosphorus enhanced phytoplankton recovery and caused an increase in biomass (M&H)[a]	Addition of phosphorus enhanced recovery of biomass (M&H)[a]		

(continued)

TABLE 7-10 (continued)

Water status	Bacteria	Reported changes			Fish
		Phytoplankton and other primary producers	Zooplankton	Benthic macro-invertebrates	
Limed body of water with preneutraliza-tion pH of 4.0 to 5.5 and low metal concen-trations (e.g., Lysevaten (Ly), Stensjon (S), and Bredvatten (B) Lakes in Sweden)	Bacterial pop-ulations in-creased result-ing in an inci-dence of fin rot (Mersey Fish Hatchery, Nova Scotia)	Initial decline in phyto-plankton biomass (Ly, S,B)	Immediate decline in biomass (Ly,S, B)	Immediate decline in biomass (Ly,S,B)	Aluminum toxicity lethal to trout and salmon (Sweden)[a]
		Change in speciation from acid-tolerant to less acid-tolerant species (Ly,S,B)	Gradual recovery of biomass, up to or occasionally greater than pre-liming levels, in several years (Ly,S,B)	Acid-tolerant chironomids replaced by less acid-tolerant species in several years (Ly,S,B)	Reproduction of acid-sensitive salmon, arctic char, brook brout, brown trout, and sea trout (Sweden)
		Phytoplankton biomass recovered in several months almost up to pre-liming levels (Ly,S,B)	Species changed from acid-tolerant clado-cerans to less acid-tolerant copepods (Ly,S,B)	Reintroduced species generally survived (S&B)	Incubation of rainbow trout, lake trout, and brook trout within crushed limestone substrates greatly enhanced hatching success and sac fry survival (George Lake, Ontario)
		Sphagnum mosses and benthic algal mats severely damaged or eradicated (Ly,S,B)			Raising pH of hatchery water by limestone filters increased sur-vival of Atlantic salmon parr during 3rd and 4th weeks after first feeding (Mersey, Nova Scotia)
Limed body of water with preneutraliza-tion pH of 5.6 to 5.7 and average or slightly high metal concen-trations (e.g., Nelson Lake (N) near Sudbury, Ontario)		No change in phytoplank-ton biomass (N)	Zooplankton biomass remained relatively constant (N)		No effects on established inshore fish communities (N)
					Reintroduced smallmouth bass successfully spawned (N)

[a]Changes related to liming that need additional research.

emissions.[25] Sweden is currently spending $5 million per year to lime
approximately 1000 lakes.[13] The costs of the neutralizing chemicals alone
on a mass basis range from $6.49 to $101.20 x 10^{-3} kg^{-1}.[26] The costs of
stream liming with limestone barriers, excluding labor, have ranged from $1000
to $7600 per project.[27]

An example of the complexities involved in undertaking a lake-liming
program is illustrated in Figure 7-4. This proposed lake restorative method
is called Contracid and has recently been reported in the Swedish press.[28]
As shown in Figure 7-4, this method would involve a physical "raking" of the
bottom of the lake in a manner similar to harrowing farm land. Appropriate
chemical mixtures (sodium hydroxide or sodium carbonate) to raise the lake
sediment's pH would be injected using a compressed air dosage system.
Theoretically, exchanging hydrogen cations for sodium cations would serve to
neutralize the acidity of hydrogen ions.

The Contracid method has been funded to perform a full-scale experimental
restoration of acidified Lake Lilla Galtsjon in southern Sweden. Follow-up
studies will continue through snowmelt in the spring of the year. Liming
strategies have not reached this stage in the United States and it will be
important to follow results closely.

Many uncertainties remain to be resolved on the short- and long-term
effects of liming of watersheds, streams, and lakes. The Electric Power
Research Institute recently completed an interim report to assess the
feasibility of utilizing liming as a technique to mitigate surface water
acidification.[13] The report identifies three broad categories requiring
additional research including liming materials and techniques; physical,
chemical, and biological changes associated with liming; and costs/benefits of
liming. The report cautions against generalizations of liming practices for
all aquatic ecosystems since every ecosystem has unique characteristics that
must be carefully considered on a site-by-site basis. Another area receiving
considerable interest from the scientific community is liming of the
terrestrial ecosystems. Terrestrial mitigation could address the problem of
aluminum leaching from the watershed into the aquatic ecosystem and the
problem of forest productivity.

An international workshop on current issues and research of liming of
acidified waters identified research needs, some of which include: developing
control strategies for episodic events; developing strategies to immobilize
metals; investigating deactivation of residual liming agents; conducting
long-term lake maintenance and reacidification studies; and developing and
monitoring restocking strategies.[29]

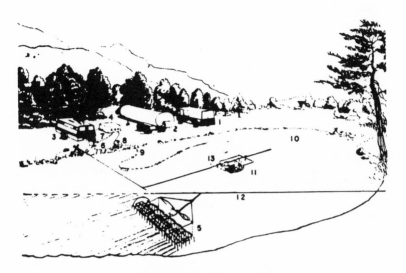

Reviving a Lake:

1. Field lab
2. Chemicals supply
3. Portable compressor
4. Chemical dilution tank
5. Harrow
6. and 7. Air feed lines
8. Air driven pump

9. Mixed chemicals supply line
10. Guide line
11. Air driven dilution pump
12. Dilution water intake
13. Pneumatic tugging arrangement

Figure 7-4. Contracid method of lake restoration.[28]

REFERENCES

1. Comptroller General of the United States. The Debate Over Acid
    Precipitation: Opposing Views, Status of Research. U.S. General
    Accounting Office, September 11, 1981.

2. Environment Reporter, Current Developments, July 30, 1982 (Vol. 13,
    No. 13). The Bureau of National Affairs, Inc., Washington, D.C.

3. Streets, D. and L. Conley. An Analysis of Proposed Legislation to
    Control Acid Rain. Argonne National Laboratory. Final Report.
    January 1983.

4. Analysis of a Senate Emission Reduction Bill (S. 3041). Prepared for the
    U.S. Environmental Protection Agency, Office of Policy and Resource
    Management, Washington, D.C. February 1983.

5. Environment Reporter, Current Developments, December 4, 1981 (Vol. 12,
    No. 32). The Bureau of National Affairs, Inc., Washington, D.C.

6. Alternative Strategies for Reducing Utility SO_2 and NO_x Emissions.
    Prepared for Argonne National Laboratory, U.S. Department of Energy, and
    U.S. Environmental Protection Agency. Draft Report. September 1981.

7. The Regional Implications of Transported Air Pollutants: An Assessment
    of Acidic Deposition and Ozone. U.S. Congress, Office of Technology
    Assessment, Washington, D.C. July 1982.

8. Department of Energy. Costs to Reduce Sulfur Dioxide Emissions. Report
    No. DOE/PE-0042. March 1982.

9. Farrand, C., Peabody Coal Company. Testimony Before the Senate
    Environment and Public Works Committee, October 19, 1981.

10. ICF, Inc. Summary of Acid Rain Analyses Undertaken by ICF for the Edison
    Electric Institute, National Wildlife Federation, and the Environmental
    Protection Agency. Prepared for Edison Electric Institute. May 1982.

11. Office of Technology Assessment. Staff Briefing Memo for the Senate
    Environment and Public Works Committee, June 2, 1982 (Revised June 4,
    1982).

12. Speyer, J. Impact of Alternative Approaches to Implement the Mitchell
    Bill on the Electric Utility and Coal Industries. Presented at the 75th
    Annual Meeting of the Air Pollution Control Assoc., New Orleans, LA, June
    1982. Paper No. 82-16.2.

13. Electric Power Research Institute. Feasibility Study to Utilize Liming
    as a Technique to Mitigate Surface Water Acidification. Interim Report,
    No. EA-2362. General Research Corporation, McLean, Virginia. April 1982

14. Henriksen, A. and M. Johannessen. Deacidification of Acid Water. SNSF Project, Report IR 5/75 Aas, Norway, 1975.

15. Grahn, O. and H. Hultberg. Development of Methods for Liming Acidic Running Waters. Swedish Water and Air Pollution Research Laboratory Report, 1975.

16. Grahn, O. and H. Hultberg. Importance of Grain Size and Geological Origin for Neutralization Effectiveness of Three Different Calcium Carbonates. Swedish Water and Air Pollution Research Laboratory Report, 1976.

17. Hultberg, H. and O. Grahn. Some Effects of Adding Lime to Lakes in W. Sweden. Swedish Water and Air Pollution Research Laboratory Report, 1975.

18. Wright, R. F. Acid Precipitation and Its Effects on Freshwater Ecosystems: An Annotated Bibliography. In: Proceedings of First International Symposium on Acid Precipitation and the Forest Ecosystem, May 12-15, 1975, Columbus, Ohio. L. S. Dochinger and T. A. Seliga, eds. U.S. Forest Service General Technical Report NE-23, U.S. Department of Agriculture, Forest Service, Northeastern Forest Experiment Station, Upper Darby, Pennsylvania. 1976. pp. 619-678.

19. Scheider, W. et al. Reclamation of Acidified Lakes near Sudbury, Ontario. Ontario Ministry of the Environment Report, Rexdale, Ontario, 1975.

20. Michalski, M. F. P. and J. Adamski. Restoration of Acidified Lakes Middle and Lohi in the Sudbury Area. In: Proceedings of the Ontario Industrial Wastes Conference. 1974. pp. 163-175.

21. Emmehn, L. Environmental Planning in Sweden--the State of Sweden's Lakes. Current Sweden, 79:1, 1977.

22. Dickson, W. Experience from Small Scale Liming in Sweden. In: Proceedings of the International Symposium on Sulfur Emissions and the Environment, London, May 1979.

23. Horn, E., J. Calquhoun, and H. Hovey. LRTAP: Acid Precipitation. J. Air Pollution Control Assoc., 30:462-466, 1980.

24. Committee on the Atmosphere and the Biosphere. National Research Council. Atmosphere-Biosphere Interactions: Toward a Better Understanding of the Ecological Consequences of Fossil Fuel Combustion. National Academy Press. Washington, D.C. 1981.

25. Barnes, R. A. Acid Rain - An International Concern. An APCA Panel Presentation. J. Air Pollution Control Assoc. 30:1089-1097, 1980.

26. Chemical Marketing Reporter. August 31, 1981.

27. Fraser, J. E. and D. L. Britt. Liming of Acidified Waters: A Review
     of Methods and Effects on Aquatic Ecosystems. Prepared for Fish and
     Wildlife Service, U.S. Department of the Interior, Washington, D.C.
     Draft Report.

28. Anonymous. A Harrowing Experience! Reviving Acidified Lakes. Sweden
     Now, 14(2):38, 1980.

29. The Liming of Acidified Waters: Issues and Research--A Report of the
     International Liming Workshop. Prepared for U.S. Department of Energy,
     Washington, D.C. ER-22-Century XY-1. December 1982.

8

Summary of Issues, Uncertainties, and Further Research Needs

This section summarizes the key issues, uncertainties, and further research needs relating to what is known of and speculated about acid rain. Table 8-1, at the end of this section, is a condensed summary of the individual issues that have surfaced from a comprehensive review of the literature. These issues, which are discussed in detail throughout the report, are organized according to the major subject areas covered: sources affecting acid rain formation; atmospheric transport, transformations, and deposition processes; monitoring programs and results; regional transport and deposition modeling; adverse and beneficial effects; and mitigative strategies. Corresponding to each issue is an indication of the level of uncertainty (viz., low, moderate, or high) as suggested in the literature. Although sometimes speculated, the level of uncertainty is often directly inferred from the literature by a lack of consensus among the experts on how a given issue relates to acid rain. In other cases, there is a clear gap in the data that prevents cause and effect relationships from being established. Finally, examination of the issues has often led to identification of specific research needs and level of intensity that may be required to alleviate the concern or uncertainty underlying an issue. These research needs are identified, where possible, to help serve as the basis for developing control alternatives and mitigative strategies.

In view of these issues and their stated levels of uncertainty, research groups and steering committees have outlined several major or aggregate issues to be addressed so that data gaps in the present knowledge on the cause and effect relationships concerning the acid rain phenomenon can be filled. The total resources required for these efforts are difficult to estimate because of the complexity and multidisciplinary talents needed to comprehensively address each issue. One of the most important of these factors is that the character of anthropogenic emissions will be constantly changing as future energy scenarios, pollution abatement procedures, mandated control requirements, and industrial processes are devised and implemented.

Several topics for future research have been identified by the "Advisory Workshop to Identify Research Needs on the Formation of Acid Precipitation" held in Alta, Utah in 1978.[1] This group of internationally-known experts in the various disciplines relating to the study of acid precipitation, stressed the following areas requiring intense investigation.

- Instrumentation: The first step should consist of accurately sampling and determining the chemical composition and controlling physical parameters involved in the formation of cloud water over temporal and spatial scales. This sampling should be supplemented with continuous aerosol monitoring.

- Field Studies: A comprehensive nationwide precipitation chemistry network is needed to document the current and future chemical composition of precipitation. Field data must be gathered for 10 key parameters controlling cloud and precipitation scavenging efficiencies and cloud chemistry.

- Modeling: Atmospheric models should incorporate heterogeneous chemical and physical processes and key variables identified in field studies.

- Laboratory Studies: Determination of the kinetics and intermediate products of sulfur and nitrogen transformation in the atmosphere is required.

- Data Analysis and Interpretation: An improved emission inventory of natural and anthropogenic sources of sulfur and nitrogen compounds is required. Emphasis should be placed on rectifying discrepancies that occur in current emission inventories when a fine grid level of analysis is used. This information must be analyzed and correlated with accurate precipitation chemistry data from field studies to show trends and variability over temporal and spatial scales.

Described in Section 1 as the forerunner to the National Acid Precipitation Assessment Plan, the Federal Acid Rain Assessment Plan,[2] prepared by the President's Acid Rain Coordination Committee, contained a comprehensive strategy to expand understanding of the phenomenon and effects of acid deposition. An abbreviated list of recommendations from the Federal Plan is presented below.

- A permanent, nationwide monitoring network (National Trends Network) for acid deposition should be established to provide a continuous high-quality record of temporal and spatial trends in the chemistry of wet and dry deposition in all major regions of the United States.

- Additional research should be initiated at once, especially in the following critical areas:

    - investigation of effects of acid precipitation on the well-being and productivity of crops, forests, soils, and aquatic ecosystems;

    - development of predictive models or simple measurements to determine the vulnerability of lakes, streams, soils, and materials to continuing acid deposition;

- development of methods for reliable measuring or estimating dry deposition; and

- development of a predictive capability to determine how changes in the spatial and temporal emission patterns affect the spatial, temporal, and chemical patterns of deposition in various regions of the United States.

• Existing information on the causes and consequences of acid deposition should be utilized fully in formulating interim approaches to the control of acid deposition and/or mitigation of its effects.

The National Acid Precipitation Assessment Plan, released in June of 1982,[3] contains a comprehensive summary of research to be carried out by the Interagency Task Force over the next 10 years. The Acid Precipitation Act of 1980, which was the authorizing legislation for the overall National Program, required that the National Plan include comprehensive research programs for:

• Identifying the sources of atmospheric emissions contributing to acid precipitation;

• Establishing and operating a nationwide, long-term monitoring network to detect and measure levels of acid precipitation;

• Conducting research in atmospheric physics and chemistry to facilitate understanding of the processes by which substances emitted into the atmosphere are transformed into acid precipitation;

• Developing and specifying the application of atmospheric transport models for use in the prediction of long-range transport of substances causing acid precipitation;

• Defining geographic areas of impact through deposition monitoring, and identifying sensitive areas and areas at risk;

• Broadening of impact data bases by consolidating existing data on water and soil chemistry and by conducting trend analyses;

• Developing dose-response functions with respect to soils, soil organisms, aquatic and amphibious organisms, crop plants, and forest plants;

• Establishing and carrying out system studies with respect to plant physiology, aquatic ecosystems, soil chemistry systems, soil microbial systems, and forest ecosystems;

• Assessing the economic effects of (a) acid precipitation on crops, forests, fisheries, and recreational and aesthetic resources and structures, and (b) alternative technologies to remedy or otherwise ameliorate any harmful effects that may result from acid precipitation;

● Documenting current federal activities related to research on acid precipitation and ensuring that such activities are coordinated to prevent needless duplication and waste of financial and technical resources;

● Effecting cooperation in current and planned acid precipitation research and development programs between affected and contributing states and with other sovereign nations having a commonality of interest; and

● Analyzing existing information on acid precipitation as a means to formulate and to present periodic recommendations to the Congress and the concerned agencies on actions that can be taken by these bodies to alleviate acid precipitation and its effects.

The issues discussed in Table 8-1 below, and those underlying the recommendations of the three groups referenced above, demonstrate that insufficient knowledge exists regarding the explicit causes and total effects of acid rain. Research efforts under the direction of the Federal Interagency Task Force as well as numerous studies funded by the private sector are focused on resolving basic issues and uncertainties. Details of these efforts are presented in Section 9.

TABLE 8-1.   SUMMARY OF ISSUES, UNCERTAINTIES, AND FURTHER RESEARCH NEEDS

Item/issue	Level of uncertainty	Need for further research
SOURCES AFFECTING ACID RAIN FORMATION		
• Magnitude assessment of naturally produced SO_x emissions relative to manmade SO_x emissions (global basis).	Moderate: Natural SO_x emission estimates have been constantly revised. The latest reported estimate attributes about 40 percent of all sulfur emissions to man's activities.	Low-Moderate: Even though some natural sources of SO_x may be significant, they are globally distributed, whereas manmade emissions are much more concentrated. The role of biogenic emissions may be significant in non-industrial areas. The quality of biogenic emission estimates should be improved.
• Magnitude assessment of naturally produced SO_x emissions relative to manmade SO_x emissions (regional basis, e.g., eastern United States, eastern Europe).	High: In the eastern United States, manmade emissions account for over 90 percent of total SO_x (based on a sulfur budget). Natural emissions account for 4 percent, with inflow to the region making up the remainder. Natural emissions of SO_x in eastern Europe have been estimated at 10 percent using sulfur budgets.	Low-Moderate: (See SO_x global). In polluted urban airsheds, it appears that anthropogenic sources of SO_x predominate. Extensive source control may not produce corresponding (linear) reductions in the acidity of rain.
• Magnitude assessment of naturally produced NO_x emissions relative to manmade NO_x emissions (global basis and regional basis).	Moderate-High: Global fluxes of nitrogen compounds are based largely on extrapolation of experimentally determined small-scale emission factors to global scale, or the use of mass balances to obtain crude estimates for unknown sources. The ratio of natural sources to anthropogenic sources has been estimated to be as low as 1:1 to as high as 15:1. Emission inventories on a regional basis are not well defined.	Low-Moderate: In spite of the uncertainty cited for natural production of NO_x, these emissions are globally distributed, whereas anthropogenic emissions are much more concentrated. In polluted urban airsheds, it appears that manmade emissions are much more significant.
• Magnitude assessment of anthropogenically produced SO_x and NO_x emissions (EPA regional emission inventory basis).	Low: There is a fairly good agreement among different inventories for SO_x and NO_x on an EPA regional basis (viz., within 20 percent – often within 10 percent).	Low: Some benefit will be realized when improvements are made in data collected at the state, AQCR, county, and facility level. A standard procedure for updating data should be developed that specifies common updating time intervals by region.
• Magnitude assessment of anthropogenically produced SO_x and NO_x emissions (state emission inventory basis).	Moderate: Comparison of emission inventories on a state basis begins to reveal point and area source discrepancies. Quality of state emission inventories can vary widely from state to state. For example, it has been observed that early 1982 (date-of-record year) NEDS files generally represented a 1978/1979 data base, with some states reporting data as old as 1975.	Moderate: Emission inventories should continue to be refined. Data reporting procedures and accuracy of data supplied by states should also be improved.

(continued)

TABLE 8-1 (continued)

Item/issue	Level of uncertainty	Need for further research
• Magnitude assessment of anthropogenically produced SO_x and NO_x emissions (AQCR, county, or facility basis).	High: Emission factors, methods of fuel allocation for area and mobile sources, and distribution of source types will affect accuracy of emission inventory estimates to a large degree. Some large discrepancies have been noted among different data bases.	High: Improvements in emission estimates and maintenance of current data in data files are required. (See state emission inventory basis, above.)
• Projections for SO_x and NO_x emissions to year 2000 based on the Second National Energy Plan (NEP II).	Moderate: Projections will depend in large part on the energy scenarios selected.	Moderate: Emission reduction scenarios based on new control technology measures and requirements should be continually updated.
• Effect of combustion variables on source emissions.	High: For older coal-fired power plants on prolonged retirement schedules, control of combustion variables may be more important than that for newer, more efficiently optimized combustion units.	High: Research has been funded and is ongoing.
• Oil-fired burners as direct sources of SO_3, SO_4, and H_2SO_4.	High: Higher SO_3 emissions result from oil-fired units than from coal-fired units, for a given amount of fuel sulfur. Emission of significant quantities of sulfates is also common from fuel oil combustion (possibly increasing emission to and formation of H_2SO_4 in the atmosphere) probably due to catalytic oxidation of trace metals in fuel oils.	High: Both SO_3 and H_2SO_4 are acidic themselves and may impact significantly on acid rain formation. The spatial scale of impacts requires investigation.
• Effect of control technology on source emissions.	High: Based on recently promulgated New Source Performance Standards, strict control levels must be maintained: viz., 0.6 lb/10^6 Btu for NO_x, (0.7 lb/10^6 Btu for lignite-fired cyclone boiler); 90 percent control of SO_x where the uncontrolled emissions are >0.6 lb/10^6 Btu but <1.2 lb/10^6 Btu, and 70 percent control of SO_x where the uncontrolled emissions are $\leq$0.6 lb/10^6 Btu.	High: Continued research on the feasibility and cost effectiveness of conventional and novel control measures for SO_x and NO_x is recommended, particularly for older relatively uncontrolled plants.
• Effect of seasonal fuel use on source emissions.	Low-Moderate: On a nationwide basis, the variation in NO_x emissions from fossil-fuel generating plants is estimated at 15 percent, with production being greatest in the summer and least in the spring. Substantial seasonal and diurnal variations associated with mobile sources have been noted.	Moderate: Data bases should be continually updated. For example, reporting mobile sources by annual emissions data may underestimate their potential for producing short-term (peak) concentrations.

(continued)

TABLE 8-1 (continued)

Item/issue	Level of uncertainty	Need for further research
• Influence of ammonia on acid precipitation formation.	Moderate: Ammonia is a known alkaline substance with acid neutralizing properties. There are large amounts of ammonia in the atmospheric background relative to the acidic forms into which it can be transformed. To the extent that neutralization occurs, the free acidity of rainfall will be reduced.	Moderate: A moderate-low level of effort should be conducted to investigate the effects of ammonia production facilities and natural sources on local environmental conditions.
• Contribution of chloride to acid precipitation.	Moderate: Chloride contribution to acid rain in the United States is suspected to result more from chlorine releases from the burning of coal than from marine salt spray, with the possible exception of coastal regions.	Low: A low level of effort should be conducted to ascertain local effects.
• The role of ozone in sulfate and nitrate formation.	Moderate-High: Chemical reactions leading to the formation of acid rain precursors have been associated with gas-phase and heterogeneous (gas-liquid and gas-solid) processes related to photochemical smog. Also, the scavenging of ozone by NO in plumes from major fuel-burning installations may lead to further nitric acid production.	Moderate-High: More research is needed to assess the synergistic role of ozone and associated photochemical products in the formation of sulfates and nitrates.
• Contribution of hydrocarbons to acid precipitation.	Moderate: Hydrocarbons interact with ozone and NO_x in photochemical smog, which may be a precursor condition for acid rain formation and precipitation.	Moderate: More research is needed to assess the synergistic role of hydrocarbons in localized acid rain formation and deposition.
• The role of carbon dioxide in acid rain formation.	Moderate: The background pH, produced by CO_2 in equilibrium with water (carbonic acid) can also be affected by other gases and soluble particles. Below a pH of 5, carbonic acid has no further acidifying (synergistic) effect on rain water.	None.
• The role of alkaline airborne dust in neutralizing acid rain.	Moderate-High: Alkaline dust from natural and anthropogenic sources may react with and neutralize acids in the atmosphere. The lower pH (6 to 7) of dust generated from eastern soils may render this area more susceptible to acid precipitation, but this may be offset by the higher pH (9 to 11) of fly ash emissions from the combustion of coal.	Moderate-High: More research is needed to determine whether residence times of dusts are sufficient to accomplish significant neutralization of acid precipitation.

(continued)

TABLE 8-1 (continued)

Item/issue	Level of uncertainty	Need for further research
• The role of airborne particulates in catalytic oxidation of SO_x to sulfates.	High: Catalytic oxidation of SO_x by suspended fly ash may occur in power plant plumes. Metallic constituents of the fly ash are suspected to act as catalysts. It has been noted that oil-fired boilers can emit higher concentrations of metallic catalysts than coal-fired boilers. The conversion of SO_x to particulate sulfates increases their atmospheric lifetime and facilitates long-range transport. The presence of manmade carbon soot particles in the atmosphere may also enhance the formation of acid rain.	High: More research is needed to define the role of metallic constituents in the catalytic oxidation of SO_x to sulfates.

ATMOSPHERIC TRANSPORT, TRANSFORMATIONS, AND DEPOSITION

Item/issue	Level of uncertainty	Need for further research
• Source to receptor transport.	High: Linkages between individual sources or source types and sensitive receptor areas are poorly established because of uncertain transport paths, interaction of sources during transport, and chemical transformations.	High: Source to receptor paths need to be more firmly established so that mitigative strategies can be tailored to the requirements of sensitive areas. Useful tools include modeling, trajectory, tracer, and trace-element ratio studies.
• Chemical transformations.	High: Major uncertainties exist in the roles of homogeneous and heterogeneous reactions in the formation of sulfates and nitrates and other acidic products. Limiting factors for these reactions and their degree of linearity have not been established in the atmosphere. Current knowledge of transformation rates and the factors controlling them rests heavily on laboratory and plume studies.	High: Development of the most cost-effective control strategies requires consideration of the roles played by all key reactants. In particular, the roles of NO_x, hydrocarbons, ozone, trace metals, organic acids, and alkaline dust need clarification. Additional measurements of chemical species in the air around cloud systems, in cloud droplets, and in rain water are needed to determine the scavenging efficiency of cloud droplets and droplet chemistry. More detailed knowledge of transformation rates is needed to determine relationships between species and transport distance. Additional laboratory and atmospheric studies are required.
• Deposition rates.	High: The relative importance of wet and dry deposition is uncertain. Knowledge of dry deposition of chemical species and its significance in the acidification of watersheds is largely unknown.	High: Representative wet deposition rates of chemical species in sensitive areas need to be more definitively established. Techniques are needed to determine dry deposition rates of significant components over natural surfaces.
• Effect of tall stacks on long-range transport.	Moderate: Increased plume height reduces local surface scavenging, increases the amount of pollutants leaving the near-stack area, and increases the time for chemical transformation before deposition.	Low: Better estimates of effects will come from improved understanding of deposition and transformation rates. Nocturnal emissions released above an inversion layer may be important.

(continued)

TABLE 8-1 (continued)

Item/issue	Level of uncertainty	Need for further research
MONITORING PROGRAMS AND RESULTS		
• Measurement of acidic deposition in North America (less than 5.6 pH).	Moderate: While it is unquestionable that acid precipitation is falling, the relative importance of wet versus dry deposition has not been reliably determined. Also, meteorological phenomena such as acid fog, frost, and dew have been essentially unstudied. Many areas in North America have also not been adequately monitored for acidity.	High: A number of monitoring networks have been set up throughout North America. A reliable method for monitoring dry deposition must be developed to determine the relative importance of wet versus dry deposition. Considerably more research is needed in the areas of acid fog, frost, and dew.
• Evidence of trends toward increasingly acidic rain over increasing areas of influence.	Moderate: Many researchers consider the evidence for increasing acidity and widening areas of influence to be significant enough to warrant regulatory action. Others insist the data are too sparse to be conclusive.	High: This issue must be settled with reasonable certainty as soon as possible. Modern networks maintained over a minimum period of about 10 years may be needed to draw firm conclusions. However, some scientists have warned that such a delay in implementing regulatory control strategies may result in irreparable damage to lake ecosystems.
• Relative importance of acidic components in rainfall.	Moderate-High: Acidic rainfall is generally considered to be composed of 60 percent sulfates, 30 percent nitrates, and 10 percent chlorides and other acidic components. These proportions vary among regions and with time and are important when determining sources. The relative importance of nitrates appears to be increasing.	Moderate: The ionic content of precipitation should continue to be monitored over a period of time for all regions. This is currently being undertaken.
• Determination of sources of acidic components of precipitation.	High: The many links between anthropogenic pollution emissions and measured acidity of rainfall are unclear. The current methods include association with fuel use patterns, evaluation of $SO_2:NO_x$ ratios, analyses of trajectories, and results of modeling.	Moderate-High: Continued research is necessary to quantify relationships between causes and effects.
• Seasonal variations in observed acidity of precipitation.	Moderate: Seasonalities have been observed in acidity monitoring data. The seasonal trends in sulfate levels correlate well but nitrate levels do not seem to have an annual variation. Better definition of trends will shed light on source contributions.	Low-Moderate: Data currently being collected should continue to be analyzed for seasonal as well as long-term trends.

(continued)

TABLE 8-1 (continued)

Item/issue	Level of uncertainty	Need for further research
• Continuity of monitoring programs.	**High:** Historically, the lack of continuity in monitoring programs has made the establishment of trends uncertain.	**High:** Agencies involved in these activities must be able to make firm commitments with support through programmatic processes.
REGIONAL TRANSPORT AND DEPOSITION MODELING		
• Regional modeling.	**High:** Models represent the link between sources and deposition and are the only means of assessing in advance the effects of changing conditions. Current regional models suitable for evaluating the acid rain problem are preliminary and involve tentative assumptions and major simplifications, including: (1) neglect of NO_x transformation; (2) linear SO_x transformation rates; (3) elementary consideration of in-cloud chemistry; (4) the use of poorly documented decay rates for wet removal of sulfates and nitrates; (5) prescription of regional wind and precipitation fields from existing networks; and (6) representation of atmosphere by one well-mixed vertical layer.	**High:** Additional development, testing and validation will be required before models can be used with confidence. This is an iterative process and improvements occur gradually as a result of more realistic assumptions and more detailed monitoring data.
• Transport.	**Moderate:** Little consensus exists among modelers as to the appropriate wind velocity data to use. Hourly simulations can be modeled, or long-term wind data can be averaged.	**Low:** Research into the processes of long-range transport has been extensive. It is now left to modelers to adequately and accurately represent these processes in models.
• Diffusion.	**Moderate:** Horizontal and vertical diffusion can be treated in many ways: separately or combined, using short-term values or long-term averages, simple parameterizations or mathematically sophisticated formulae, or single or multi-layered treatments.	**Moderate:** More realistic assumptions are required and more sophisticated techniques are needed in order to accurately represent these processes in models.
• Chemistry.	**High:** Sulfur transformations have been simulated with linear parameterizations. However, nitrogen chemistry, total acids, and neutralization processes all have not been simulated.	**High:** More research is needed to better represent the various chemical processes in models.
• Deposition.	**Moderate:** There are large variations in empirical relationships for deposition wet deposition. Parameterized coefficients and power law approximations are used equally. Dry deposition velocities also show wide variations.	**High:** No research has been conducted on deposition parameters for nitrogen compounds, which are becoming more important in evaluating the acid rain phenomenon.

(continued)

TABLE 8-1 (continued)

Item/issue	Level of uncertainty	Need for further research
• Spatial and temporal variations.	High: Wind fields, decay rates, diffusion parameters, and chemical transformations all exhibit spatial and temporal variations. No sophisticated treatments are currently being modeled.	High: More accurate treatment of these spatial and temporal variations will greatly improve models.
• Data bases.	Moderate: Meteorological data are available, but not always spatially applicable; they can be hourly or long-term averages. Emission inventories generally provide reasonably adequate data, although measured pH data for model validation purposes are limited.	Moderate: Additional testing and validation of models will depend heavily on the quality of data bases used.

ADVERSE AND BENEFICIAL EFFECTS OF ACID PRECIPITATION

Item/issue	Level of uncertainty	Need for further research
• How can we evaluate whether acidification of a lake has occurred? What effects can be predicted?	High: A quantification of the extent of the problem requires adoption of accepted criteria to identify an acidified water body or system.	High: A useful and generally accepted model needs to be developed. Such a model would require large amounts of background data on lake chemistry and other areas.
• How fast will a given lake become acidified? How and why do lakes vary in their susceptibility to acidification?	Moderate: These data would enable a better quantification of the extent of acidification and provide a true measure of regions of special sensitivity.	High: A sensitivity analysis is required. Such an analysis requires a large data base. This analysis would have to include: the watershed/lake area; lake elevation; SO_4 reduction system; denitrification system; geological substrate; buffering of acid input by canopy, litter, soil, stream channels, etc.
• Long-term, comparative studies of carefully selected lakes. These studies should include quantitative analysis of vegetation, soils, geology, and hydrology of watersheds.	Moderate: Work done to date has concentrated on short-term acute impacts of acidification. Long-term effects of chronic acidic inputs have been relegated to a lower priority. Concern will undoubtedly increase to High as short-term impacts and mechanisms of acidification are resolved.	High: Long-term studies invariably are complex and costly.
• Carefully planned laboratory and field studies need to be conducted to elucidate mechanisms and quantify effects of acidification on aquatic and terrestrial ecosystems. Specific areas of research could include:	High: Effects on aquatic species/ecosystems and terrestrial ecosystems are the primary concern regarding acidic precipitation. Both short-term acute effects and long-term chronic impacts are of importance.	Variable: Research effort will vary depending on the effects being investigated. Some questions could be resolved with a minimum expenditure of time and money; others would require extensive commitments of resources and personnel. Examples of areas of research and necessary levels of effort are listed below. Obviously there are many more areas that could be listed. These serve only to illustrate the complexity of the problem.

(continued)

TABLE 8-1 (continued)

Item/issue	Level of uncertainty	Need for further research
- bioassay of all forms of aquatic organisms for pH sensitivity and heavy metal toxicity.		Moderate-High
- physiological and behavioral studies of all kinds of organisms under stress at low pH via exposure to sulfuric and nitric acid in proportion to real world situations (e.g., 2:1, 1:1, 0.6:1 in various locations) and with exposure to neutralized salts.		Moderate-High
- long-term monitoring of sensitive organisms or communities to identify potentially sensitive ecosystems.		Moderate-High
- physical and chemical characterization of dissolved organic matter.		Low-Moderate
- identification of chemical species of aluminum and toxicity of these species especially at pH 4-6.		Low-Moderate
- chemical transformations during draining through soils.		Moderate-High
- the biomass and productivity of algal and invertebrate communities in acid waters.		Moderate-High
- mechanisms of the development of benthic sphagnum and algal mats and their influence on ionic exchange at the sediment/water interface.		Moderate-High
- exchange of nutrients and metals in acid waters.		Moderate-High
- mercury transfer and accumulation processes in lakes.		Moderate-High

(continued)

TABLE 8-1 (continued)

Item/issue	Level of uncertainty		Need for further research
- the components and characteristics of buffer systems in acid lakes.		Moderate-High	
- response of fish to short-term pH depression.		Low-Moderate	
- better evaluation of the sensitive stages in the life history of all kinds of organisms.		Moderate-High	
- better elucidation of the mechanisms responsible for population extinction of both invertebrate fauna and fish.		High	
- quantification of metals leached from watersheds.		Moderate-High	
- synergistic/antagonistic effects of pH, Ca, Al, and Mn.		High	
- the limits of acclimation and genetics in certain species.		Low-Moderate	
● What are the effects of wet and dry deposition on forest canopies and other vegetation?	High: Effects on vegetation must be elucidated to better understand the acidification process through the entire ecosystem.	Moderate-High	Moderate-High: Research is needed to determine the solubility of deposited particles under various moisture and chemical regimes and the magnitude of nutrients leached from vegetation.
● Quantitative work on different acidity sources and sinks in the same soil needs to be conducted. For example:	High: As above. Especially of concern are effects of acidification of soils as this affects food crops.	Moderate-High	Moderate-High: Again, level of effort depends on parameter to be quantified. However, elucidation of effects of acid precipitation on soil systems has in the past generally proved to require detailed effort.
- H+ contribution from plant acids and decomposition processes.			
- quantification of weathering and cation exchange processes and the effects of percolate composition.			

(continued)

TABLE 8-1 (continued)

Item/issue	Level of uncertainty	Need for further research
- rates of, and conditions for, nitrate and sulfate reduction.		
- mobilization of heavy metals in acid soils.		
• Quantification of the effects of acidic rainfall on soil systems, in general, including:	High: As above.	Moderate-High: As above.
- the theoretical soil chemistry of low level chronic acid inputs to soils.		
- applied measurements of acidification rates in laboratory and field studies.		
- methods of evaluating the interaction of acid inputs and plant systems on soil acidity.		
- the soil fertility change and modification of nutrient cycles.		
• Long-term effects of rainfall acidity on soil and soil/plant systems.	High: Concern is high about chronic impacts of acidic precipitation on terrestrial ecosystems, especially forest systems.	Moderate-High: Systems models could be generated to predict long-term effects. Actual in situ monitoring of long-term effects would be a major undertaking. Chronic effects could be simulated in the laboratory, but true extrapolation to the natural condition would be tenuous.
• What are the effects on surface water quality of changing land use patterns?	Moderate-High: This area has not received enough study. Resolution of this question would contribute to a true quantification of the effects of acidic precipitation apart from other factors.	Moderate-High: A broad data base would be required.
• What are the long-term effects of habitat damage on wildlife?	High: Evidence indicates that the food chain is adversely affected by acidic precipitation, thus wildlife may also be affected.	Low-Moderate: A better understanding of the effects on aquatic and terrestrial ecosystems is required to begin resolving this issue.

(continued)

TABLE 8-1 (continued)

Item/issue	Level of uncertainty	Need for further research
• What will be the ecological/biological consequences if acidic precipitation is eliminated?	Low: Concern at present is primarily directed at effects caused by the presence of acidic precipitation, not the converse. However, this area deserves careful study and evaluation, especially because some data indicate beneficial impacts of acidic precipitation.	Moderate: This area cannot be truly investigated without a clear picture of the impacts of acid rain on the systems affected.
• What are the impacts of acidic precipitation on human health and well-being?	High: This question is of primary importance. Impacts should not only be assumed to represent health hazards but must also take into account loss of recreational and leisure activities, degradation of structures, monuments and other manmade objects, and effects on crops, forests, and aesthetic values, in general.	Variable: Minimal research efforts could quantify levels of trace toxic metals in potable waters and aquatic species and estimate impacts on health based on a broad background of toxicological information. Some estimates could easily be made to ascertain monetary loss resulting from crop damage, etc. Evaluation of the long-term effects of exposure to sulfuric acid aerosols in normal humans and the interactions with other pollutants is required. The other areas of concern, many of which fall within the broad area generally recognized as quality of life, are less easily determined.
• Quantify a sulfate loading which would protect aquatic ecosystems already acidified.	High: A quantification requires the adoption of accepted criteria to characterize an acidified aquatic ecosystem.	High: Current predictive models need to be modified to determine the rate of acidification of surface waters, the buffering capacity of the watershed, and the rate of recovery following reduced acid deposition.
MITIGATIVE STRATEGIES		
• How may the impacts of acid precipitation be mitigated?	Moderate-High: This question assumes all recognized impacts of acidic precipitation are detrimental. This has not been demonstrated to the satisfaction of all investigators involved in acidic precipitation research. Answering this question hinges on resolving most of the issues presented above, and involves evaluating both adverse and beneficial aspects of acidic precipitation.	Moderate-High: Mitigative strategies may be conceptualized with minimal difficulty once the effects of acid precipitation are quantified both chemically and physically.
• The feasibility/desirability of liming as a mitigative strategy needs to be evaluated.	Moderate: Consideration of liming or other mitigative strategies has not received much attention in the United States to date.	Variable: The level of research effort required to evaluate liming as a mitigative strategy depends on the aspect of the strategy under study. Benefit-cost analyses may be made with moderate effort assuming true impacts of acidification on a given lake or water body are known and if a realistic estimate of the logistics involved in liming a given area is available. Investigation into chemical, biological or ecological long-term effects of liming would be a major undertaking.

REFERENCES

1.   Sigma Research, Inc. In: Proceedings of the Advisory Workshop to
      Identify Research Needs on the Formation of Acid Precipitation, Alta,
      Utah. Electric Power Research Institute, 1978.

2.   Acid Rain Coordination Committee. The Federal Acid Rain Assessment
      Plan. Executive Office of the President, Council on Environmental
      Quality, Draft Report, August 1980.

3.   Interagency Task Force on Acid Precipitation. National Acid
      Precipitation Assessment Plan. Washington, D.C., June 1982.

9

Current and Proposed Research on Acid Precipitation

Many organizations in the United States sponsor research on acid rain. The Federal Government, for example, proposes to fund more than $20 million in acid rain research during FY 1983.[1] Several states and a wide range of private organizations also conduct sizeable acid rain research programs. This section provides a brief overview of the organizations involved in acid rain research and the types of projects that they sponsor. It also discusses two projects, now underway, that are designed to provide more comprehensive inventories of federal, state, and private sector research on acid rain. Most of the research described in this section is either currently underway or scheduled to begin shortly. Previous sections of this report, as well as the earlier edition of GCA's Acid Rain Information Book,[2] discuss research that has already been completed. This section also focuses almost exclusively on research that is performed in the United States and specifically designed to provide information on acid precipitation; international research on acid rain, as well as all basic research on related topics such as SO_2 and NO_x control technology and atmospheric processes, are only briefly discussed.

FEDERAL RESEARCH ON ACID PRECIPITATION

Federal research on acid precipitation is being coordinated by the Interagency Task Force on Acid Precipitation (ITFAP). This Task Force, which was created by the Acid Precipitation Act of 1980, is jointly chaired by the Department of Agriculture (DOA), the Environmental Protection Agency (EPA), and the National Oceanic and Atmospheric Administration (NOAA). The other participating federal organizations are: the Departments of the Interior (DOI), Health and Human Services (HHS), Commerce (DOC), Energy (DOE), and State (DOS); the National Aeronautics and Space Administration (NASA); the Council on Environmental Quality (CEQ); the National Science Foundation (NSF); and the Tennessee Valley Authority (TVA). The Task Force also includes four Presidential appointees and the Directors of the Argonne National Laboratory, Brookhaven National Laboratory, Oak Ridge National Laboratory, and the Pacific Northwest National Laboratory.

The Task Force's primary responsibility is to develop and implement a comprehensive, 10-year National Acid Precipitation Assessment Program (NAPAP). In June 1982, the Task Force published the National Acid Precipitation Assessment Plan,[1] which outlines the scope and proposed organization of this 10-year federal research effort. This plan divides research needs into nine basic categories: (a) natural sources; (b) manmade sources; (c) atmospheric processes; (d) deposition monitoring; (e) aquatic impacts; (f) terrestrial impacts; (g) effects on materials and cultural resources; (h) control technologies; and (i) assessment and policy analysis.

As Figure 9-1 indicates, the Task Force has set up individual task groups to coordinate research in each of these nine areas, as well as a task group on international activities that is responsible for compiling information on acid precipitation research in other countries. The Task Force has designated a specific agency (such as DOE, EPA) to coordinate the work of each task group.

Table 9-1 summarizes the research tasks proposed by the Task Force in each of these research categories. This table, which was included as an appendix to the National Plan,[1] outlines when the research is scheduled to take place, which federal agencies will be involved, and the priority level assigned to each research task. Priority 1 denotes the most urgently needed research that offers the opportunity for relatively rapid generation of crucial information. Tasks of slightly less urgency are given a priority 2, and priority 3 indicates important research but where the need for results is least urgent.

The task groups are currently developing detailed operation plans that indicate more precisely how each of these research tasks will be addressed. According to the National Plan,[1] the interagency budget (and, thus, the research plan outlined in Table 9-1) does not include research activities that are not specifically designed to address crucial policy questions concerning acid precipitation. For instance, the National Science Foundation (NSF) supports extensive basic research programs relevant to acid precipitation. NSF's funding of these activities is not included in the interagency budget, although NSF is a full participant in the Task Force and the studies it supports are coordinated with the rest of the National Program. Similarly, federal support of research and development on control technology is not included in the Task Force's interagency budget because there are many other reasons for controlling emissions of SO_2 and NO_x that are not directly related to the formation of acid precipitation. However, the Task Force maintains a control technology task group to monitor the federal activities and expenditures on relevant control technologies.

The Task Force has several other responsibilities in addition to developing and implementing the comprehensive research program outlined above. The responsibilities include:

- Maintaining an inventory of federally-funded acid precipitation research projects;

- Developing an annual interagency budget for the federal program;

- Providing Annual Reports on the program's progress and implications of the existing knowledge;

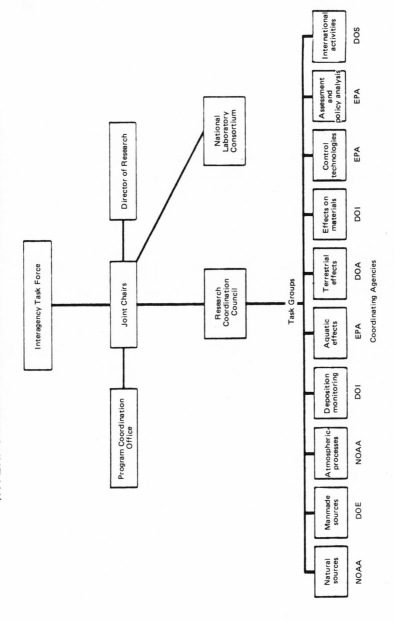

Figure 9-1. Organization Chart, Interagency Task Force on Acid Precipitation.[1]

TABLE 9-1.   NATIONAL ACID PRECIPITATION ASSESSMENT PROGRAM – SUMMARY OF RESEARCH[1]

Research Task (Coordinating Agency)	Priority	Duration (FY)	Agency involvement[a] (Participating = 1)				(Contributing = 2)			
			DOA	EPA	NOAA	DOI	DOE	NSF	TVA	Other
A. Natural Sources (NOAA)										
1. Analysis & Assessment of Natural Sources of Acid Deposition	1	1981-1986		2	1	2	2	2		NASA
2. Case Studies of Neutralizing Materials in the Atmosphere	1	1981-1986	2	2	1	2	2	2	2	NASA
B. Manmade Sources (DOE)										
1. Inventories of Current Emissions of Pollutants of Interest	1	1981-1990		1			1		2	
2. Developing Models for Emissions & Economic Analysis	1	1982-1990		1			1		2	
3. Baseline Emission Projections	1	1982-1990		1			1		2	
4. Analysis of Historic Emission Trends	2	1982-1986		1			1		2	
5. Detailed Analyses of Factors Affecting Emissions from Manmade Sources	2	1983-1990		1			1		2	
C. Atmospheric Processes (NOAA)										
1. Research on Long-Range Transport & Dispersion	1	1982-1987		1	1	1	2	2	2	NASA
2. Determining Global & Regional Circulation of Acidic Materials	1	1980-1986		1	1		1	2	2	NASA
3. Investigating Chemical & Physical Transformations	1	1980-1990		1	1		1	2	1	NASA
4. Research on the Scavenging of Particles & Gases by Clouds	1	1980-1990		1	1		1	2		NASA
5. Improving Modeling Data Bases	3	1981-1985		2	2		1		2	
6. Improving Computer Simulation	1	1980-1985		1	1		1			
D. Deposition Monitoring (DOI)										
1. Continued Improvement & Evaluation of the Global Trends Networks (GTN)	1	1980-1990		1	1		2			
2. Further Development of National Trends Network (NTN)	1	1980-1990	1	1	1	1	2		1	
3. Developing Methods for Sampling Dry Measurements	1	1982-1987	2	1	1	2	1			
4. Expansion & Improvement of the Research Support Networks	1	1980-1990		1	1	1	1		2	
E. Aquatic Impacts (EPA)										
1. Monitoring National & Regional Water Quality	1	1982-1987		1		1	1		1	
2. Determining Factors that Control Lake Susceptibility	1	1980-1985		1		1	1	2	1	
3. Determining Relative Contribution of Nitric and Sulfuric Acid Inputs	1	1981-1986		1		1		2	1	
4. Evaluating the Significance of Mobilization of Toxic Metals	2	1982-1987		1		1	2		1	

(continued)

TABLE 9-1 (continued).

Research Task (Coordinating Agency)	Priority	Duration (FY)	Agency involvement[a] (Participating = 1)				(Contributing = 2)			Other
			DOA	EPA	NOAA	DOI	DOE	NSF	TVA	
5. Modeling Watershed Dose/Response Relationship	1	1981–1986	1	1		1	2	2	1	
6. Studying Acidification of Drinking-Water Sources	1	1980–1984		1		1				HHS
7. Monitoring Drinking-Water & Evaluating Treatment Methods	2	1983–1986		1		1				HHS
8. Monitoring Regional Trends in Biological Effects	1	1980–1984		1		1	2	2	2	
9. Studying Watershed Productivity	1	1980–1990	1	1		1	2	2	1	
10. Identifying Vulnerable Growth Stages	1	1980–1985		1		1	2			
11. Studying Metal Contamination of Fish	2	1981–1983		2		1	2			
12. Analyzing Mitigation Strategies for Acidified Lakes	2	1982–1987	1	1		1			1	
F. Terrestrial Impacts (DOA)										
1. Studying Effects of Growth & Productivity of Forest Trees and Range Plants	1	1980–1990		1		1	2	2	1	
2. Identifying Vulnerable Growth Stages in Plants	2	1980–1990	1	2		1	2			
3. Investigating Effects on Metabolic Functions and Cellular Structures	1	1982–1992	1				2	2		
4. Analyzing Acid Deposition Induced Predisposition of Forest and Range Plants to Diseases and Insects	1	1982–1987	1	2						
5. Screening of Crop Species Sensitivity	1	1980–1985	1	1			2	2	1	
6. Developing Dose-Response Relationships for Crop Growth and Yield	2	1982–1987	1	1		1	2		2	
7. Investigating Acid Deposition Induced Predispositions of Crops to Susceptibility to Diseases and Insects	3	1982–1987	1	1					1	
8. Analyzing Metal Contamination of Crops	3	1982–1984	1	1						
9. Characterizing Soil Vulnerability	1	1982–1985	1	1		1	2			HHS
10. Studying Effects on the Ability of Soils to Support Vegetation	1	1980–1985	1	1		1		2	2	
11. Analyzing Soil Degradation Mechanisms & Mitigation Measures	3	1982–1987	1	1						
12. Analyzing the Buffering Capacity & Response of Watersheds to Acid Deposition	1	1981–1986	1	1		2	2	2	1	
G. Materials & Cultural Resources (DOI)										
1. Investigating Effects on Materials and Cultural Resources	1	1980–1985				1				GSA; DOD;NBS
2. Determining the Susceptibility of Cultural Resources	1	1982–1987				1				GSA;NBS
3. Estimating the Costs of Materials Damage	2	1984–1987		1		2	2			GSA,NBS
4. Research on Protective Coatings & Mitigative Treatments	3	1983–1986		1		1				GSA; DOD;NBS

(continued)

TABLE 9-1 (continued).

Research Task (Coordinating Agency)	Priority	Duration (FY)	DOA	EPA	NOAA	DOI	DOE	NSF	TVA	Other
I. Assessments & Policy Analysis (EPA)										
1. Compilation and evaluation of Costs and Performance of Potential Mitigation Measures	1	1982–1991	2	1		2	2			
2. Integrated Assessment of the Acid Precipitation Phenomenon and Potential Mitigation Measures	1	1982–1990	2	1		2	1			CEQ
3. Preparing Special Scientific and Policy Assessment Documents	1	1981–1990	1	1	1	1	1	2	2	DOS; HHS; NASA
4. Program Information and Coordination Activities	1	Ongoing	1	1	1	1	1	1	1	CEQ(1) DOS; HHS;
5. Special Assessments and Analyses (Program's First 5-Years)	1	-- --	1	1	1	1	1	2	1	NASA; NBS
a. National Survey of Sensitive Lakes and Streams (EPA)		1982–1983								
b. Deposition Monitoring Strategy (DOI)		1982–1983								
c. Analysis of Trends in Acid Deposition (EPA)		1983–1984								
d. Atmospheric Processes Analysis (NOAA)		1983–1984								
e. Effects on Agricultural Terrestrial Systems (DOA)		1983–1984								
f. State-of-the-Art in Control Technology (EPA)		1983–1984								
g. Man-made Sources Assessment (DOE)		1983–1984								
h. Effects on Nonagricultural Terrestrial Systems (DOA)		1984–1985								
i. Damage Assessment for Materials and Cultural Resources (DOI)		1984–1985								
j. Natural Sources Assessment (NOAA)		1984–1985								
k. Second Critical Assessment of Scientific Knowledge and Policy Implications (EPA)		1985–1986								

Column group heading: Agency involvement[a] (Participating = 1) (Contributing = 2)

[a] Agencies are considered participating in a task when they have resources specifically committed to it. Contributing agencies are ones conducting work that is relevant to the task but not directly involved as principals in the project.

- Providing productive interaction between the federal program and private sector, academic, state and local governmental, and international activities; and

- Obtaining non-federal input to the planning, review, and program activities.

Figures 9-2 and 9-3[1] summarize the federal funding commitment to acid rain research in FY 1982, by agency and by research category, respectively. The remainder of the discussion on federal research briefly outlines the type of research that is sponsored by the six agencies described in Figure 9-2, and provides additional information on the eight research categories identified in Figure 9-3.

Federal Agencies Sponsoring Acid Precipitation Research

As Table 9-1 indicates, six agencies (DOA, EPA, NOAA, DOI, DOE, and TVA) play a lead role in most of the proposed NAPAP research tasks. The following descriptions, adopted from more detailed profiles contained in the National Plan, briefly indicate the type of research each agency sponsors.

Department of Agriculture (DOA)--
The Department of Agriculture is charged with overall responsibility for preserving and strengthening the productivity of agricultural, forest, and related natural resources of the United States. DOA acid precipitation research includes documenting trends in the distribution and intensity of acid rain, determining effects of acid deposition, and identifying ways to minimize harmful effects on crops, soils, forests, and rangelands. For example, DOA established the National Atmospheric Deposition Program (NADP) to provide a long-term system for monitoring chemical changes in atmospheric deposition and acid precipitation in various regions of the United States and to determine the effects of the deposited substances on crops, forests, soils, surface waters, and materials. The program is organized through the regional research program of the Cooperative State Research Service (CSRS) and the State Agricultural Experiment Stations. (Many of the monitoring stations supported by NADP are scheduled to become part of the National Trends Network being established through the Interagency Task Force). DOA's Forest Service (FS) conducts extensive research on the extent, nature, and biological effects of atmospheric deposition. Multidisciplinary teams of scientists are conducting research at laboratories and in field areas (including over 20 calibrated watersheds). Much of DOA's work is done cooperatively with universities and other state and federal agencies.

DOA, which is one of three agencies that jointly chair the Interagency Task Force, has responsibility for coordinating the work of the Terrestrial Effects Task Group.

Environmental Protection Agency (EPA)--
The Environmental Protection Agency is charged with protecting the quality of the air, land, and water resources of the United States. EPA supports both applied and basic research to obtain better understanding of the

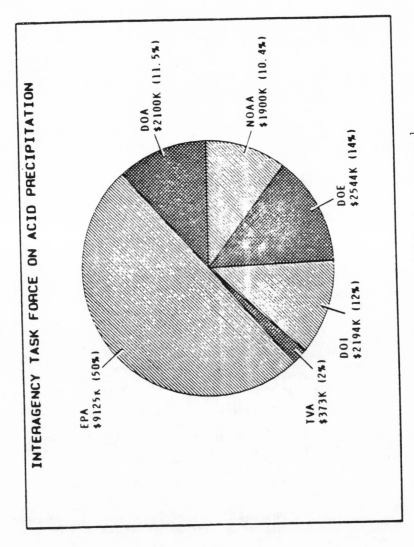

Figure 9-2. Fiscal year 1982 funding by agency.[1]

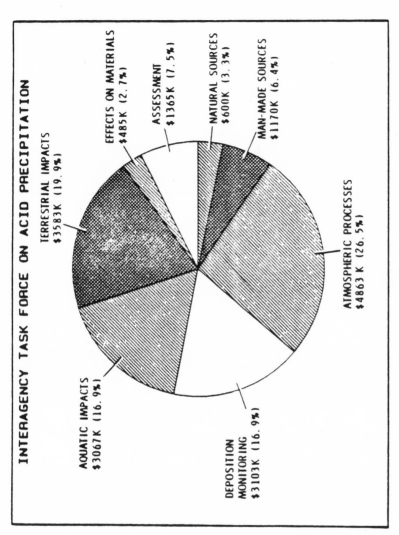

Figure 9–3. Fiscal year 1982 funding by research category.[1]

acid rain environmental phenomenon. A major agency activity is the assessment of environmental research information generated both by EPA and others. Criteria documents are written when the assessment process indicates that regulations are appropriate. EPA also has primary responsibility for setting control standards for the manmade emissions of precursors to acid precipitation.

The EPA Acid Precipitation Research Program is coordinated by the Office of Exploratory Research within the Office of Research and Development. Research is conducted in five primary areas: monitoring, atmospheric processes, environmental effects, control technology, and mitigation strategies. Participants in EPA-supported research include four EPA laboratories, more than 20 academic institutions, and currently, 11 non-EPA governmental agencies and laboratories. EPA efforts to monitor acid deposition include: joint support, with DOA, DOI, and NOAA, of the National Atmospheric Deposition Program (NADP) network; and joint support, with NOAA, of a global acid rain monitoring network. EPA established and maintains the national precipitation chemistry data base. Regional atmospheric transport modeling is another ongoing EPA activity, both through the Multistate Atmospheric Power Production Pollution Study (MAP3S) and the regional modeling program at the EPA Environmental Sciences Research Laboratory (ESRL). Among other activities, these programs are developing a coordinated strategy for the development and evaluation of refined acid deposition models. EPA is also conducting research on the environmental effects of acid precipitation on lakes and streams, drinking water, soils, crops, forests, and materials. EPA has a major cooperative agreement with North Carolina State University to guide the investigation of the effects of acid precipitation on both aquatic and terrestrial ecosystems.

EPA, which shares the chairmanship of the Interagency Task Force with DOA and NOAA, also has responsibility for overseeing the work of three task groups: Aquatic Effects, Control Technologies, and Assessment and Policy Analyses.

National Oceanic and Atmospheric Administration (NOAA)--
    The National Oceanic and Atmospheric Administration (NOAA) conducts the major portion of the acid rain-related activities of the Department of Commerce. One of NOAA's major missions is to measure and interpret atmospheric and oceanographic parameters to increase understanding of weather and climate. An important aspect of this work is to document and analyze changes in the chemical cycles in the atmosphere. These cycles include: (1) transport of trace substances that enter the atmosphere; (2) chemical transformations that occur during transit; and (3) final removal and deposition of the trace materials on the earth's surface.

To determine where airborne materials would be deposited, NOAA has developed various transport models. NOAA's Air Resources Laboratories (ARL) operational trajectory model is used to study and predict the transport of acidic materials and their final deposition through precipitation. NOAA also conducts research on chemical transformations in the atmosphere and the Aeronomy Laboratory (AL) has been especially concerned with photochemical reactions in the atmosphere.

NOAA began ground monitoring of precipitation chemistry in the mid-1950's, when the first national collection network was established. NOAA - National Weather Service (NWS) facilities have been used as collection sites for many other networks; at present, most of the World Meteorological Organization (WMO) regional and baseline stations also are at NWS locations. Special studies of data collected at NOAA baseline sites have been useful in determining the background acidity in precipitation. NOAA support of university research has included: an intercomparison of precipitation chemistry collectors across the United States-Canadian border; the development of new techniques to measure the chemistry of rain on a real-time basis; special studies of dry atmospheric deposition; and atmospheric nitric acid measurements.

In addition to chairing the Interagency Task Force together with DOA and EPA, NOAA also coordinates the activities of the Natural Sources and Atmospheric Processes task groups.

Department of the Interior (DOI)--
The Department of the Interior is responsible for the protection and conservation of the Nation's natural resources. As a result, various Bureaus of DOI are extensively involved in the National effort to define the extent of acid precipitation and the actions required to deal with it.

The U.S. Geological Survey (USGS) is studying the nature of atmospheric dusts and the gases and solid materials emitted by volcanoes and geysers. After emissions enter the atmosphere, the Bureau of Reclamation (BUREC) weather modification research program uses sophisticated radar, instrumented research aircraft, and other facilities to investigate the rate of vertical mixing and the cloud conditions under which rainout of various materials occurs. Such research is readily adaptable to a full-scale study of acid precipitation. Both the National Park Service (NPS) and BUREC are developing mathematical models of atmospheric transport.

The National Park Service, Bureau of Land Management (BLM), and the U.S. Geological Survey all operate monitoring sites as part of the National Atmospheric Deposition Program. In addition, the USGS is providing standards of quality assurance for the chemical analysis of atmospheric deposition by NADP's Central Analytical Laboratory. The Office of Water Research and Technology (OWRT) has provided funding for a range of acid rain-related research projects to complement work of other Interior Bureaus.

DOI is also involved in research on the effects of acid precipitation. The United States Fish and Wildlife Service (FWS), NPS, and USGS are all conducting investigations on the effects of acid precipitation on lake and stream chemistry. Research on the adverse effects of alterations in water chemistry on plants and animal life is also being supported by FWS and NPS. In addition, USGS soil physicists are studying the movement of water and solutes in the unsaturated zone and USGS hydrologists are studying geochemical processes and developing rainfall-runoff and solute-transport models for both surface water and ground water. NPS also supports research on the chemical changes in precipitation passing through terrestrial ecosystems.

DOI's responsibilities on the Interagency Task Force involve coordination of the Deposition Monitoring and Effects on Materials task groups.

Department of Energy (DOE)--
The Department of Energy is responsible for overseeing the development of the Nation's energy resources; part of this responsibility includes conducting research on the effects of producing and using energy. DOE's program of acid precipitation research has included work in emissions monitoring, atmospheric processes, ecological effects, and control technology evaluation.

In 1976, one of DOE's predecessors, the Energy Research and Development Administration (ERDA), initiated the Multistate Atmospheric Power Production Pollution Study (MAP3S), which had as its major goals the improvement of the Nation's capability to understand and predict the atmospheric effects of emissions from fossil-fueled electric generation plants. Although DOE transferred most of its MAP3S program and its major ecological effects studies to EPA in FY 1979, it continues to cooperate with EPA in supporting the MAP3S Precipitation Chemistry Network.

The Environmental Measurements Laboratory, in late 1976, began studies of the effects of the Nation's changing patterns of energy use upon the major element and trace element chemical composition of precipitation, dry deposition, and total deposition. Any relationship between changing rates of use of various fuels (especially coal) and the deposition trend data are fully examined. The emphasis in DOE research in atmospheric processes continues to be on the development of improved transport models, improved modeling of deposition processes, and application of these tools to establish source-receptor relationships. For example, DOE is sponsoring a climatological analysis of 3 years' of Hubbard Brook precipitation chemistry data to determine whether source-receptor relationships can be established.

Ecological research by DOE is designed to provide information on the sensitivity of representative ecosystems and plant species to acid rain, and to begin to determine the ecological and economic costs of acid deposition. Current studies include analyses of the effects of acid rain on fish, forest soils, and ground water.

Within the Interagency Task Force, DOE is responsible for coordinating the work of the Manmade Sources task group.

Tennessee Valley Authority (TVA)--
During the construction of its first large coal-fired power plant at New Johnsonville, Tennessee in the early 1950's, the Tennessee Valley Authority became involved in research on the dispersion and environmental effects of power plant pollutants. In cooperation with other federal agencies and research organizations, this effort has continued and includes research on all aspects of power plant pollution, such as emissions characterization; dispersion, chemistry, and long-range transport; fate and effects; and control of emissions.

In 1968, TVA became concerned about the potential problem of acid precipitation and initiated preoperational studies in the vicinity of its Cumberland Steam Plant to determine the local impacts of its emissions on the quality of wet/dry deposition and the forest resources of the area. A wet/dry deposition monitoring network was established at Cumberland in 1971.

In 1975, two highly instrumented experimental watersheds were established cooperatively by TVA and EPA on potentially sensitive soils to determine the fate and effects of wet/dry deposition of sulfur on deciduous hardwood forests and the surface waters draining the watersheds. These watersheds and Oak Ridge National Laboratory's (ORNL) Walker Branch watershed are also being used in cooperative research with the Electric Power Research Institute (EPRI) to determine the effects of wet/dry deposition of nitrogen oxides and nitrates on forest ecosystems.

Research Projects Coordinated through ITFAP Task Groups

Each of the task groups within ITFAP is currently drafting a detailed operation plan. These plans identify current and proposed research projects sponsored by the six agencies described above (and others) that are designed to address the research tasks outlined in the National Plan[1] and summarized in Table 9-1, presented earlier. The following tables summarize the research projects described in the draft operation plans of the eight task groups:[3] natural sources (Table 9-2), manmade sources (Table 9-3), atmospheric processes (Table 9-4), deposition monitoring (Table 9-5), aquatic impacts (Table 9-6), terrestrial impacts (Table 9-7), effects on materials (Table 9-8), and assessments and policy analysis (Table 9-9). All of the information in these tables is subject to change either as a result of internal Task Force, agency or other review processes currently underway or due to changes in research priorities at a later time.

The projects listed in Tables 9-2 through 9-9 are not organized according to the research tasks outlined in the National Plan.[1] In some cases, the task groups' draft operation plans did not specify which research tasks individual projects were designed to address. More commonly, however, the project descriptions provided in the plans reveal that many of the individual projects are designed to address several of the research tasks. As Table 9-6 indicates, the task group on aquatic impacts (which is coordinating more than 50 research projects totaling over $3.5 million in FY 1983) chose to group its projects into five broad research objectives instead of the 12 more specific research tasks outlined in the National Plan.[1]

The funding estimates contained in the draft plans were often incomplete, and occasionally required some interpretation before they could be incorporated into the tables presented in this section. Funding estimates for many projects were reported only for FY 1982 and FY 1983; missing funding estimates are indicated in the tables by a dash. In a few cases, the tables contain funding estimates for fiscal years before or after the period of performance specified for the project. These apparent discrepancies in the tables reflect similar inconsistencies in the draft operation plans themselves.

TABLE 9-2. RESEARCH COORDINATED BY THE NATURAL SOURCES TASK GROUP[a]

Project title	Funding agency	Funding estimates ($1000s)				Period of performance	
		FY 1982	FY 1983	FY 1984	FY 1985	Begin	End
Modeling the Source Strengths and the Distributions of Natural NO_x and Sulfur Sources	NOAA	34	39	39	-	10/81	9/86
Studies of the Reactions of Natural Source Precursors of Acid Materials	NOAA	51	58	58	-	10/82	9/90
Field Measurements of Natural Emissions of Nitrogen Compounds Related to Acid Deposition	NOAA	55	68	68	-	10/82	9/87
Analytical Investigations of Trapping and Detection Techniques for Sulfur Compounds	NOAA	30	30	30	-	10/82	9/84
The Role of Oceanic Processes in Determining the Hydrogen Ion Content of Precipitation	NOAA	50	100	100	-	10/82	9/86
Marine Source Strength of Reduced Sulfur Compounds	NOAA	50	100	100	-	3/82	9/83
Intercomparison of Techniques to Measure Natural Emissions of Sulfur Compounds	NOAA	70	70	70	-	FY 1982	Renewable
Source Strengths of Natural Terrestrial Sulfur Emissions: Initial Assessment and Field Measurements	NOAA	100	100	100	-	FY 1982	Renewable
Biogenic Sources of Atmospheric Sulfur Compounds	NOAA	70	70	70	-	FY 1982	Renewable
Assessment of the Contribution of Natural Alkaline Materials to Precipitation	NOAA	30	30	30	-	FY 1982	Renewable

[a]Information derived from Reference 3.

TABLE 9-3. RESEARCH COORDINATED BY THE MANMADE SOURCES TASK GROUP[a]

Project title	Funding agency	Funding estimates ($1000s)				Period of performance	
		FY 1982	FY 1983	FY 1984	FY 1985	Begin	End
Acid Precipitation Precursor Study	DOE	200	200	-	-	-	-
Acid Rain Data Base	DOE	40	10	-	-	9/80	Ongoing
Advanced Utility Simulation Model	EPA	821	650	-	-	9/81	-
Characterization of Sources of Acid Precipitation	DOE	60	90	-	-	9/82	Ongoing
Development and Maintenance of Comprehensive Emissions Inventories	EPA	50	230	300	-	6/82	Cont.
Industrial Combustion Emissions Model	EPA	50	170	300	-	9/82	12/85
Projects Currently Being Considered for Funding (Not Formally Approved)							
Industrial Processes Emissions Model							
Mobile Sources Emissions Model							
Residential/Commercial Emissions Model							
Study of Factors Which Affect Emissions from Selected Sources							

[a]Information derived from Reference 3.

TABLE 9-4. RESEARCH COORDINATED BY THE ATMOSPHERIC PROCESSES TASK GROUP[a]

Project title	Funding agency	Funding estimates ($1000s)				Period of performance	
		FY 1982	FY 1983	FY 1984	FY 1985	Begin	End
Parameterization of Dry Deposition in Eulerian Modeling	EPA	-	30	35	-	10/82	9/86
Micrometeorological Studies of the Dry Deposition of Acid Aerosols and Precursors	EPA	-	190	200	-	10/81	6/86
Mixing Characteristics of the Planetary Boundary Layer in Late Afternoon	EPA	-	0	100	-	In progress	FY 1986
Improved Parameterization of PBL Mixing Characteristics for Eulerian Framework Model	EPA	-	50	50	-	Ongoing	FY 1985
Experimental Field Studies of Vertical Transport and Chemical Transformation due to Nonprecipitation Cumulus Activity	EPA	-	100	320	-	FY 1983	FY 1986
Parametric Methodologies of Vertical Mass Transport due to Convective Clouds for Eulerian Framework Model	EPA	-	20	100	-	FY 1983	FY 1986
Meteorological and Transport Model for the Regional Scale Eulerian Acid Deposition Model	EPA	-	-	110	-	10/83	9/86
Surface-Based Remote and In-Situ Measurements of Flow Near Clouds; Seasonal Correlation Between PBL and Cumulus Activity	EPA	-	40	50	-	In progress	9/85
Theoretical Investigation of the Predictability of Source Impacts at Long Range	EPA	-	75	100	-	10/82	9/85
Investigate Role of Isentropic Transport of Acid Precursors Vented into Cloud Layers on Source-Receptor Relationships	EPA	-	120	160	-	FY 1983	FY 1986
Acid Transport Studies on Regional Scale with CAPTEX	EPA	-	200	-	-	10/82	9/85
Development of Prototype Air Parcel Marking System and Experimental Design for Studies of the Predictability of Long-Range Transport	EPA	-	125	-	-	10/82	9/84
Flow Into and Through Convective Storm Systems	EPA	-	40	-	-	10/83	9/86
Flow Into and Through Frontal Systems	EPA	-	40	-	-	10/82	9/86
Investigation of Feasibility and Application of Tracer Methods to Studies of Flows in Precipitation Systems	EPA	-	60	-	-	10/83	9/84
Precipitation Scavenging Module Development	EPA	-	120	120	120	10/82	9/86
Theoretical Techniques for Scavenging Analysis	EPA	-	175	285	285	10/82	9/86
Precipitation Chemistry Network (MAP3S/RAINE)	EPA	-	217	217	250	In progress	Open

(continued)

TABLE 9-4 (continued)

Project title	Funding agency	Funding estimates ($1000s)				Period of performance	
		FY 1982	FY 1983	FY 1984	FY 1985	Begin	End
Precipitation Scavenging: Field Studies and Data Interpretation	EPA	-	221	340	380	10/82	9/85
Vertical Profiles of Acid-Forming Substances: Aerosols, Gases, and Equilibrium Phenomena	EPA	-	120	315	220	10/82	9/85
Aircraft Measurement Systems and Quality Control	EPA	-	220	300	320	10/82	9/86
Chemical and Physical Instruments/Methods	EPA	-	75	200	-	10/82	9/86
Gas-Phase Chemical Transformations	EPA	-	20	20	-	10/82	9/85
Aqueous-Phase Chemical Transformations	EPA	-	200	200	-	10/82	9/86
Chemical Modules for Eulerian Framework Model	EPA	-	20	20	-	10/82	9/86
Technical Plan for Regional Acid Deposition Eulerian Model	EPA	-	0	-	-	6/82	6/83
Development of the Regional Acid Deposition Eulerian Framework Model	EPA	-	600	700	800	10/82	12/87
Technical Design Plan for Regional Acid Deposition Field Experiment	EPA	-	500	50	-	10/82	9/84
Mesoscale Model Evaluation for Acid Deposition Studies	EPA	-	250	250	100	10/82	9/85
Evaluation of the Numerical Integrater Schemes for the Mainframe Eulerian Model	EPA	-	80	20	-	10/82	9/84
Sulfur Transport Eulerian Model (STEM)	EPA	-	57	63	-	In progress	9/84
Improvement of Lagrangian Models of Acid Deposition	EPA	-	110	120	-	In progress	6/85
Data Management for Acid Deposition Field Studies and Modeling	EPA	-	100	250	275	10/82	9/85
Land-use and Topographic Files	EPA	-	0	40	0	10/83	9/84
Climatological Analysis of Mesoscale Storms	EPA	-	25	30	30	10/82	9/85
Long-range Transport and Dispersion	NOAA	85	90	90	-	4/82	1988
Hemispheric and Global Circulation of Acidic and Pre-acidic Materials	NOAA	265	360	360	-	6/82	1988
Field Investigations of Atmospheric Chemical Transformation and Scavenging Processes Involving Acid-Related Materials	NOAA	0	200	200	-	10/82	9/90

(continued)

TABLE 9-4 (continued)

Project title	Funding agency	Funding estimates ($1000s)				Period of performance	
		FY 1982	FY 1983	FY 1984	FY 1985	Begin	End
Modeling the Atmospheric Photochemistry of SO_2, NO_x, and HO_x	NOAA	30	100	100	-	10/81	9/90
Laboratory Studies of Atmospheric Chemical Processes Associated with Acid Precipitation	NOAA	45	150	150	-	10/82	9/95
Sources of Cloud Water Acidity	NOAA	100	150	150	-	FY 1982	-
Air Pollution Scavenging	DOE	250	260	-	-	1963	Cont.
Atmospheric-Canopy Interactions	DOE	150	165	-	-	1976	Cont.
MAP3S Precipitation Chemistry Network	DOE	117	120	-	-	1976	Cont.
Maintenance of a Rural Precipitation Chemistry Station at Whiteface Mountain	DOE	75	0	-	-	1976	Cont.
Evaluation of Regional Air Quality Models	NPS	50	50	50	-	1980	1984
Projects Sponsored by "Contributing" Agencies (Not included in Acid Rain Research Budget)							
Measurement of the Oceans' Content and Fluxes of Carbonyl Sulfide	NSF	5	-	-	-	-	-
Continued Development and Application of Stochastic Models for Wet Removal of Atmospheric Trace Species	NSF	13	-	-	-	-	-
Studies in Cloud Chemistry	NSF	30	-	-	-	-	-
Oxidation of Sulfur Dioxide by Hydrogen Peroxide in Atmospheric Aerosols	NSF	9	-	-	-	-	-
Atmospheric Acidity: The Dry Deposition of Nitric Acid Vapor	NSF	15	-	-	-	-	-
Laboratory Studies of Tropospheric and Stratospheric Chemistry: Gas-Phase Kinetics of the HS Radical	NSF	17	-	-	-	-	-
Optical Sensing of Sulfate Compounds in Atmospheric Aerosols	NSF	21	-	-	-	-	-
Measurement of Crustal Aerosol Composition	NSF	23	-	-	-	-	-
SO_2 Oxidation Rate on Well-Characterized Surfaces—A Laboratory Study	NSF	20	-	-	-	-	-
The Flux of Reduced Sulfur Compounds from the Oceans to the Atmosphere	NSF	-	-	-	-	-	-

(continued)

TABLE 9-4 (continued)

Project title	Funding agency	Funding estimates ($1000s)				Period of performance	
		FY 1982	FY 1983	FY 1984	FY 1985	Begin	End
Episode Characterization-Intensive Monitoring for the Southern Blue Ridge Province	Not specified	-	-	225	225	10/83	9/86
Determination of Favored Transport Pathways and Associated Synoptic Meteorological Patterns Heading to High Deposition Rates in the Blue Ridge Province	Not specified	-	55	90	85	3/83	9/86
The Production of Secondary Acid Pollutants in Power Plant Plumes – Mechanistic Studies	Not specified	120	70	90	-	FY 1983	FY 1985
Smog Chamber Studies of Secondary Pollutant Formation in Power Plant Plumes-Effect of the Application of Control Technology on Acid Aerosol Formation	Not specified	120	50	60	-	FY 1983	FY 1984
Trajectory Model Validation	Not specified	-	80	120	-	FY 1983	FY 1985
Dry Deposition of Acidic Substances	Not specified	-	-	-	-	-	-
The Photochemistry of Tropospheric CO and NO_x and the Impact of Anthropogenic Emission	NASA	-	-	-	-	-	-
Satellite Sensing of Air Pollution	NASA	-	-	-	-	-	-
The Chemistry of NH_3, HNO_3, and NH_x in the Troposphere	NASA	-	-	-	-	-	-
Airborne UV Dial System Development and Application	NASA	-	-	-	-	-	-
The Development of an Airborne Laser-Photofragmentation/Laser Induced Florescence System for the Detection of Atmospheric Trace Gases	NASA	-	-	-	-	-	-
Development of an In-Situ Measurement Technique for Tropospheric NO_x in the Part Per Trillion Range Using Resonant Ionization Laser Spectroscopy	NASA	-	-	-	-	-	-

[a] Information derived from Reference 3.

TABLE 9-5. RESEARCH COORDINATED BY THE DEPOSITION MONITORING TASK GROUP[a]

Project title	Funding agency	Funding estimates ($1000s)				Period of performance	
		FY 1982	FY 1983	FY 1984	FY 1985	Begin	End
NPS Atmospheric Trend Monitoring Program	NPS	75	100	-	-	1980	Cont.
Monitoring Atmospheric Deposition	USGS	475	1174	-	-	1982	Cont.
Analysis of Data From National Trends Network	USGS	0	75	-	-	1983	Cont.
Quality Assurance of Acid Rain Activities	USGS	110	200	-	-	1982	Cont.
Background Precipitation Quality - Tennessee Valley	TVA	18	22	-	-	1978	1988
Dry Deposition Processes and Methods Development	NOAA	150	100	-	-	1981	Cont.
Support for WMO Regional Stations in the National Trends Network	NOAA	100	50	-	-	1982	Cont.
Atmospheric Research Sites	NOAA	300	200	-	-	1982	1987
Global Trends Network	NOAA	50	50	-	-	1980	1984
Development of New Collection, Analyses and Siting Criteria	NOAA	100	100	-	-	1982	Cont.
Deposition Monitoring	USDA-CSRS	259	259	-	-	1978	Cont.
Atmospheric Deposition Monitoring	USFS	127	145	-	-	1978	Cont.
Monitoring Data System Support	EPA	125	145	145	-	FY 1980	Cont.
Study of Spatial and Temporal Variability of Deposition Data	EPA	65	65	85	-	FY 1982	Cont.
Quality Assurance Support for Acid Precipitation Networks	EPA	20	155	100	-	FY 1982	Cont.
Deposition Monitoring for Effects Research	EPA	75	45	-	-	1980	1983
Development of Chemical Methods for Dry Deposition Measurement and Monitoring	EPA	100	150	200	-	10/82	Open
Monitoring Methods for Acid Rain	EPA	0	150	175	-	1983	Ongoing
Evaluation of Procedures for Determining Precision and Accuracy of Acid Precipitation Chemical and Physical Properties	EPA	35	65	65	-	FY 1982	FY 1984

(continued)

TABLE 9-5 (continued)

Project title	Funding agency	Funding estimates ($1000s)				Period of performance	
		FY 1982	FY 1983	FY 1984	FY 1985	Begin	End
Development of Real Time Acid Precipitation Measurement Methods	EPA	0	70	85	-	FY 1983	FY 1986
Standardization of pH Measurements in Acidic Precipitation	EPA	65	100	100	-	FY 1982	FY 1985
Development of Similarity/Heat Budget Method for Dry Deposition	EPA	0	100	110	120	10/82	Open
Dry Deposition Monitoring Intercomparisons and Parameterizations	EPA	100	100	110	120	10/82	Open
Precipitation Chemistry in the Conterminous U.S.	DOE	340	340	-	-	1976	Cont.
Deposition Monitoring in Western U.S.	BLM	60	65	75	-	1979	1989

aInformation derived from Reference 3.

TABLE 9-6.   RESEARCH COORDINATED BY THE AQUATIC IMPACTS TASK GROUP[a]

Project title	Funding agency	Funding estimates ($1000s)				Period of performance	
		FY 1982	FY 1983	FY 1984	FY 1985	Begin	End
Quantification of the Extent of Acidification and Sensitivity of Lakes, Streams, and Groundwaters in the United States							
Inventory of Available Data Relevant to a National Assessment of the Extent of Surface Water Sensitivity and Acidification	EPA	280	197	-	-	1982	1983
Extent of Acidification (Water Quality) and Acidification Effects (Biotic) on Lakes and Streams in Minnesota, Wisconsin, and Michigan	EPA	200	60	60	-	1980	Indef.
Identification of Areas Containing Waters Sensitive to Acidification by Acid Deposition	USGS	75	100	-	-	1981	1987
Assessment of the Extent of Surface Water Sensitivity and Acidification-Tennessee Valley Region	EPA	45	100	-	-	4/82	9/83
Atmospheric Deposition-Related Changes Within Aquatic and Riparian Remote Natural Environments	NPS	98	148	298	-	FY 1982	FY 1992+
The Impact of Forest Management Practices and Atmospheric Deposition on Stream Chemistry in Terms of Water Quality and Stream Biota	USDA-FS	30	30	-	-	1978	-
Water Quality Management in Northern Lake State Forests	USDA-FS	45	45	-	-	1978	-
The Effects of Acid Precipitation and Alternative Forest Management Practices on Water Yield and Quality in the Southern Appalachian Mountains and Piedmont Region	USDA-FS	30	55	-	-	1978	-
The Impact of Atmospheric Deposition on Water Quality From Appalachian Forests	USDA-FS	20	45	-	-	1978	-
The Impact of Atmospheric Deposition and Land Use Practices on Water Quality From Municipal Watersheds	USDA-FS	10	35	-	-̈	1978	-
Mapping Acid Sensitivity of Surface Waters in the United States	EPA	38	50	-	-	1981	1983
Assessment of Acidic Precipitation Effects on Surface and Groundwater	EPA	183	158	0	-	10/80	Cont.
Monitoring Atmospheric Deposition Effects in Lakes, Streams, and Groundwater	USGS	200	200	-	-	1982	1986
Time Histories and Toxic Substances in Acidified Aquatic Ecosystems	DOE	250	275	275	-	1982	-
Trace Element Analysis in Calibrated Watershed Studies	USGS	78	45	-	-	1982	Cont.

(continued)

TABLE 9-6 (continued)

Project title	Funding agency	Funding estimates ($1000s)				Period of performance	
		FY 1982	FY 1983	FY 1984	FY 1985	Begin	End
Extent of Acidification and Sensitivity of Reservoirs in the Southern Blue Ridge Province (Southeast U.S.)	Not specified	-	65	125	175	10/82	9/87
Acid Sensitivity of Selected Reservoirs in the Tennessee Valley Region	EPA	20	20	20	-	9/82	9/90
Assessment of the Extent of Surface Water Sensitivity and Acidification—Tennessee Valley Region	EPA	45	100	125	-	4/82	9/84
Long-Term Monitoring of Surface Waters	EPA	60	200	0	-	1982-83	To be determined
Identification, Quantification, and Predictive Modeling of the Factors that Control the Susceptibility of Natural Waters to Acidification							
Identify Factors Affecting the Acidification of Surface Waters	EPA	-	-	-	-	1980	1983
Comparative Analysis of Aluminum Biogeochemistry in Forested Watersheds Exposed to Acidic Deposition	EPA	125	0	0	-	12/82	7/85
Chemistry, Transport, and Fate of Aluminum in Dilute Acidified Lake Systems	EPA	35	0	0	-	12/82	7/84
Effects of Soil Infiltration Characteristics on the Chemistry of Throughflow Delivered to Aquatic Systems	EPA	60	0	0	-	12/82	8/85
Predictive Modeling of the Effects of Acidic Deposition on the Chemistry of Natural Waters	EPA	-	100	-	-	10/82	1988
Changes in Surface Water and Soil Chemistry Related to Flow Paths and Reaction Mechanisms in Soil and Bedrock	USGS	95	75	-	-	1982	1986
Effects of Surface Water Acidification on the Chemical Fluxes in Streams, Lakes and Groundwater	USGS	97	25	-	-	1982	1986
Empirical Modeling of Regional Trends in Surface Water Acidification	EPA	50	150	0	-	10/80	Cont.
Susceptibility of Streams to Acidification in the Southern Blue Ridge Province (Southeast U.S.)	TVA	-	75	-	-	10/82	9/86
Susceptibility of Reservoirs to Acidification in the Southern Blue Ridge Province (Southeast U.S.)	TVA	-	35	-	-	10/82	9/86

(continued)

TABLE 9-6 (continued)

Identify and Quantify the Effects of Surface Water Acidification on Biological Processes and Populations

Project title	Funding agency	Funding estimates ($1000s)				Period of performance	
		FY 1982	FY 1983	FY 1984	FY 1985	Begin	End
Methods for Identification of Fish Populations at Risk From Acidic Precipitation	EPA	0	15	0	-	10/82	11/83
Correlations Between Water Quality and Fish Populations in Oligotrophic Surface Waters Receiving Acidic Precipitation	EPA	0	70	0	-	1/83	1/86
Response of Smallmouth Bass to pH Dependent Water Quality Perturbations	EPA	0	30	0	-	FY 1983	FY 1984
Biological Indicators of the Impacts of Acid Rain and Inorganic Contaminants on Coldwater and Warmwater Fish	USFWS	200	208	150	-	1982	3/85
Predicting and Evaluating the Effects of Acidic Precipitation on Water Chemistry and Endemic Fish	EPA	70	0	0	-	FY 1984	FY 1987
Impacts of Acid Precipitation and Trace Metals on Fishery Resources in Northern Wisconsin Streams	USFWS	23	112	-	-	1982	12/84
Determine the Relative Sensitivity to Acid Precipitation of Fish Species Likely to be Exposed to this Stress	EPA	75	100	100	-	11/82	10/84
Impacts of Surface Water Acidification on Commercially and Recreationally Important Salmonid Fishes of the Western United States	EPA	15	15	15	-	4/82	3/84
Microcosm Studies to Assess Factors Affecting Surface Water Sensitivity and Biological Response	EPA	0	150	0	-	1/83	12/86
Effects of Acid Precipitation on the Aquatic Habitat and Ecology of Waterflow and Fish	USFWS (EPA pass-through)	47	53	70	100	5/82	1/84
Effects on Wildlife of Metals Associated with Acid Precipitation	USFWS	0	85	85	-	1982	1984
Effects of Acidification on Free-living Wetland Wildlife	USFWS (EPA pass through)	70	95	-	-	4/82	7/85
Ecosystem Effects of Experimentally Acidified Wetlands	USFWS	51	100	100	-	1/82	9/84

(continued)

TABLE 9-6 (continued)

Project title	Funding agency	Funding estimates ($1000s)				Period of performance	
		FY 1982	FY 1983	FY 1984	FY 1985	Begin	End
Evaluation of Stream Benthos as Bioindicator Organisms of Stress From Acid Precipitation	USFWS	47	40	-	-	6/82	5/85
Fish Community Structure and Trace Metal Concentrations in Potentially Acid-Sensitive and Insensitive Streams of the Southern Blue Ridge Province	USFWS (EPA pass through)	30	62	0	-	7/82	9/82
Effects of Varying Acidic Conditions on the Survival, Development, and Growth of Salmonid Fishes	EPA	75	50	0	-	7/82	6/83
Effects of pH on Metal Form and Metal Toxicity	EPA	0	75	0	-	-	-
Effects of Acidification on Low-order Stream Ecosystems in the Eastern U.S.	EPA	0	0	0	-	FY 1984	FY 1987
Effect of Acid Rain on Amphibians in Temporary Forest Ponds	USFWS (EPA pass-through)	22	18	-	-	1982	1984
Effects of the Benthic Algal Mat of an Acidic Adirondack Lake on Phosphorus Cycling and Other Ions	USFWS (EPA pass-through)	5	-	-	-	6/82	4/83
Test of the Hypothesis that Single Species or Certain Taxonomic Groups Can Serve as Indicators of Acid Impact	EPA	0	150	0	-	1/83	1/84
Responses of Stream Ecosystems to Low pH: Population, Community, and Functional Process Level Effects	EPA	0	0	300	-	10/84	2/87
Quantitative Methodology for Evaluating Long-term Effects of Acidic Deposition on Fish Population Dynamics and Trophic Interactions	EPA	0	0	0	-	FY 1984	FY 1987
Assessment of the Potential Effects of Acid Precipitation to Human Health in Aquatic Systems							
Effects of Acid Rain on Water Supplies	EPA	100	0	-	-	9/80	3/83
Effects of Acidification ot Aquatic Ecosystems on the Bioaccumulate of Toxic Materials in Aquatic Food Chains	EPA	-	-	-	-	FY 1984	-

(continued)

TABLE 9-6 (continued)

Project title	Funding agency	Funding estimates ($1000s)				Period of performance	
		FY 1982	FY 1983	FY 1984	FY 1985	Begin	End
Toxic Substances in the Biota of Acidified Aquatic Ecosystems	DOE	Included in DOE-funded project under Research Objective No. 1.				1982	-
Develop Mitigation Strategies for Restoring or Protecting Acidified Lakes and Streams							
Development and Analysis of Mitigation Strategies for Acidified Aquatic Systems	USFWS (EPA pass-through)	125	150	300	300	10/81	10/86
Liming Acidified Waters	USFWS (EPA pass-through)	32	2	-	-	2/82	11/82
Limestone Contactors for Corrosion Control in Small Water Supply Systems	EPA	50	100	0	-	7/82	6/84
Lake and Stream Acidification Effects and Recovery by Liming and Other Neutralizing Agents	USFWS (EPA pass-through)	0	0	200	200	1983	1986
Emplacement of a Limestone Gravel in Spring Upwelling as a Possible Mitigation Measure in Acidic Brook Trout Lakes	USFWS (EPA pass-through)	44	94	100	-	1982	1985

a Information derived from Reference 3.

TABLE 9-7. RESEARCH COORDINATED BY THE TERRESTRIAL IMPACTS TASK GROUP[a]

Project title	Funding agency	Funding estimates ($1000s)				Period of performance	
		FY 1982	FY 1983	FY 1984	FY 1985	Begin	End
Dendroecological Analysis of Forest Growth Responses	EPA (DOI-USGS)	110	150	150	–	1982	1985
Forest Dieback in the Northeastern United States	EPA (USDA-FS)	39	0	0	–	1982	1983
Effects of Acid Deposition on Sensitive Life Stages and Critical Processes Influencing Plant Growth and Survival	EPA	25	40	60	–	1982	1986
Direct and Interactive Effects of Aluminum on Tree Species as Influenced by Acidic Deposition	EPA	35	35	40	–	1982	1985
Effects of Simulated Acidic Precipitation on Foliar Diseases, Root Diseases, and Mycorrhizal Associations of Forest Trees	EPA	15	15	20	–	1979	1985
Interactive Effects of Acid Rain, Gaseous Pollutants, and Other Environmental Stresses on Plant Growth	EPA-USDA	30	45	80	–	1978	Cont.
Effects of Acid Rain, Natural Acidification, and Harvesting on Cation Removal from Forest Soils	EPA	150	150	150	–	4/82	4/85
Effects of Soil Infiltration Characteristics on the Chemistry of Throughflow Delivered to Aquatic Systems	EPA	60	60	40	–	8/82	8/85
Aluminum Movement Through Soils as Affected by Acidic Deposition	EPA	40	80	100	–	1983	1985
Effects of Acidic Deposition on Mineral Weathering Rates	EPA	35	35	40	–	1982	1985
Predicting Soil Sensitivity as Affected by Acidic Deposition	EPA	50	0	100	–	1982	1985
Effects of Acid Precipitation on Selected Soils of the Southeastern United States	EPA	40	40	50	–	1980	1985
Influence of Acid Deposition on Accumulation, Depletion, and Exchange of Nutrients Within Forested Watersheds	USDA-FS, EPA	0	150	170	–	1983	Cont.
A Comparative Analysis of Aluminum Biogeochemistry in Forested Watersheds Exposed to Acidic Deposition	EPA	100	100	50	–	1982	1985

(continued)

TABLE 9-7 (continued)

Project title	Funding agency	Funding estimates ($1000s)				Period of performance	
		FY 1982	FY 1983	FY 1984	FY 1985	Begin	End
The Effect of Acid Precipitation and Its Gaseous Precursors on Forest Composition, Structure, Growth, and Productivity	USDA-FS	125	223	-	-	1975	-
Cycling of Materials from Atmospheric Deposition in Urban Forest Ecosystems	USDA-FS	100	235	-	-	1982	-
Effects of Acid Precipitation on Nutrient Cycling and Weathering of Minerals in Appalachian Watersheds	USDA-FS	160	210	-	-	1979	-
Effects of Acid Precipitation on Nutrient Cycling, Soil Fertility, and Release of Toxic Metals in New England Hardwood Ecosystems	USDA-FS	30	240	-	-	1978	-
Water Quality Management in Northern Lake State Forests	USDA-FS	110	240	-	-	1978	-
Effects of Acid Precipitation on Nutrient Cycling in Terrestrial Ecosystems of Southern Appalachian and Piedmont Watersheds	USDA-FS	45	110	-	-	1982	-
Effects of Surface Water Acidification on the Chemical Fluxes in Streams, Lakes, and Ground Water	EPA, DOI-USGS	170	241	-	-	1982	1986
Identification of Areas Containing Waters Sensitive to Acidification by Acid Deposition	DOI-USGS	75	145	-	-	1981	1987
Changes in Surface Water and Soil Chemistry Related to Flow Paths and Reaction Mechanisms in Soil and Bedrock	USGS	125	195	-	-	1982	1986
Atmospheric Deposition-Related Changes Within the Riparian and Terrestrial Remote Natural Environments Managed by the NPS	DOI-NPS	186	229	529	-	1982	-
Terrestrial Impacts of Acidic Deposition on Deciduous Forests in the TVA Region—Modeling Atmospheric Inputs—I	EPA/TVA	-	150	-	-	1982	1983
Effects of Acid Precipitation of Forest Soils and Watershed Biogeochemistry in New England	DOE	66	-	-	-	1981	1982
Effects on Terrestrial Ecosystems	USDA-CSRS	148	148	-	-	1978	-
Determine the Effects of Simulated Sulfuric-Nitric Acid Precipitation on Field Crops	USDA-ARS	110	610	610	-	1982	1988
Interactions Between Acid Deposition and Other Air Pollutants that Affect Plant Growth	USDA-ARS	0	161	169	-	1982	1988

(continued)

TABLE 9-7 (continued)

Project title	Funding agency	Funding estimates ($1000s)				Period of performance	
		FY 1982	FY 1983	FY 1984	FY 1985	Begin	End
The Effect of Acid Precipitation on Leaching of Basic Ions from Soils and on Their Movement Through Watersheds	USDA-ARS	0	200	200	-	1983	1988
Effects of Acid Precipitation on Crop Productivity in Major Growing Areas	EPA	160	225	250	-	1982	1986
Factors Relevant to Extrapolation from Specific Sites to Regional Assessments	EPA	245	200	200	-	1982	1986
Effects of Acid Rain, Alone and in Combination with Gaseous Pollutants on Growth and Yield of Crop Plants	EPA	61	70	75	-	1978	Cont.
Qualitative and Quantitative Status of a Field Grown Potato Crop Stressed by Acidified Rain	DOE	56	-	-	-	1981	1983
Impacts of Acidic Deposition on Perennial Grass/Legume Pastures in the Tennessee Valley Region	TVA	66	0	165	-	1978	1986
Mediating Effects of the Vegetation and Soil Mantle on Soil Water Chemistry	TVA	0	0	235	-	1983	1986

aInformation derived from Reference 3.

TABLE 9-8.   RESEARCH COORDINATED BY THE EFFECTS ON MATERIALS TASK GROUP[a]

Project title	Funding agency	Funding estimates ($1000s)				Period of performance	
		FY 1982	FY 1983	FY 1984	FY 1985	Begin	End
Spatial Analysis of Materials Using Land-Use Mapping and Multi-spectral Imaging	USGS	-	-	150	150	10/83	9/85
Geochemical and Petrographic Analyses of Deterioration in Representative Building Stones for Remote Sensing Assessments of Material Damage	USGS	-	50	100	100	10/82	9/85
Passive Monitor Calibration	EPA	25	10	0	-	6/82	1/84
Effects of Acid Deposition on Corrosion of Structural Materials	EPA	80	80	80	-	5/81	Cont.
Acid Rain Simulator Exposure	EPA	0	0	150	-	4/84	5/88
Acidic Deposition on Materials: West Coast	EPA	0	0	150	-	1/84	5/88
Deterioration of Non-Metallic Materials	EPA	0	0	100	-	1/84	5/88
Chemical of Dew on Materials	EPA	0	45	100	-	5/83	5/88
Material Damage: Photochemical Chamber Studies	EPA	0	0	100	-	2/84	12/87
Acid Deposition Study: Program Coordination	EPA	0	50	100	-	10/83	Cont.
Retrospective Air Quality Model for Estimating Damage to Materials	EPA	40	28	50	-	9/82	10/84
Determination of Materials Distribution in Suburban and Rural Areas	EPA	60	37	100	-	9/82	12/87
Prevailing Practices and Mitigation Strategies for Coping with Damages from Acid Deposition	EPA	0	100	100	-	1/83	12/87
Materials Damage Benefit Model Refinement and Application	EPA	0	60	100	-	1/83	12/89
Special Measurement Report FY-85	EPA	0	0	70	-	1/84	7/85
Damage Measurement Technology	NPS	0	90	150	150	10/82	9/85
Field Exposure Tests of Statuary Metals	NPS	0	45	70	100	10/82	Ongoing
Resource Specific Monitoring	NPS	24	50	100	150	4/82	Ongoing
National Historic Landmark Plaques Study	NPS	20	35	50	0	5/82	9/84
Air Quality Histories	NPS	16	50	100	150	8/82	9/85

(continued)

TABLE 9-8 (continued)

Project title	Funding agency	Funding estimates ($1000s)				Period of performance	
		FY 1982	FY 1983	FY 1984	FY 1985	Begin	End
Industry Sites—Correlation Existing Deterioration Rate Data With Environmental Data	NPS	25	90	100	100	6/82	9/83
Distribution of Cultural Properties	NPS	0	0	50	50	10/83	10/85
Sources of Masonry Materials	NPS	30	25	50	50	8/82	9/84
Historical Patterns of Material Use	NPS	0	0	40	60	11/83	9/85
Cultural Resource Values	NPS	0	15	50	50	10/83	9/84
Maintenance Cost Search	NPS	0	15	30	50	1/83	9/85
Treatment Costs—Manufacturers' Suggested Life Cycles	NPS	0	0	80	60	10/83	9/85
Census of Treated Masonry Buildings	NPS	20	20	40	40	10/80	Ongoing
Weather Chamber Tests of Treated Materials	NPS	0	40	50	60	10/82	9/83

aInformation derived from Reference 3.

TABLE 9-9. RESEARCH COORDINATED BY THE ASSESSMENTS AND POLICY ANALYSIS TASK GROUP[a]

Project title	Funding agency	Funding estimates ($1000s)[b]				Period of performance	
		FY 1982	FY 1983	FY 1984	FY 1985	Begin	End
Integrated Assessment Methods Development							
Development of Methods for Empirical Estimates of Benefits	EPA, DOE	-	125 (50)	-	-	-	-
Development of Advanced Effects Assessment Methodology	EPA	-	75	-	-	-	-
Development of Advanced Methods for Source/Receptor Assessment	-	-	-	-	-	-	-
Develop Integrated Methods for Constructing Emission Control and Mitigation Strategies							
- Integrated Emission Control Strategies	EPA	-	235	-	-	-	-
- Integrated Receptor-Oriented Mitigation Strategies	-	-	-	-	-	-	-
- Incorporating Uncertainty into Strategy Assessment	-	-	-	-	-	-	-
- Evaluate Factors Which Affect Retirement Age for Energy Facilities	EPA	-	75	-	-	-	-
Develop Advanced Methods for Integrated Assessment							
- Development of Advanced Integrated Assessment Methodology	EPA	-	220	-	-	-	-
- Systems Analysis/Mass Flows	EPA	-	160	-	-	-	-
- Optimum Configuration for Assessment Regions	EPA	-	65	-	-	-	-
- Development and Testing of Methods for Uncertainty Estimations	DOE	-	50	-	-	-	-
- Assessment of Uncertainty Associated with Emission Control and Mitigation Strategies	DOE	-	100	-	-	-	-
- Generation of Uncertainty Parameters	DOE	-	40	-	-	-	-

(continued)

TABLE 9-9 (continued)

Project title	Funding agency	Funding estimates ($1000s)[b]				Period of performance	
		FY 1982	FY 1983	FY 1984	FY 1985	Begin	End
Integrated Assessment Coordination and Integration							
Overall Coordination and Reporting Support	EPA, DOE	-	65 (220)	-	-	-	-
Coordinate Data Base Construction Activities	EPA, DOE	-	35 (120)	-	-	-	-
Coordinate Model Development and Validation Activities	EPA, DOE	-	10 (60)	-	-	-	-
Coordinate Model and Data Base Integration	-	-	-	-	-	-	-
Integrated Assessment Applications and Special Assessments							
Perform and Participate in Special Scientific/Technical Assessments							
- Short-Term Policy Studies and Special Reports	EPA	-	140	-	-	-	-
- Coordination of Special Assessment Activities	EPA, DOE	-	10 (50)	-	-	-	-
- Acidic Deposition Critical Assessment Document	EPA	-	75	-	-	-	-
- Assessment of Historical Acid Precipitation Data	EPA	-	160	-	-	-	-
- Comprehensive Trend Analysis	-	-	-	-	-	-	-
- Assessment of Source-Receptor Relationships	-	-	-	-	-	-	-
- Primary/Secondary Sulfate; Short- vs. Long-Range Transport	EPA, DOE	-	80 (15)	-	-	-	-
Provide Alternative Control/Mitigation Strategies	EPA	-	0	-	-	-	-
Policy Analysis Studies/Application of Assessment Methodologies	EPA	-	0	-	-	-	-
Review of Policy Issues	EPA, DOE	-	40 (20)	-	-	-	-

[a] Information obtained from Acid Deposition Assessment Staff.

[b] ( ) indicates DOE funds not contained in FY 1983 NAPAP budget.

The Interagency Task Force has contracted with the Oak Ridge National Laboratory to develop an inventory of all federal- and state-sponsored acid precipitation research. This inventory, which is scheduled to be completed in December 1982, will contain a description of all research projects funded under the NAPAP (including those listed in Tables 9-2 through 9-9). Whenever possible, these project descriptions will contain the following information:*

- Project title

- Funding organization

- Name and phone number of project officer

- Principal investigator

- Name, address, and phone number of research organization

- Brief summary of research objectives, project approach, and milestones.

Plans for publishing the inventory, and maintaining and updating this valuable data base, have not yet been finalized.

NON-FEDERAL RESEARCH ON ACID PRECIPITATION

Although the Federal Government conducts the largest acid precipitation research program in the country, state governments, industry, trade, and research organizations, and environmental interest groups also sponsor several million dollars of acid rain research each year. The remainder of this section focuses on the extensive acid precipitation research program sponsored by the Electric Power Research Institute (EPRI); it also describes current efforts to inventory other acid rain research sponsored by state governments and private sector organizations.

Electric Power Research Institute

The Electric Power Research Institute (EPRI) is a nonprofit research arm of the United States electric utility industry. Over the past 3 years, EPRI has spent over $12 million on acid rain research and anticipates spending over $6 million per year for each of the next 5 years.[4] As Tables 9-10 and 9-11 indicate, EPRI's current and completed research focuses on both the environmental physics and chemistry of acid deposition and its ecological effects. EPRI has also undertaken three projects designed to facilitate cost-benefit analyses of acid precipitation control measures. All of EPRI's acid rain research is being performed under contract, much of it with universities and DOE's national laboratories.

---

*Personal Communication between Lisa Baci, GCA, and Dr. Gloria Caton, Oak Ridge National Laboratory, September 17, 1982.

TABLE 9-10. EPRI ACIDIC PRECIPITATION RESEARCH (CURRENT AND COMPLETE) ENVIRONMENTAL PHYSICS AND CHEMISTRY PROGRAM[a]

Project Number	Title	Project Term
EMISSIONS		
RP862[b]	Sulfate Regional Experiment	1976-1981
PHYSICAL AND CHEMICAL TRANSFORMATION		
RP1369[b]	NO_x Transformation in Power Plant Plumes	1979-1982
RP1434[b]	The Effects of Aerosols and Cloud Droplets on the Nighttime Transformation of Sulfur Oxides	1978-1983
RP1630-12	Development of a Method to Measure for H_2O_2 in Air, Cloudwater, and Rainwater	1981-1982
RP2022	Cloud Model Application to Identify Important Chemical Mechanisms	1981-1982
DILUTION AND TRANSPORT		
RP862[b]	Sulfate Regional Experiment (listed above)	1976-1981
RP1311	Atmospheric Chemistry Related to the Formation of Acid Precipitation (North Sea Study)	1978-1981
RP1630[b]	Regional Air Quality Studies	1979-1985
IN-CLOUD CHEMISTRY		
RP1311	Atmospheric Chemistry Related to the Formation of Acid Precipitation (North Sea Study--listed above)	1978-1981
RP2023	Cloud Water Acidity Measurements and Formation Mechanisms	1981-1985
DEPOSITION		
RP1155	Characterization of Acid Precipitation in the Adirondack Region	1977-1979
RP1306	Modeling of Dry Deposition of SO_2 and Sulfate Aerosols	1978-1980
RP1376	Monitoring of Precipitation Chemistry in the Eastern United States	1976-1980

[a]Modified from Reference 4.

[b]Refers to projects that are relative to acidic precipitation but were not started exclusively as acidic precipitation studies.

TABLE 9-11.   EPRI ACIDIC PRECIPITATION RESEARCH (CURRENT AND COMPLETE) ECOLOGICAL STUDIES PROGRAM[a]

Project Number	Title	Project Term
SOILS		
RP1904	Response of Agricultural Soils to Acid Precipitation	1981
LAKE ACIDIFICATION		
RP1109	Integrated Lake Watershed Acidification Study (ILWAS)	1977-1982
RP1910	Effects of Acid Rain on Aquatic Processes: Methodology Development	1981-1984
RP2174	Regional Integrated Lake Watershed Acidification Study (RILWAS)	1982-1985
TERRESTRIAL FAUNA		
No work yet underway.		
CROPS		
RP1812	Effects of Acid Precipitation on Agricultural Crops - Northeast	1980-1983
RP1908	Effects of Acid Precipitation on Agricultural Crops - Midwest, Southeast, Southwest	1981-1984
FORESTS AND GRASSLANDS		
RP1632	Microcosm Evaluation of Acidic Deposition on Forest Ecosystems	1980-1982
RP1727	Evaluation of Nitrogen Deposition on Forested Watersheds	1980-1984
RP1813	Effects of Acid Rain on Nutrient Status of Forest Ecosystem	1980-1984
RP1907	Acid Rain/Forest Canopy Interactions	1981-1983

[a]Modified from Reference 4.

Several of EPRI's research projects have attracted considerable attention, particularly its Integrated Lake-Watershed Acidification Study. In this study, scientists from several distinguished universities and research organizations are studying three lakes of differing acidities located in the Adirondack region of New York. One of the major goals of this multimillion dollar project, which is near completion, is to produce a model that predicts how acid rain interacts with elements of the environment to affect lake acidity. EPRI has decided to fund a multimillion dollar follow-on project,[4] entitled Regional Integrated Lake Watershed Acidification Study, which is designed to extend the methodology already developed to a regional scale, and test the applicability of the lake acidification model in areas outside of the Adirondacks.

Inventories of Non-Federal Acid Precipitation Research

There are currently two major efforts underway to inventory acid precipitation research sponsored by organizations other than the Federal Government. The Interagency Task Force on Acid Precipitation hopes to include information on state-funded research in the inventory being compiled by Oak Ridge National Laboratory* and described above. The Task Force plans to sponsor a meeting in November 1982 to bring together representatives of federal, state, and private sector organizations sponsoring acid rain research.[†] Its contractor for this meeting has just begun to develop a preliminary list[‡] of states that should be invited to the meeting. This list, which is still tentative and not yet complete, indicates that at least six states sponsor or plan to undertake state-funded acid rain research programs.

A comprehensive inventory of private sector research has been recently completed.[5] This project was equally co-funded by the American Petroleum Institute (A.P.I.), Edison Electric Institute (E.E.I.), Electric Power Research Institute (EPRI), and the Gas Research Institute (G.R.I.). The following industries/interest groups were contacted: electric utilities, gas, petroleum, cement, chemicals, coal, environmental, fishing, paper/forest products, iron and steel, motor vehicles, paints/coatings, and smelting. For each project identified, the report contains a brief description that includes the following information:

---

*Personal Communication between Lisa Baci, GCA, and Dr. Gloria Caton, Oak Ridge National Laboratory, September 17, 1982.

†Personal Communication between Lisa Baci, GCA, and Interagency Task Force on Acid Precipitation Staff, September 16, 1982.

‡Personal Communication between Lisa Baci, GCA, and Alexis Hoskins, Schwartz and Connolly, September 20, 1982.

- Project title

- Funding organization(s)

- Project officer

- Research organization(s)

- Principal investigator(s)

- Project period of performance

- Funding levels

- Research objectives

- Project description

- Expected outputs/delivery dates.

A total of 124 research projects were identified and described. Total private sector funding for these projects was approximately $3.1, $7.1, and $8.5 million in 1980, 1981, and 1982, respectively. The electric utility industry provided approximately 80 percent of these funds. The motor vehicles industry, coal industry, and the petroleum industry supplied 8, 6, and 4 percent of these research funds, respectively. Approximately 43 percent of the funding was devoted to research on the environmental effects of acid deposition; research on atmospheric processes and emissions/monitoring received approximately 22 and 33 percent of the total funds expended, respectively.

REFERENCES

1.   Interagency Task Force on Acid Precipitation. National Acid
      Precipitation Assessment Plan. Washington, DC, June 1982.

2.   GCA Corporation. Acid Rain Information Book. DOE/EP-0018, Dist. Cat.
      UC-11. May 1981.

3.   Interagency Task Force on Acid Precipitation. Series of Task Force
      Report Appendices: Task Group A--Natural Sources (NOAA); Task Group B--
      Manmade Sources (DOE); Task Group C--Atmospheric Processes (NOAA); Task
      Group D--Deposition Monitoring (DOI); Task Group E--Aquatic Impacts
      (EPA); Task Group F--Terrestrial Impacts (DOA); Task Group G--Effects on
      Materials (DOI); and Task Group I--Assessments and Policy Analysis (EPA).
      Draft Appendices. 1982.

4.   Allan, M. A. Acidic Precipitation Research at EPRI. Electric Power
      Research Institute. July 1982.

5.   Kinsman, J. D. and J. Wisniewski. Inventory of Acid Rain Research
      Projects Funded by the Private Sector. General Research Corporation.
      McLean, VA, 1982.

ELECTROSTATIC PRECIPITATOR MANUAL

by

Jack R. McDonald   Alan H. Dean

Southern Research Institute

Pollution Technology Review No. 91

This manual covers the fundamentals of electrostatic precipitation (ESP); mechanical and electrical components of electrostatic precipitators; factors influencing precipitator performance; measurement of important parameters; advantages and disadvantages of cold-side, hot-side, and flue gas conditioned electrostatic precipitators; safety aspects; maintenance procedures; troubleshooting procedures; the usage of a computer model for electrostatic precipitation; and features of a well-equipped electrostatic precipitator.

The manual is a summary of the results of studies performed by various individuals and organizations on the applications of electrostatic precipitators to the collection of fly ash particles produced in the combustion of pulverized coal. These studies include comprehensive performance evaluations of full-scale precipitators, in-situ and laboratory measurement of fly ash resistivity, rapping reentrainment investigations, tests to evaluate the effects of flue gas conditioning agents on precipitator performance, investigations into the fundamental operation of hot-side precipitators, basic laboratory experiments, and development of a mathematical model of electrostatic precipitation.

A condensed table of contents listing **chapter titles and selected subtitles** is given below.

ISBN 0-8155-0895-6 (1982)   **484 pages**

Other Noyes Publications

HANDBOOK FOR
FLUE GAS DESULFURIZATION SCRUBBING
WITH LIMESTONE

by

D.S. Henzel
B.A. Laseke
PEDCo Environmental, Inc.

E.O. Smith
D.O. Swenson
Black & Veatch Consulting Engineers

Pollution Technology Review No. 94

This up-to-date and thorough handbook provides guidance for the selection, installation, and operation of limestone flue gas desulfurization (FGD) scrubber systems. The book covers all of the stages of the project from inception, through design, procurement, operation, and maintenance of the system.

Of the many available processes for FGD, the limestone wet scrubbing process is widely used and is continually being improved by numerous technological advances. The limestone wet scrubbing process generates wet sludge as a "throwaway" product or gypsum as a recoverable by-product. The book deals extensively with optional process features and recent innovative modifications that enhance the efficiency of a system.

The emphasis throughout is on practical applications. For example, the discussion of system design and performance provides the kind of information requested by regulatory agencies. This information can also be applied in evaluating preliminary studies and recommendations of a consulting architectural/engineering firm. Further, it can be used in developing detailed equipment specifications and assessing the performance predictions of various scrubber suppliers.

The condensed table of contents given below lists **chapter titles and selected subtitles.**

ISBN 0-8155-0912-X (1982)

424 pages

Other Noyes Publications

EMERGING TECHNOLOGIES
FOR THE CONTROL OF HAZARDOUS WASTES

by

B.H. Edwards   **J.N. Paullin**   **K. Coghlan-Jordan**

Ebon Research Systems
Washington, DC

Pollution Technology Review No. 99

This book reviews and assesses emerging technologies or novel variations of established technologies for the control of hazardous wastes. Most of the hazardous wastes considered in the study are organic substances.

Current interest in hazardous waste handling methods and disposal practices is apparent almost daily in the news media. Methods which might reduce the ultimate disposal problems facing industry and/or decrease the actual quantity of wastes generated are actively being sought.

Three major technologies are covered in detail in the book—molten salt combustion, fluidized bed incineration, and ultraviolet (UV)/ozone destruction. Theory, unit operations, specific wastes treated, and economics are discussed for each of these.

Several other technologies in the developmental stages are also described. Included in this category are catalyzed wet oxidation, dehalogenation by treatment with UV irradiation and hydrogen, electron bombardment of trace toxic organic compounds, UV/chlorinolysis of aqueous organics, and catalytic hydrogenation-dechlorination of polychlorinated biphenyls (PCBs).

Among the wastes to be treated by these emerging technologies are various dioxins, PCBs, pesticides, herbicides, chemical warfare agents, explosives, propellants, nitrobenzene, plus hydrazine and its derivatives.

A **condensed table of contents** is listed below.

ISBN 0-8155-0943-X(1983)   **146 pages**

70939

REMEDIAL ACTION TECHNOLOGY FOR WASTE DISPOSAL SITES

by

P. Rogoshewski   **H. Bryson**   **K. Wagner**

JRB Associates, Inc.
for the U.S. Environmental Protection Agency

Pollution Technology Review No. 101

The remedial actions which can be applied to control, contain, treat, or remove contaminants from uncontrolled hazardous waste sites and the nature of contamination at waste disposal sites are described in this comprehensive handbook. Improper disposal of industrial, commercial, and municipal solid and hazardous wastes is one of the nation's most pressing environmental problems. The quantity of wastes generated and disposed of annually is tremendous and growing. Cases of improper waste management have resulted in contamination of local groundwater, surface water, land, air, and food and forage crops.

As a result of clean-up operations that have already been conducted, and in anticipation of site clean-up activities that will result from recent regulatory action, many technologies have and are being developed. Those technologies specifically designed for clean-up of waste disposal sites are called "remedial actions." Remedial actions include surface, groundwater, leachate and gas migration controls; direct treatment methods; techniques for contaminated water and sewer lines; and processes for contaminated sediment removal.

The book details available technologies and describes how they may be selected and applied for the clean-up of disposal sites, with particular emphasis on hazardous waste sites. Information on each remedial action includes a general description; applications; design, construction, and/or operating considerations; advantages and disadvantages; and installation and annual operating costs, with examples where possible. **Chapter titles and selected subtitles** are given below.

ISBN 0-8155-0947-2

500 pages